C000230359

The Walmsley Society
www.walmsleysoc.org

Leo Walmsley

THE
GOLDEN
WATERWHEEL

An Autobiographical Novel by

Leo Walmsley

The Walmsley Society

First published in 1954 by Collins
This edition published in 2012 by
The Walmsley Society
www.walmsleysoc.org

ISBN   978-0-9561151-4-0

British Library Cataloguing-in-Publication Data:
A catalogue record is available for this book
from the British Library.

Printed and bound by

SRP
Exeter

TO GRETA & FRED

for their long friendship and encouragement

Foreword

This, so far as the author can trust his memory, is a substantially true story. The places described in it are real places, the characters real people, including the author himself, his wife and family.

But, as he has used the same places and some of the same people in other novels and books he has written, he claims poetic licence in this one and has kept to the fictitious names.

CONTENTS

PART ONE

page 1

PART TWO

page 215

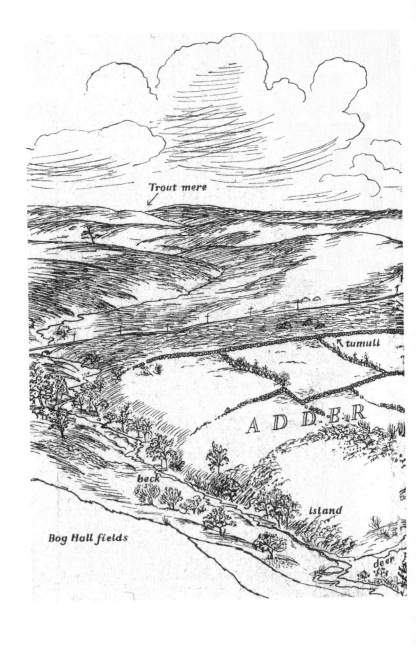

Trout mere

tumuli

A D D E R

beck

island

Bog Hall fields

deer fis

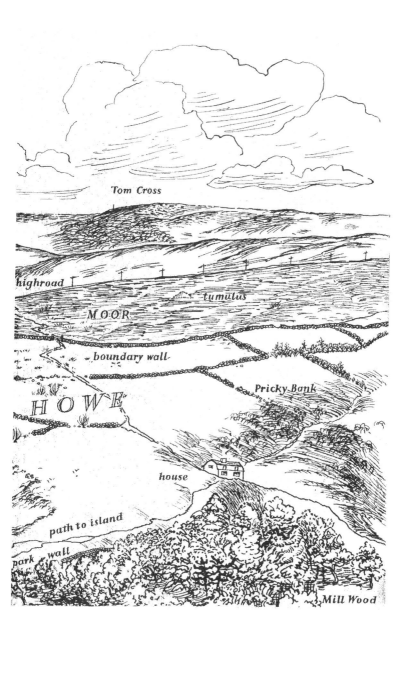

Tom Cross

highroad

MOOR

tumulus

boundary wall

Pricky Bank

HOWE

house

path to island

park wall

Mill Wood

PART ONE

1

WHEN AT last Dain and I decided to leave our Cornish home where we had lived for nearly four eventful and happy years, and make a new home on our well-loved and remembered Yorkshire coast, burning our boats, for it seemed likely we should never be able to return, we thought of all the things we had against living in Cornwall, and of all the things that were in favour of going North. By doing this we were going to make it easier and less painful to pull out our roots from this in many ways pleasant but alien soil; for we were Yorkshire born and bred, and we had come to Cornwall only because of a combination of awkward circumstances, chiefly financial, which no longer bothered us. By hard work and frugal living, and by a good luck that had never for long deserted us, we had achieved a modest solvency.

The finding of our home was typical of our good luck, for at that period our capital was only forty pounds, the price of a short story I had sold to an American magazine. It was an army hut, a timber bunkhouse of the

Kaiser's war. It measured sixty by twenty feet, built sectionally, and it had been bought and re-erected after the war by the firm of J. Hoskins and Sons, the leading shipwrights in the seaport of St Jude, as a workshop.

The firm, which had prospered during the war and during the post-war boom, had bought a section of the foreshore adjoining land on one of the harbour's sheltered creeks, and had constructed a slip so that fair-sized vessels could be grounded on it for survey and repairs. The hut had been erected close to the slip in a little valley through which ran a stream. The ground was not level so that it had been put on piles like a lake dwelling. The piles had been so high at the end nearest the shore that it had been decided to let the hut slope down in this direction, and there was a drop of four feet from one end to the other, a gradient of one in fifteen. This gradient would not have greatly troubled the workmen used to working on the cambered decks of ships, and we had got used to it ourselves in time. But it meant that all our furniture, which we made ourselves, had to be chocked; beds and tables given odd legs, and that in walking across the hut you had to lean slightly to one side and to the other side walking back.

The hut had proved a white elephant for the firm. The post-war boom in ship repairing had been followed by a slump. Eventually Hoskins had gone bankrupt and had been allowed to carry on only by the grace of its creditors. No purchaser could be found for the hut or the land, but a tenant had been found for the hut and half of it had been partitioned to form a four-roomed bungalow. That first tenant had kept goats in the tradition of

Robinson Crusoe, and a valuable legacy was an accumulation of dry dung under the floor between the piles, which had a great deal to do with the unusual fecundity of our garden. He had not stayed long. The legacies of successive tenants had been mostly tin cans, beer bottles, old boots, radio batteries, and ashes distributed round the hut and in the course of the little stream, the mud in which, if we had left it undisturbed, might have proved of interest to some archaeologist in the distant future.

The last human tenants had done a moonlight flit, and judging by their remains they had lived on a diet of beer, condensed milk and cockles; but they had left behind a colony of sub-tenants in the shape of rats, mice, fleas and cockroaches. The roof leaked. The cooking stove was broken and obviously smoked. There was a large vegetable garden grown over with docks, nettles and brambles. The beach of a little cove was strewn with tin cans, pieces of rusty corrugated iron and broken bottles. But to us (we had no children then), homeless, with no capital except our precious forty pounds, but very much in love and full of belief in ourselves, the whole place had seemed a potential paradise.

The rent for the hut, the cove and foreshore, and eight acres rough land was three shillings a week. The disillusioned, cynical, and yet unfailingly good-natured senior member of the bankrupt firm, old Joe Hoskins, whom we had liked immensely from the start, had told us that we could alter the hut as we liked, and he had agreed to give us a cooking range, a bath and lavatory from a salvaged yacht, and throw in a second-hand

3

dinghy at a nominal price. We'd need that as the place was virtually an island.

We'd known that we could make a home of it, where I could write the books I had in mind and where, if they went well, we could safely start our family. And that we had done. We had made the roof watertight. We had installed the bath. We had altered the partitioning to make a big and comfortable kitchen living-room, with its only snag the sloping floor. We had lined the walls of all the rooms with cloth cut from old sails that Joe had given us. We had cleared and fenced in the vegetable garden, cleared the stream and made flowerbeds on its banks. We had made our furniture chiefly from timber taken from the hulls of derelict sailing ships lying in the creek and driftwood washed up in our cove. I had written the first of my novels, and, if it hadn't been a bestseller, it had been well noticed by the critics, and it had earned enough for us to invest in a second-hand ship's lifeboat which, with an ancient engine, we had converted into a cabin cruiser. We had taken our first-born, Amelia, on our first short voyage in it.

We could think of many things we had against this place, now that we had decided to leave it. We had kept one half of the hut, the one nearest the cove, as a lounge, and we had put in a large window which gave a splendid view. We had designed and built an open fireplace with a hearth wide enough to burn big logs. It was a failure. It would draw fiercely in hot weather, when we didn't need it. In winter, no matter how the wind was blowing, it would sulk and smoke and we could never get the room warm enough to sit in it for long.

Although it looked so good, and functioned so well at the wrong time, that fireplace was a perpetual annoyance to me, for I could not discover why it behaved as it did.

"My love," I said to Dain. "One of the most important things in planning our new house, if not the most important thing of all, will be the fireplace of our sitting-room. We must get expert advice on that, anyway. We must make certain that it will burn any sort of fuel, and in all conditions of weather."

"Yes, darling, and especially *cold* weather."

We were in the sitting-room, starting to sort out our things for packing. It was an evening in late spring. There was a cold blustery wind and it had been raining all day. The fire wouldn't draw and we were using an oil stove to take the chill off the room.

"But we do want it to burn logs," Dain went on. "I suppose it will be just as good there for finding driftwood as here."

"Better, much better. After a rough sea the whole beach is often strewn with wood."

"We'll have to have coal for the kitchen fireplace, though. It will be lovely having a modern range, and hot water all the time, and a proper bathroom."

"Yes. And all floors level. I wish we could have electricity, but we'd have to find a site near to a town for that. I wish there was a site with a stream near it, where we could have a dam and a waterwheel and make our own electricity, and breed our own trout too. That would be ideal. Browe Beck would be no good for that. And the old mill on Mill Beck would be no use to us."

"No. And the dam would be dangerous for the

children. We can't have everything, darling. The fishing will be better there than here, anyway. There are two trout streams, and the one over the moor with the mere, where we caught such a lot of fish that evening. Do you remember?"

"Yes, rather. But I should think that by this time the mere is choked with weed, and all the trout killed off. In any case, it's probably been bought by some war profiteer, and all of it strictly preserved. We ought to get some good sea fishing, though, better than here. It's a pity we can't take the motorboat. Still, we could have a dinghy, provided it was light enough to haul up well above high-water mark."

"It's all terribly exciting, isn't it? Making a new home, and yet in a place we both love! I'm dying to see the North Sea again, and the moors. It will be just too wonderful if we can have a pony and ride again. It's a wonderful country for riding."

It was, in every way, a wonderful country. We were going to build there, or have built for us, for we were only amateurs, an ideal house, preferably of Yorkshire freestone, with a red pantiled roof like the farm buildings and cottages of the district. We didn't want another army hut, or any other sort of existing building. We wanted to start from the beginning, design it and watch it being built exactly to our own ideas of what our home should be. We did not know yet exactly where it was going to be, or even that we could find and be able to purchase a site. But we had one place in mind that seemed perfection.

It was four years since we had left the district. I had spent all my boyhood and most of my youth there, and there was not a field or copse or lane I did not know. In my boyhood practically all of the farm land, woods and moors, and most of the village itself had been owned by the titled but non-resident Lord of the Manor, and two resident squires. One of the squires, who owned the lower part of one of the two becks which ran down from the moors to the shores of the bay, was to me a terror. He was a powerful man, more than six feet tall. He was not married, and he lived in the Hall with his unmarried sister who was almost as tall and as fierce looking as himself. He was a magistrate, and his pet aversion was trespassers and particularly poachers. He owned the mill and the mill dam which had some fine trout in it, and the only time I had ever seen him smile was the time he had caught me poaching in it—a very grim smile indeed.

The other squire, whose mansion stood near the same stream but higher up the valley near the moors, was by contrast almost a dwarf. He, too, hated trespassers and poachers, but I was never really afraid of him. He was a religious man, and went to church twice on Sundays, wearing a frock-coat and a bowler hat, and driving there and back in a little dog-cart. He was an authority on ecclesiastical architecture and had written at least one book on the subject.

He took a peculiar interest in the farms he owned. At one of them he rebuilt a cowshed with hand-dressed stone with carved church windows and louvres, and an arched doorway with an iron-studded oak door, again like that of a church. The stalls were all of carved oak and looked almost like pews. At another farm he built a pigsty which was an exact replica in miniature of a

Grecian temple, only there were two storeys, in the topmost one of which the pigs were supposed to sleep, and there was a special staircase for them. They preferred the ground floor however. Neither cowshed nor pigsty had water laid on. Nor did he ever think of laying water on, or installing sinks or bathrooms in any of his farms or cottages for the use of his human tenants.

Both squires were dead by the end of the Kaiser's war. Their estates had been split up and sold, most of the farms being bought by their tenants, who had done well during the war. But the boom in farming, like that in shipping, had been succeeded by a slump. Before we had left several of the farmers had been obliged to sell up: their live and dead stock, the farms themselves, going for ridiculously low prices. Some were snapped up by speculators from Yorkshire's industrial towns who, perhaps, had a hunch that some day another war and another boom might come. Some of the farmers had hung on.

There had been so many changes we did not know what the present situation of ownership was. We could only pray that the one who owned the particular site we had in mind was not a speculator, and that he would wish to sell, and at a reasonable price. We'd got three hundred pounds in the bank, and with that we had to purchase the site and put down a sufficient proportion of the total cost of construction to get a building society loan.

Each of the two becks ran into the bay down wooded valleys that formed gaps in the low liassic cliff to the south of the old village. The mill stood about a hundred yards back from the mouth of the beck nearer to the

8

village. In rough weather, and spring tides, the waves actually washed its foundations. From its cove a good cart road led up the south side of the valley into the country, passing the small hamlet called Browe with a railway station, and connecting with the moorland highway to Burnharbour. But there was no connection between the village of Bramblewick and the Mill Cove for wheeled traffic except along the beach, and this only when the tide was down. The beach was partly rock, partly shingle and sand. Motors ventured it only at their peril.

The second beck was about half a mile farther to the south. Here was another road, but steep and dangerous. Our site was on the top of the cliff on the north side of the cove of this beck, overlooking the cove and the whole sweep of the bay. The steep road was on the opposite side of the cove, and was of no significance to our scheme. What was of utmost importance was the existence of a cart lane, just wide enough for motor trucks, leading back over the fields to the road from the other beck and the railway station about a mile and a half distant. There would be no difficulty in the transport of building material. A matter of equal importance was the existence of a spring, not more than twenty feet down the valley from the level patch where our house would be built. It was piped into a stone cattle trough. How often as a boy had I bent my face down into this trough to quench my thirst, heedless of the water-boatmen on its surface, or the newts which in spring-time could be seen on its muddy bottom.

That side of the valley faced south, and in spring was

carpeted with primroses and violets. A bridle-path led down it to the beck where there was a ford and a wooden footbridge giving access to the other road. It was a smaller and slightly shorter stream than the Mill Beck, never so good for trout. But its cove had a shingle beach which rough seas had piled up to make a natural dam, and usually there was a wide and fairly deep pool extending from below the bridge for more than a hundred yards upstream into the wood. When there were periods of heavy continuous rain, and the beck was in spate, the shingle dam was scoured away, and the pool emptied. If this did not happen in a whole year you could get reasonably sized trout, and occasionally salmon.

What a place to have within a stone's throw of your own home! When the tide was halfway down there was a wide stretch of clean firm sand bounded by the flat, curving scaurs which ran parallel to the curve of the bay. This sand extended beyond low water for nearly a mile and was one of the best boat fishing grounds on the coast. Here with long lines or hand lines you could get plaice, soles, dabs, skate, and in the summer, whiting galore, and big ones too.

Nor did you need a boat to get first-rate fishing. In summer swarms of billet and cod and mackerel came close in to the beach hunting the vast shoals of herring sile. You stood on the scaur ends and fished with a long rod and a white feather bait. In winter, especially when there was a swell rolling, you could get big cod by casting out from the shore. The pools between the scaurs teemed with marine life. At low water, spring tides, you could find lobsters and crabs in the crevices of the scaurs, and haul them out with a long iron hook. The cove itself and the shore as far as the headland cliff of High Batts was a wonderful place for finding things when the sea was rough with an on-shore wind. And apart from flotsam and jetsam the shingle which lay along the cliff foot abounded with semi-precious stones like agates, carnelians and jet, washed out of the shale. The shale itself was full of fossils.

Our house would have to be well built, with draught-proof doors and windows to withstand the winter gales. The view would be splendid. It would face south-east, and we should be able to watch the sun rising from the sea and lighting up the huge cliff of High Batts. That cliff was composed of sandstone crags overlying the liassic shales. In profile it was like an immense sculptured sphinx, with feet stretched out into the sea. In rainy or misty weather, when its crags and shale beds were wet, it was grey and gloomy and forbidding. When dry and lit with sun it would look sometimes as though it had been carved from solid gold. Its aspects were infinitely varied. Perhaps it looked most exciting of all after or immediately before a July thunderstorm, with monstrous leaden and ivory nimbus clouds piled up behind it, and a shaft of farewell or welcoming sunshine trained like an intensely powerful searchlight on its cliffs.

The whole place was beautiful and exciting and so varied in its attractions. There was the sea and the seashore; the cliffs, the woods and becks, and miles of unspoilt moorland dotted with tumuli, and prehistoric earthworks, all within easy reach of where we were going to live. There was the village of Bramblewick, alas, no longer with active fishermen living in it, but still immensely interesting to us who knew its past. And within six miles was the busy port of Burnharbour. Burnharbour would be less than twenty minutes by rail from our station.

Yet, with all our wishful thinking, we could not pretend that the place we were going to leave had not its many attractions and advantages, that we had not come to have an immense affection for it, that we were not going to miss it, and even yearn for it, no matter how happy we were to be in Yorkshire.

The view through the window of our too big and draughty, and un-heatable front room, down to the cove and the creek was unbelievably lovely at times. There were no other houses in sight. Across the creek from our cove, a distance of about two hundred yards, the land rose steeply, with outcrops of naked rock. Between the outcrops there was bracken, and clumps of gorse (which in Yorkshire we call whins), blackthorn and hawthorn and gnarled stunted oaks. With the tide high, and no wind, the surface of the water would be like a sheet of polished glass, and the whole of the bank would be reflected in it.

In autumn when the oaks and bracken had turned, the colour would almost take your breath away. The banks of mud exposed when the tide was out might be a nuisance to us in grounding our boats, but they had a special beauty and interest, for they attracted flocks of birds: gulls, curlews, sandpipers, terns, oyster-catchers, and almost always at the edge of the tide you could see a heron fishing, either dead still, or stealthily wading through the shallows. The oaks were bare in winter but the dead bracken remained to glow and warm the eye whenever the sun came out.

In early spring, much earlier than in Yorkshire, came the primroses and violets, and the gorse. Before the last primrose had withered, and before the perpendicular shoots of the new bracken had broken through the old dead fronds, both the bank opposite to us and our own land would be covered with bluebells, among which would be clumps of red campions, here deeper red, and with bigger flowers than in Yorkshire. Then the blackthorn would bloom, looking as though patches of snow had fallen on the hillsides. Already the buds of the oaks were swelling and starting to burst. The bracken would mount, fighting and at last beating the bluebells, but not the red campions, which before late spring would be reinforced with the foxgloves, growing taller than any bracken frond, and lasting into summer, and outliving the may blossom and the full leafage of bush and tree.

We could not pretend that the North Sea was ever quite so blue as that which washed the Cornish coasts or that except in long periods of calm summer weather, ever so clear, or even quite so warm. We could not pretend that the sea coast within reach even of our dinghy in calm weather could not, although it was nowhere half the height of High Batts, in many ways knock spots off anything we had in Yorkshire. It had the enormous advantage of facing south. It was broken by innumerable coves with sand or shingle beaches hemmed in with fantastically shaped and coloured rocks.

There was one such cove, not more than half an

hour's pull from our creek, where the rocks were composed entirely of serpentine, exquisitely marked and tinted. The water was colder here than in our own creek, but it was so clear you could see the bottom at ten fathoms, and after a dip you could stretch yourself on the smooth wave-polished rocks like a seal, and feel the sun's heat radiating from the rock warming and drying you, giving you the courage to dive in again.

These things we should miss, and in the years to come undoubtedly yearn for. We should have to sell our cruiser, and our dinghy, for there would be no safe anchorage near our new home, and while we would certainly have a boat it would have to be one light enough to carry well above high-water mark. We simply could not, we told ourselves, expect to have everything. And the most important thing after all was the future of our family, for we already had two children, Amelia aged three and Jane aged six months, and it was probable that we should have more.

We believed that it was a good thing to bring children up in the country, and a country that bordered on the sea; that the most important foundation for their lives was good health, and a sanity induced by a close contact with nature: fresh air, good food, space, a garden, woods, lanes, streams, hills, beaches for them to explore as they grew bigger. The good, simple things first! But we did not wish them to grow into Eskimos or Masai warriors. Their ultimate jungle would be that of modern civilisation: their hunting when they grew up would be for careers, money, fame, love. That would be their own affair. Whatever they wanted to do, or became, they would be no worse off for having learnt at first hand the ways of natural things, for knowing about trees and flowers, and birds and fishes and insects and the weather, for having learnt to swim in the sea, and climb a cliff and sail a boat or ride a pony.

But it was essential too that they should have early practice in the ways, the conventions and disciplines of human society. It was right that they should have a decent house to live in, with level floors, real ceilings, a roof that hadn't to be patched after (and often during) every storm; with a real bathroom and water hot and cold, and possibly with electric light and power.

We loved Cornwall, we had loved the home we had built there. It had served its purpose. We knew that it was right to go.

2

WE HAD many friends in the district, but we had been afraid of making any inquiries about our piece of land in case one of the speculators got wind of our intention and got in before us. We were assuming that one had not done so already. The first thing we must do was visit the place, make certain that our memories were not at fault about its size and exact position in relation to the cart lane; whether this lane was private or public property; whether the spring was adequate for our water supply (I had never known the trough dry, but springs *were* known to dry up altogether, or find another outlet); and then, if all *was* satisfactory, discreetly discover who the landlord was, then meet him and discuss business.

I felt uneasy about this. If we had to deal with one of those hard-headed Yorkshire city men who'd been investing their money in land we'd be at a big disadvantage from the start. If it was one of the old farmers who still owned it, he'd be hard too, when it came to a matter of 'brass'; besides, as a boy, I had never been popular with the local farmers; indeed, we had been natural enemies, for like the squires they hated anyone walking over their fields or through their woods and copses no matter how careful one might be to close gates and not tread on crops. In my bird-nesting or natural history expeditions, or when I was after trout or daffodils or blackberries or mushrooms, I'd always keep well away from the farm buildings, and avoid fields where men were working, and run for my life if by any chance I saw anyone of them coming towards me even if I were walking on a public lane. They were a rough lot, much rougher than the fishermen, with loud harsh voices, which when they were driving their cattle or sheep, or even just ploughing, could be heard for miles.

It was a day in early June when we set out on our first reconnaissance. During our last few days in Cornwall, and actually up to the time of our departure, the weather had been cold and rainy, with strong south-west winds and overcast skies. This had made the parting from our home even easier to bear. Our creek and cove and little valley, all of which could look so ravishingly beautiful, were at their worst when from the hired motor boat that transported us across the harbour to the station of St Jude's we took what we believed to be our last sight of them. The sun, and a clear blue sky, and an incipient anticyclone had welcomed our return to Yorkshire.

The summer visitor season which, since the decline in inshore fishing, was the main industry of the coast had begun. Through friends and house agents we had tried to find temporary accommodation in the village. Every cottage was let, and we had been obliged to take a quarterly lease of a large unfurnished house midway between Bramblewick and Burnharbour.

This house was another white elephant. It had been built before the war by a wealthy retired butcher from Bradford to his own specifications, and almost everything about it was wrong, although it must have cost a small fortune. It was built in a hollow of a large boggy pasture field bordered by a ragged wood that obscured any view of coast or moorland. Its exterior was hideous yellow brick, half-timbered, with gabled upper windows and a roof of flat, almost pink, tiles, so unlike the lovely warm red curved pantiles of the farms and village cottages. The downstairs windows had their clear glass bordered with stained, leaded patterned panes, and the gabled porch and front door were similarly decorated and embellished with fancy ironwork. Inside all the woodwork, including the staircase, was of varnished pitch-pine, but in the lounge (which was half-panelled) this was stained almost black. This room contained an imitation Elizabethan fireplace, which judging by the smoke stains on the wall above it was no more efficient than the one we had built in our big room. The dining-room and another reception room had tiled Victorian fireplaces, and built-in, fretted mantelpieces with bevelled mirrors, and their walls were covered with varnished lincrusta. There were five bedrooms, the walls of the principal one being covered with a paper on which was printed in multiple repetition a picture of a pair of blue jays, perched facing each other on a branch of twisting vine which bore bunches of grapes, four bunches for each pair of birds.

It was not surprising that the owner and builder of the house had died of a heart attack six months after taking up his residence in it, and that his widow had gone to spend her remaining years in a Burnharbour boarding house; and that no purchaser or tenant had subsequently been found for it. It was a dreadful place. It had filled us with dismay on our arrival, invoked a powerful nostalgia for the home we had left, even for the slanting floors. But the rent was low. Within two miles was an intermediate railway station from which we could get to the station that was near to our site. If everything went well we should be out of it, into our new home before the winter came. And a genial aunt of ours, who loved the country, and liked and got on well with children, had agreed to come and help us through the summer months at least.

It had taken us four days of almost non-stop work to clean and settle ourselves into that house which we had privately named Butcher's Folly. The aunt had arrived. We had left her happily in charge of the children, and had caught the afternoon train. The promise of an

18

anticyclone had been fulfilled. It was a blazing hot day, with a cloudless sky and not a breath of wind. We could not recall a hotter day in Cornwall during the whole time we had lived there.

How remote Cornwall seemed as we stepped out of the train on to the platform of the little railway station of Browe, so familiar to us both. This was the country. Dain's roots in it were not so deep as my own. Like my own parents, hers had been "foreigners" and they had come to live here at a much later date and had since moved. But it was here that we had first met and found that our interests in, and likings for, the countryside and the seashore were shared. We had rambled together along the cliffs and shore, and over the moors, taking food with us, and a billycan, making fires of driftwood or heather roots and turf. We had caught lobsters on the low spring ebbs, or in winter set scaur lines for cod. We had done a little innocent poaching.

The one thing I had not completely shared with Dain was her passion for riding. She had been given, by a school friend of hers who had married and gone to live in India, a spirited but temperamental pony called Dick, which had an incurable dislike for the sound of a motor car changing gear. With this went either an uncanny sense of hearing, or a vivid imagination, for he would rear up and then break into a mad gallop on a course of his own choice, leaping hedges and stone walls, splashing through boggy streams and ponds, and nothing would stop him except complete exhaustion, which meant of course that his rider, if she hadn't already been left behind, would have to walk him home—a distance which might be anything up to a dozen miles.

I liked riding, but it was an expensive pastime, and I'd never had much practice in it. On one occasion I'd been persuaded by Dain into hiring a pony, recommended by its owner as quiet and obedient, and we'd gone for what was to have been an easy ride over the moors. No pony, unless decrepit, is willing to maintain a steady gait when its companion breaks into a hell-for-leather gallop. This had happened, and I had taken part in an involuntary steeplechase, which, if exhilarating had made me so stiff and sore that I had been unable to walk or sit down in comfort for a week after. Unfortunately (or perhaps fortunately—for Dick's phobia was decidedly dangerous) he had stampeded from his paddock one day, tried a fence that had barbed wire in it, severed an artery and had to be destroyed.

It was good to be back. It was a grand country to be in. From the station the road curved down into a little wooded valley, crossing a stream which was a miniature tributary of the Mill Beck, then rose again to the level. We couldn't see the sea yet, but we could see the edge of High Browe Moor rising nearly nine hundred feet from the green valley of Browe Beck, soon visible to the south of the road.

Nothing had changed, at least visually, during the years of our voluntary exile. The farms, there were several of them in view, looked just as they had always looked.

I knew little about farming. Unless I had looked at the actual plants, I could not have told the difference between a field of oats or barley or wheat, or sown grass or old meadow. Had I known then what I was to learn later I should have been able to detect on every side of us the signs of neglect and bad husbandry, of inadequate tillage, of crops and pastures suffering from lack of lime and fertiliser, of neglected fences and drains. The stock looked healthy, and well-nourished, but I did not realise that the herds of milkers and young cattle were numerically a fraction of what this land, with capital and modern mechanical and chemical methods, was capable of supporting. I hadn't realised to what extent the British farmer had been affected by the general world slump, especially the small farmer. And if I had recognised all the signs of it here, it would only have encouraged our hopes of getting our piece of land, which in any case could not be of high agricultural value.

What did encourage me was seeing no signs of the invading speculator, who as a business man might have helped his tenants and himself by buying tractors and modern machinery. We passed a meadow which one man and a youth were cutting with an ancient rusty mowing machine drawn by a mare that looked at least as old as the machine. I did not recognise either the man or the youth, but Dain knew the horse, which was called Daisy and was blind in one eye.

The road itself was deserted and, although macadamed, showed little signs of use by motor cars. It ended at the Mill Cove cul-de-sac, and we knew that the tide was up. It had a slight slope towards the coast although the cliffs between the two coves were relatively high, and soon we got our first glimpse of the sea itself, far out, just a narrow ribbon showing between the cliff edge and the horizon. It was dead smooth, shining like glass, and the smoke from a large passing steamer trailed along the horizon line in a thin level cloud. We hadn't far to go. We came to a group of farm buildings and cottages with a lane branching to them on our left and continuing down into the valley of the Mill Beck about half a mile above the Mill itself. Where this lane branched off there was a narrower one leading opposite to the right, to Browe back cove, and our still invisible site. It was gated and there was a stone stile by the gate itself, and both these were familiar to us. The lane was only about half a mile in length. For about the first half of it it went slightly uphill, the land forming a watershed between the two becks. It was narrow, with untrimmed thorn hedges and banks; but it was, I noted with satisfaction, just wide enough to take a builder's motor truck, and although its surface was encrusted with dry clay and cow dung there was metal underneath. If there were pot-holes, or soft spots, it would be a simple matter to fill them with shingle from the beach . . . No motor trucks, or cars, or even carts, had been along it for a considerable time, judging by its condition.

We hurried. There were cornfields on our left, actually reaching to the cliff edge. I was sure that these fields had belonged to the Mill farm. The Mill farm had belonged to the big squire. The lane, I was pretty certain, had actually marked part of the boundary between the estates of the two squires, but the foreshore of the entire bay (and our patch more or less bordered on the shore) had belonged to the Lord of the Manor.

We reached the highest point in the lane where it

began to slope gently down towards the top of the valley of the beck. The hedges were still high but we could see the gate at the lane end and beyond it the topmost trees of the wood. We ran the remaining distance, swung open the gate, and there it was, the piece of land itself.

In contrasting this place with our Cornish cove we had inevitably attributed to it an altogether sterner beauty. My own most vivid memories of it were with the sea rough, with huge waves breaking on the outlying scaurs of the bay, rolling in to the shore and cliff foot. I had never pictured it in a June heat wave. The tide was high, and from the beach to the horizon there was not a visible ripple on the sea, except for the wake of the passing steamer, and several dark patches with flocks of sea birds wheeling over them, which I knew were caused by shoals of herring sile driven to the surface by shoals of mackerel or billet. We could not, because of the tall thorn hedge of the last cornfield, see the south end of the bay or the village itself, but we could see the whole shore and range of cliffs to High Batts. Its crags were trembling in the heat, and the whole headland was reflected in the sea as in a perfect mirror, and although it was too early for the real heather to be in bloom the escarpment of the High Moor and the debris of the old alum quarries below the moor edge were patched with the purple of heath and the gold of broom and whins.

"It's better," I said, "than I thought."

"It's a wonderful place to build our home! Won't the children love the beach! There's no mud here when the tide goes down."

"They'll have the beck too. I've never seen the pool

under the bridge so big, although it's never dangerously deep. There can't have been any heavy rains during the winter to wash the bar away. It would make a perfect harbour for our dinghy when we get one, only it would have to be hauled over the bar, and it would have to be a very light one. I think I can see trout, or salmon smolt rising in the pool."

"Do you remember the big salmon we caught higher up the wood with our hands? I wonder who owns the wood? It would be wonderful if we could buy that too, then it wouldn't be poaching if we did get salmon."

"We haven't," I said, bringing us down to earth, "bought *this* place yet. We may not be able to buy it. It may not be for sale. It may not be suitable anyway. We've got to look at the spring. We wouldn't be allowed to build a house unless it had a good water supply."

"Well, I know that's all right. Dick was always most fussy about drinking. He'd never drink at the pool because there was always a little salt water in it. But coming or going, he'd never pass the trough."

From the gate and the end of the lane the piece of land made a rough rectangle bordered by the hedge of the cornfield, the top of the wood, and a thicket of bramble and thorn reaching, with breaks of grass, down to the beck. There was an almost level space of about half an acre at the top across which the bridle path took a diagonal course, leaving on either side of it ample room for both house and garden, but the path was unfenced, unmetalled, and could easily be diverted. The grass here was closely cropped, evidently by cattle. There was no livestock on it now. The trough lay some twenty feet down the bank. The bridle path passed it. We hurried down and there it was: a long trough carved out of a single block of sandstone, brimming over with clear water which fell from an old cast-iron pipe projecting from the bank which was grown with moss and liverwort and hart's tongue ferns; good evidence that the spring was permanent. We had a drink in celebration, and how cool and good it was! It was a snag that it was so far below the level of the nearest possible site. But the flow was sufficient to work a ram: a device which, automatically, will lift a proportion of any flowing water to any reasonable height. It would be one more expense, but once installed it would cost nothing for upkeep, whereas with a council supply there would be a water rate, amounting in time to much more than the cost of our own installation.

We sat down on a patch of dry ground close by the trough, and summed things up with great satisfaction. The water was all right. So was the lane. There was ample room on the level for building, for vegetable and flower gardens. The lay of the land was suitable for the construction of a septic tank for sewage disposal. We were within easy range of a railway station. We could shop either at Bramblewick or Burnharbour, and there were grocers and butchers at both places who had country delivery vans. Milk we could get at one of the farms at the lane end. Coal (and we'd be able to economise on this with driftwood from the beach) could be delivered from the railway station. For lighting we should have to depend on oil at first, but if we made money we could get our own plant, engine driven, or perhaps by wind. There would be plenty of wind at most times of the year.

The one big thing I wished, for it would have fulfilled one of my most cherished ambitions, was that the stream was nearer and that we could possess at least a part of it. What would have made the place ideal was the stream running alongside the house (as it had done in Cornwall), but one big enough to contain trout, no matter how small at first. It would be swift flowing through a gorge that could be inexpensively dammed, so as to make a permanent pool, which, stocked with the right plants, would provide food on which the trout would thrive and grow fat like those in the mill dam I had poached as a boy. (How, in those days, I had envied the miller!) In addition to the trout, the stream and pool should have the requisite volume and height to drive a waterwheel, not like the miller's to grind corn, but to work a dynamo providing free electricity, for lighting, heating, power, giving us all the advantages of living in a town, with none of the disadvantages. . .

We couldn't have everything. This was as near the ideal as any human beings of our tastes and ambitions could expect, and we'd be very fortunate if we were able to buy it at a price low enough to be able to build our house. The next thing was to find out who the owner was, and the obvious way to do that was to go back along the lane to the crossroads, and inquire at one of the farms or cottages that stood near.

Some of the old uneasiness came back to me as we got up to go. It was hardly likely that we were going to find anyone as amenable and generous as Joe Hoskins. We must prepare ourselves, I said, for getting unfavourable news. The very fact that the place was such a splendid site for a house, and that no house was on it, might have an unfortunate significance. To which Dain answered with an encouraging, if not completely convincing, optimism:

"No one's built a house here because no one's ever thought of it. Most people would think it was too isolated, too far away from shops and cinemas. It's just right for us and the children, and we've simply got to have it, and I'm certain the owner will sell it to us when he knows how much we want it."

"That," I protested, "is the last thing we've got to let him know. Our line must be that we don't want it much. That we've got dozens of other places to choose from, and that we might be persuaded to buy this if it were going cheap."

"But there aren't any other places. There's not a place anywhere near the sea where we could build, and where there's water, and a road too."

I knew that only too well. We had, when we had first thought of leaving Cornwall, gone over in our minds every yard of the coastline within the prescribed south, and north limits of where we wanted to live. This was the only possibility. We had burnt our boats. If we couldn't get this place the only alternative was to make the best of Butcher's Folly, a thought so dreadful that I dared not put it into words. We did not continue the discussion. As we turned to move towards the bridle path Dain paused, and said:

"Listen, there's someone on horseback coming up the

path. Perhaps it's a farmer, and he'll be able to tell us about the place and who owns it. Let's wait for him."

The lower end of the path, the footbridge and ford, were hidden by the thorn thicket from where we now halted. There now appeared in sight an old man in shirt sleeves, and wearing a tattered straw hat, mounted on a white pony.

"It's old Isaac Benson!" Dain cried. "I'd recognise his pony a mile off. He's called Snowball. Isaac used to go to hunt meets with him, but he was always too fat to jump, and always went through gates. He lives in one of the cottages at the lane end. He's a grumpy man. I never liked him. But he'll know who owns the land."

I did recognise him as he approached. He had been one of the tenants of the little squire, and I had an uncomfortable feeling that I'd had trouble with him long ago. I could not recall the precise incident. He was stout, clean shaven with a tuft of white hair showing under his hat. He looked extremely hot, and he was trying rather ineffectually to keep the flies from his pony's eyes, and himself, with a bunch of bracken fronds. Despite the weight he was carrying, and his own age, the pony was making a brave job of the hill.

"I bet Snowball's got his mind on the trough," Dain said. "Poor old thing. He must be at least thirty years old."

She was right. We had to stand back a yard or so to let them pass to the trough. The old man had given us what I took to be an unfriendly glance, with no sign of recognition in it. He'd take us to be summer visitors, and as such to be regarded with deeper distrust than the 'foreigners' who had been settled in the district for years.

I knew better than speak to him straightaway. Dain was less cautious. She took a move towards the pony.

"Isn't this Snowball?"

The old man gave her a suspicious look which was not completely unfriendly.

"Aye."

Snowball was already drinking, Dain had the confidence to move up to him and put a hand on his flanks and start caressing him. The old man stared at her, evidently not resenting the familiarity.

"I know your face," he suddenly remarked. "Aren't you the lass that used to ride a black gallower called Dick?"

Dain gave him a sweet smile.

"Yes."

"I thought so. And he had to be put off. Lucky for you. He'd have broke your neck if you'd gone on riding him. A gallower's no use these days unless he can stand motor cars. The danged things is everywhere."

He turned to give me a suspicious look.

"What's your name?"

I told him.

He cogitated for a moment, and I wondered if his memory was going to prove better than mine. Had he once seen me in his orchard, or climbing one of his fences, or just trespassing?

"I thought I'd seen you afore. You were a mischievous beggar when you were a lad. I remember t'awd squire tellin' me to watch out for you, and skelp your backside if ever I caught you in mischief. But you've been away from this spot a long while I reckon, and you'll have been

29

in the war. Last time I clepped eyes on you you were in khaki. Are you two courtin' or are you wed?"

"Wed," I said. "And we've got two children. We're back here, looking for a piece of land to build a house on."

"So you've got some brass? "

"Not much."

Clearly he was weighing me up.

"Nay, none of us have got much of that these days, except them beggars from away who've bin buying up farms round here since t'war ended. And where d'ye think you're going to find a spot for a house?"

"We've got several spots in mind."

He was evidently interested.

"How much land d'ye want?"

"About an acre, but it would have to be rough ground and cheap. We've been having a look round this place, between here and the end of the lane. Could you tell us who the present owner is?"

He stared hard at me.

"Who's the owner of *this?* Why—it's me. It goes with my cottage at t'lane end, along with two acres of pasture back o' t' cottage, scarce big enough to feed a couple of cows. When t'squire died and his estate was sold up I had to quit Whinbank Farm. I was gettin' ower awd for a big spot like that anyway, and both my lads was set on emigrating to Canada. There was nobbut missus and me. We bought spot where we are now, and forty acres of grazing up near Low Moor, with grazing on t'moor for fifty ewes. Adder Howe, they call that spot. But it's a long way away, and I've had to sell my ewes."

Both of us had good reason to remember Adder

Howe. It was on the upper part of the Mill Beck, not far from its source on the moor. A mile or so over the moor, across the coastal watershed, was another beck which ran south and finally joined a river discharging into the Yorkshire Ouse. This beck had always contained trout, but it was small, the water peaty, and fish normally never grew to any size. At one place the then owner of the moor (a wealthy and, except in the grouse shooting season, absentee landlord) had built a concrete dam across the valley, making a mere of about three acres. Its purpose had been to attract waterfowl, especially duck. The original trout in the beck, presumably trapped when the wall was completed, had found in it an abundant and inexhaustible supply of food, stimulating to growth and reproduction, and we had discovered this one evening when we were on our way back from a futile fishing of the lower reaches of the beck. The whole surface of the mere was rippled with rising fish, some of them really big.

As I'd been given permission to fish the beck years before, I did not feel that I should be poaching, although I knew that the moor had changed ownership several times since my permission had been granted. There was no notice board near the mere. Besides, the whole moor was regarded as common land. The weather had been warm and close, without any wind. For a long time the fish refused to take artificial fly, although I tried every variety. Then just at dusk a sudden wind sprang up, blowing away the real fly the fish were feeding on, and from that moment every cast I made resulted in a rise. I caught nearly a score and there was not one under a pound in weight.

The lateness of the hour, and the signs of an approaching thunderstorm, had compelled us to give up while the fish were still rising. Our shortest way back to the village was by way of Adder Howe. Close by the beck there was an old, partly ruined barn, and we were in sight of the place when the storm broke with tremendous violence. Many of its slates were off, but we found shelter in it and we'd made a fire on the stone floor of sticks and turf we'd pulled from a turf stack nearby. How often in Cornwall we had thought of that adventure, recalling the smell of the turf, the taste of the trout we had grilled over it. Certainly the biggest advantage this place had over Cornwall was its variety. There were moors in Cornwall, and trout streams, but none near to where we had lived. Here we had both.

I was closely studying the expression on the old man's face. I saw nothing in it to suggest that in him we had encountered another Joe Hoskins. He looked as hard as nails. I was aware of a dryness in my mouth, of a shakiness in my voice when I asked the question on his answer to which the whole of our future hung.

"I don't suppose," I said, "you'd think of selling us a bit of this land?"

The look I saw in his eyes then was, I thought, one of cupidity. He did not, to my temporary relief, answer at once. He jerked the reins of his pony.

"Come on, Snowball." And as he turned the pony round for the path he said: "I've never thought of sellin' this spot. We'll have a look at it from t'hill top."

We followed him up to the level patch, not daring to

speak. He stopped. For nearly a minute, and it seemed like hours, we stood there in silence. And then he said:

"It's a bit of good grass this. I put a ton of slag on it last back-end, and it's fetched t'clover up. So you want to build a house here, do you? How much of it would you want?"

"I shouldn't mind buying the lot, if you didn't ask too big a price."

"You couldn't build anywhere on the bank. It's all soft ground there in wintertime, and bottom half on it is slowly slipping into t' beck."

"No. It would have to be up here on the level, but we'd need the water, or at least the right to use it."

"Aye, of course. You couldn't build a house where there wasn't water. It's a good spring that. It never dries up."

He wouldn't, I thought with rising hopes, have talked like this if he hadn't got it in his mind to sell. He was just trying to make up his mind how much he dare ask for it.

"Did you say you'd seen some other spots?"

"We haven't seen them yet. We've only been thinking about them. This place would suit us all right, especially as it's got a spring. We've only been back in Yorkshire a few days. We haven't had time to look around."

There was another long and dreadful silence. And then he said:

"Nay. I'm not goin' to sell this spot, either whole or a bit on it. It's the only spare bit o' grazin' there is handy. I've got to think of my missus. Doctors have told me I've got a bad heart, and that I mightn't last much longer. Missus has always been used to having some cows an' calves to look after. When I'm gone, she'll need this spot. You can't build your house here."

For a moment I felt that I could not believe that I heard what he said. It was the sort of thing that happens in a nightmare. It was incredible that all that we had planned and hoped for could just suddenly come to nothing like this. I looked at Dain. There were tears in her eyes. I said:

"Do you really mean it? We don't intend to build a big house. We could manage with quite a small plot, and we'd give you a good price for it."

The old man jerked at the reins, and the pony which had started to crop the grass, reluctantly raised its head.

"Nay. I'm not going to sell. But I tell you what. I'll sell you a bit of land up at Adder Howe, and cheap too. There's plenty of water there. I'll sell you an acre for twenty quid, and choose where you like."

"Adder Howe? But we want to be near the sea. That's why this place looked like suiting us. Adder Howe's miles from the sea."

"Aye, of course. It's on the moor edge gettin' on for three miles from the sea. You'd need a gallower, if you weren't too fond of walking like me. But you're close by the high road to Burnharbour, with buses running every half hour in summer time."

I looked at Dain again. She seemed suddenly cheerful.

"We certainly ought to go and look at Adder Howe," she said. "It isn't such a long way from the sea. If we got a quiet pony, we could have panniers for the children, or we might even have a trap. We could get down to the shore whenever we liked."

"Aye. You'd want a gallower summat like Snowball, but a bit younger. I had a trap for her, but woodworm got into it, and the wheels fell to bits. I've still got the harness . . . Now, if you want to see Adder Howe I'll take you up now. I've got some bullocks grazin' there an' I haven't seen 'em for a week. I've been ower badly."

I felt no enthusiasm. To live three miles from the sea would, in effect, be as bad as living twenty miles from it, or out of sight or sound of it completely. We should not be able to keep a boat, for a boat on this coast needed constant vigilance. We should rarely be able to be 'first-on' along the beach after the ebb of a rough sea, and if we were, and found anything that had washed up, we'd never be able to carry it home if it were heavy. Adder Howe was at least five hundred feet above sea level, the lanes that led to it, if I remembered them rightly, were very steep in parts, and any pony—even if we could ever afford one—would find it hard going pulling a trap. Yet, without transport, we should never be able to get to and from the beach with the children unless we took a whole day for it. Even this place was not so good as Cornwall in that respect. There the sea had been at our front door, and if our boats dried out on the ebb tide, even in the wildest weather, they were safe at their moorings. But there was no going back to Cornwall. I thought of Butcher's Folly. And I said grimly:

"All right. We'll have a look at Adder Howe."

3

IT WAS awful, turning our backs against the sea, and that entrancing view which we had imagined was to be permanently ours; walking back along the lane, which only a few minutes before I had surveyed with such satisfaction. I felt angry with the old man. To think that we were going to be denied the fulfilment of our dream for the sake of a couple of wretched cows which undoubtedly would thrive better and be happier on hay and cake, fed to them in a cowshed, where at least there would be no flies to worry them on a summer's day. I thought of presenting this argument to him. Of suggesting that we might give him sufficient money for a piece of his land for him to buy fodder, or rent grazing on a neighbour's farm. I knew that he had made up his mind and that no argument, however logical, would move him.

We progressed along the lane without speaking. There was no sound except the pony's hoofs, and his breathing, and the buzz of the flies round his head. We opened the gate at the crossroads, and we turned up the road towards the station. The heat which we had found so exhilarating at the start of our expedition had now become oppressive, although the sky was blue as ever, and there was no sign of a thunderstorm. I'd thought that if all had gone well about ,the site we'd have celebrated by walking down to the beach and having our first swim for many years in the North Sea. It had looked every bit as warm and as enticing as one of our Cornish coves.

Soon we were even out of sight of the sea. But the old man had begun to talk, to give us a long and intimate account of his bodily afflictions. It wasn't only his heart that was bad. He'd got rheumatics, and gallstones. He'd been laid up with shingles a while back. All his body had been covered with sores. His stomach was bad. He couldn't eat a proper meal without having indigestion. He couldn't drink a pint of beer without wishing he hadn't. If it wasn't for Snowball he wouldn't be able to get anywhere, for the rheumatics in his legs were so bad he could scarcely walk at all.

We reached Browe railway station, passed by another farm and began to climb a steep grass road. To my relief, although it did not make him more cheerful, he changed the subject of his monologue from disease to farming. Things were bad, and they were getting worse. They hadn't been so bad during the war. You could get fair prices for stock and poultry, butter and eggs. Butter had been up to four bob a pound in winter time, eggs as much a dozen, and always a market for 'em. You'd get a good price for lambs and bullocks and pigs. Sheep were worth keeping then. Fleece from the moor sheep would fetch two shillings a pound. Now the price wasn't worth the job of shearing them. Farmers were being robbed and ruined. . .

He went on and on. Soon I was only half-listening to him for as the road climbed the view was opening up.

Glancing back, one could see the sea again, and the whole sweep of the bay between its two headlands. The level fields reaching to the cliff edge of the middle part of the bay had become a mosaic, broken by the wooded valley of the two becks, and rising on both sides of us to the edge of the moors. We were almost level with the lowest part of the moor. As though she had read my thoughts, Dain remarked:

"It *is* lovely up here. Look—there's Black Howes, where we found the flint spear head. Do you remember the bog just beyond it, with the cotton grass, and the red sundew plants that catch flies? And the smell of the bog-myrtle?"

Black Howes (the word 'Howe' signifies a tumulus) was a group of three tumuli near the edge of the moor, on the seaward slope of the land that formed the watershed between our becks and the one that ran south, the one that had on it the artificial mere with the trout. It was on the tip of my tongue to ask the old man who owned the moor now, but I thought better of it.

It was undoubtedly lovely. There had been nothing near our Cornish home to compare with this. As we drew near to the top of the hill the whole breadth of the moor came in sight, and due west it reached to the horizon in a series of gently rising hills, almost like waves, with no field to break them and only an occasional wind-bent pine. On almost every hill crest, either singly or in groups, were tumuli. This was all real heather moor, with no bloom on it yet. It was predominately brown with small patches of green where the bracken had got a hold. In another month it would be a sea of purple.

The hill we were climbing, although not so high as that of High Moor, was higher than the nearest margin of Low Moor, still about a mile distant. At its top, the grass road became a cart lane, with high dry-stone walls, and there was a gentle gradient to the west, so that when we gained it we lost sight of the sea again. The hill indeed formed a sort of ridge, and to the north and south of it fields sloped down into the valleys of Mill and Browe Beck, which were still wooded, although not so thickly as near the sea. Mill Beck was now much nearer to us than the other one. We could see the Hall where the little squire had lived, and a lane leading up the opposite side of its valley, above the wood, and giving access to several widely separated farms by joining lanes. The beck here was called Howe Beck, and one of the farms, close by the beck itself, was called Howe Beck Mill. There was a stone bridge, and there had once been a mill, but it had been washed away in a flood. The land on the moor side of the Mill, up to the moor itself, was known as Adder Howe. Apart from the barn we had sheltered in, there were no buildings on it. I pointed.

"Is that it?"

"Aye. That's Adder Howe, on t' other side of the beck. It goes up from the beck, above Howe Beck Mill Wood, alongside Pricky Bank. That's Jimmy Bond's spot, to the moor edge. There's five fields more or less level, and I believe they were once ploughed and grew corn, but that was afore my time. They've been let gan to rack and ruin. There's a stone wall running along the moor, and a thorn fence between my spot and Jimmy Bond's. But I'll bet that his ewes and lambs is all on my land now. He'll do nowt

39

to stop 'em straying. It's my belief Jimmy trains his sheep to break down fences."

It was the first funny remark that the old man had made and, as we laughed, he qualified it.

"Aye, he's a smart chap is Jimmy. Cunning—that's what he is. He can talk the hind legs off a donkey. A great hand at borrowin' things and forgetting to pay 'em back. He's nowt of a farmer, except for moor sheep. I've never yet found one of Matt Pashby's sheep on my land. Matt's at Bog Hall. His land runs from this side of the beck. Matt, like me, is getting on in years, and he's nobbut in a poor way for brass."

The names of both these farmers were only vaguely familiar to me.

"Who owns the beck?" I asked.

"I do, from above the mill as far as the moor."

"Who lives at the mill farm now?"

"A chap called Sam Briggs. Another smart 'un. A foreigner too. He's only been here ten years. Full of modern ideas about farming. But it's my opinion he knows nowt. His wife never stops yapping. She's like a cackling hen. Sam owns the beck only where it runs through the wood. The rest of it is mine."

"I believe there are trout in it," said Dain.

"They're very small," I said, speaking from longer experience. "It's too rocky, and too swift."

For the moment, my sense of disappointment about Browe Beck Cove was revived. Nothing, I felt, could ever have half of its attractions and advantages. I felt a renewed irritation against the old man who was leading us farther and farther away from what we really wanted.

The walled cart road led into a fir plantation, then to a crossroads, with one lane leading straight on to the farm of Bog Hall, and another downhill through the plantation towards Howe Beck Mill and Wood.

We turned into this lane, which followed the course of a tiny, boggy stream, a tributary of the main beck. Our view of Adder Howe and the moors was shut off by the trees: firs to the right of us, oaks to the left, taller as we drew into the shelter of the valley. Soon we saw below us the tiles of the mill farm, and then, a hundred yards or so short of the farm, we came to a gate on our left, and a narrow lane leading into the wood. It was a stout oak gate, beautifully made, and hung on massive posts of dressed sandstone. There was a panel on the top bar, with the word PRIVATE cut into it: a relic of the reign of the little squire. It had always been padlocked when I was a boy. Now it was just latched.

We entered the wood. Here there was only an unfenced and muddy cart track. The oaks were tall, and close together. They were in full leaf, and the sunlight penetrated them in narrow beams which dappled the moist and luxuriant undergrowth of ferns and wild garlic and wood anemones. It was cool and still with no sound except the buzzing of the flies until we neared the beck, with its low chuckling. We came upon it at a bend in the lane. I had forgotten how beautiful and clear it was. It wasn't big. There was a level, gravelly ford, and here the stream was scarcely half an inch deep. Immediately below there were two big jagged sandstone blocks thickly grown with moss, and between them the water narrowed and fell into a pool, fringed with tall

41

ferns. Snowball made for the pool, and I saw the flash of a small trout as he bent down to drink.

"Whose is the wood?" I asked. "It isn't yours is it?"

"Nay. This belongs to Sam Briggs of Howe Beck Mill. But I've got a right of way through it to Adder Howe. We'll come to my gate in a minute."

He pulled at the reins again, and we crossed the beck. The road now was scarcely discernible, but the pony knew the way and, inspired with his drink, moved up the opposite bank almost at a trot. We came to a high stone wall, the boundary of the wood itself. There was another gate. It was broken, its latch missing, and it was tied to its post with rusty wire and binder twine. Beyond it and above it the land, mostly covered with whins and bramble and bracken, rose steeply, and there was another watercourse up which the road climbed for about fifty yards to a small relatively level area, above which it continued out of sight. On this level area stood the old barn where we had sheltered from the thunderstorm. Another minute we had reached it, and the old man drew up, and at once started to curse.

"I thought as much! I thought as much! There's Jimmy Bond's bloody sheep everywhere."

We had heard the bleating of sheep and lambs even before we had entered the wood. And now we saw them. Some were inside the building, which was divided in the middle into a cow byre and barn proper, with a doorway to each, but no door; some were cropping the rough grass on the bank above, others were in the watercourse, which here ran parallel to the length of the building. They were black-faced, moorland sheep: ewes with half-grown lambs which certainly looked most picturesque and attractive to us but evidently not to Isaac, for he cursed and shouted at them, driving them away.

The building was in a worse state than when we had seen it last. More of its slates were off. There was a dip in the ridge of the roof which suggested its rafters were rotting, and not far short of complete collapse. My immediate interest was not in the building, but in the view. The sea had become visible again over the top of the wood, down the valley of Howe and Mill Beck between the slopes of the ridge we had walked along, and the high ground to the north where the little squire's Hall stood. Both the headlands of the bay were hidden, but it looked as though we would get the whole bay if we found a suitable site, higher up the hill. There was a view of the moors too, to the south. Black Howes was clearly visible. From the actual top of the hill we were on there should be a magnificent panorama. It *was* a long way from the sea, but as second best Adder Howe had distinct possibilities. Dain was more interested in the building. The old man was still shouting at the sheep, and she said to me excitedly:

"It would make a wonderful stable, wouldn't it, if we mended the roof. Do let's ask him if he'll let it to us, if we bought a piece of land from him. He might even sell it to us. I think this place would be almost as good as the other. I *like* it."

"It's not bad," I said. "But we've got to see the whole place first. There's no room to build here. We've got to see the top fields, and don't forget we've got to have a water supply, *and* a road. No lorry could ever get up the way we've come, but I think there is some sort of track across the moor to the highway. The higher we go the farther we get from the beck. This little stream doesn't look any good."

Indeed, it scarcely was a stream, the one close to the barn. It was more like a bog, with sedges growing thickly round it and the water itself liquid mud churned up by the sheep and mixed with their droppings. I was struck by the fact that, if it had been clear, it would have borne an extraordinary resemblance to the stream which ran alongside our Cornish hut. The old man turned to us again.

"There's no sign of them beasts o' mine. I'll have to ride along the hedges and walls, and find 'em, and see where these bloody sheep is gettin' in, so if you want to see the whole spot you'd best come. We'll go up alongside Jimmy Bond's first."

He led the way across the bog. There was a path leading up and slightly to the right, among the whins and brambles, and it brought us soon to the boundary fence, when it turned to follow the fence straight up the hill to the first of the Adder Howe fields. It was not level, for the land was still rising towards the invisible moorland boundary, but it had a much lesser gradient than the bank we had climbed. It was patched with whins, themselves cropped by sheep as closely as a privet hedge, and the grass between was beaten down by their feet and the traffic of rabbits. There had been dry walls between this field and the next. Only a few stones, and a single upright stone gatepost remained of them. The view was widening, and still we were not at the top.

Even here the upward slope was not so steep that it would have precluded building. But we were a long way from the beck. There was no sign of any spring.

We kept along the boundary fence which was of overgrown thorn, interlaced in the thin parts with barbed wire and rusty netting. Suddenly Snowball whinnied. From the other side of the fence came an answering whinny, and then the sound of cantering hoofs, and just ahead of us we saw a man on a handsome chestnut horse pull up at a place where the fence was low, evidently waiting for us. I knew him by sight. I didn't know his name. He was middle-aged, well built, with a pleasant, good-humoured face, and a faintly mocking expression. I guessed rightly that it was Jimmy Bond, and by the scowl on Isaac's face I thought we were going to witness a row. But Jimmy smiled and gave him a disarming greeting.

"Now, Mr Benson. How are you keeping? I haven't seen you for a while."

We stopped.

"Nay," The old man growled. "I've been badly with me stomach and rheumatics."

Jimmy looked most sympathetic.

"I'm sorry to hear that. Very sorry. I'm riding round looking for some ewes and lambs of mine. You haven't seen owt on 'em, have you?"

"You must be deaf if you can't hear 'em." The old man retorted smartly. "T'beggars is all on my land, down by the barn."

Jimmy looked surprised.

"*Are* they? Aye, I can hear 'em now. I wonder how

they've got in. This hedge is all right. It must be that gate on the moor wall. Your bullocks broke that down the other day. I found 'em in my barley, and drove 'em back and mended the gate."

"Where are they now? Have you seen 'em?"

"Aye. They're down by the beck, at top end of your wood. Least they were there this morning, when I rode round."

"Queer you didn't see them straying ewes of yours same time."

"Aye. But I didn't ride across your land. Well, I'll get 'em driven out. I'll have a look at that gate. . . So long."

He swung his horse round and cantered away up his field and we saw that he was accompanied by a black and white collie. The old man was fuming.

"He's a sly beggar. He only came cantering up because he heard us. I'll lay he drove them sheep in hissen, and that they've been in since last time I was up. But I'll lay my bullocks wouldn't have a mouthful of his barley before he had 'em driven out."

He led on to the next field. Here the whins were less frequent, but there were patches of bracken, the grass was coarse, and there was no continuous fence. It was almost level, however, and when we reached the middle of it what slope there was was towards the moor, only one field away. We had gained the highest point of Adder Howe, and the view, as I had expected, was magnificent in every direction. There were miles of almost unbroken moor reaching due west. The whole vale of Bramblewick, with its mosaic of fields, lay below us to the east. The headland of High Batts was foreshortened, and its profile less bold, but there was the whole bay, with the roofs of the village making a red patch at the northern end. The view was certainly more extensive and perhaps more beautiful than the one we would have had from Browe Beck Cove. One could not, however, choose a site for a house just for its view, and of more practical interest was the aspect we were now given of the whole of Adder Howe, and its boundaries. The old man had sighted his bullocks, sheltering from the sun under a clump of rowan trees at the far end of the valley of the beck, and he pulled up.

"Aye. There they are. They look all right. Now what about this bit of land you said you wanted?"

"Did you say we could pick where we liked?"

I had a suspicion that he hesitated before he answered.

"Aye. That's what I said."

"Is there any road to Adder Howe apart from the lane we came up to the barn?"

"I won't say there's a real road, but there's an old cart track leading from my gate across the moor to the high road. You can see it from here."

There was one more field between us and the edge of the moor and the boundary wall. It would be about five acres, with no whins in it, but with a patch of encroaching bracken at the farther end, and here and there outcrops of lightish-coloured weathered rock. Clearly this was land that had originally been moor. It could have been of little value except for grazing. About a quarter of a mile across the moor was the main motor road, with telegraph poles, and a fairly busy traffic of private cars, trucks, and holiday charabancs. There were two red, single-deck buses in sight, moving in opposite directions. There was a gate in the boundary wall. Jimmy, who must have had a similar gate in his own field and ridden with self-righteous haste along the moor, was just passing through it. There was a distinct track leading from the gate, across what looked like fairly boggy ground to the highway. The same track ran from inside the gate, through more clumps of whins, down to the barn. Was the track metalled, I asked? He didn't know, but it was hard enough in dry weather. There were plenty of stones lying on the moor to fill up the boggy bits.

The land fell in the direction of the high road, and it would be out of sight of the sea. Here, where we stood, would be admirable if we were thinking only of the view and lines of communication. It would be very exposed, however, and while there was a great advantage in being near a road where there were buses it was a snag being as near as this. And there was another supremely important matter.

"Is there any water on this part of the land?"

"Nay. It's too well-drained. There's plenty of water in the beck down below. But the only other water is that that goes past the barn."

"But that's all muddy."

"Not where it comes out of the ground among the whins above the barn. It's a good spring that. We'll go and have a look at it."

As we moved off again, Dain gave me a nudge, and whispered:

"That's the place for us, close to the barn. I'm certain

he'd let us use the barn if we mended the roof and looked after it for him, and kept the sheep away."

"I don't think there's room there. It looks as though the barn itself occupies all the level land."

I felt no enthusiasm. Indeed I was having a powerful longing for our Cornish home, wishing we had never left it, our little cove, and our boats. Things were simple there. Here everything looked complicated and difficult. We were moving down towards the barn, Snowball picking his own way between the clumps of whins. Farther along the bank, Jimmy had just finished rounding up his sheep, and was driving them up towards the moor gate. The old man glared in his direction, but said nothing. We reached the barn, and he stopped. Then he said, ill-temperedly:

"Now then. You can have a look at that spring by yoursens. I've had enough of trapesing about. And you'd best make up your minds quick as to whether you want to buy a bit o' land or not. I've got to get back for milkin', and I don't want to waste any more of my time up here."

It was not an encouraging speech, and I felt like making an angry retort, telling him to go to the devil with his bit of land. After all, it was he who had suggested our coming up. I said nothing. He was a genuinely sick man. This business of his neighbour's sheep had obviously upset him deeply. We made our way up a little gully reaching from the bog. There were alders and sallow growing between the sedges, and moss, but no more mud, and soon we saw the trickle of clean water among the undergrowth. I forced my way through a clump of bramble and whins, and saw the water emerging from

49

the ground. It was a real spring. It was not more than fifty yards from the barn, and it was at least thirty feet above it. We retraced our footsteps. The old man still looked truculent.

"Well, did you find it?"

"Yes. It seems a good spring. But there doesn't seem to be any level spot down here where we could build a house, except close up to the barn."

"Well, that's not my fault, is it?" he said testily.

There was, I thought, just about room between the barn and the bog to build a small house, and it was almost level. The barn itself was built on the edge of what was practically a cliff falling to the edge of the wood. Had it not been there we should have had ample space for all we wanted, for our garden could have been made on the slope of the hill on the other side of the bog. Without much hope, I said:

"I suppose you wouldn't sell us an acre round here, including the barn itself?"

"Nay. I'm not sellin' the barn. And if you can't find another spot to suit, then we might as well give it up, and gan our ways. And dammit it'll be a nuisance anyway, having the land split up. You'd best give up the idea altogether and look for another spot. I'll not sell just a bit on it. I've changed my mind about that."

My heart sank.

"What do you mean?"

"I mean that I'll sell the whole spot, or nowt at all. And there it is. Take it or leave it."

I looked at Dain. I could see that she was stunned. Again I felt furious. It looked as though he had got us up here under false pretences. But I kept my anger down. I said, and I meant it ironically:

"And how much do you want for the whole place?"

I was prepared for him to say (and I had multiplied his twenty pounds for an acre by forty) eight hundred or perhaps even a thousand pounds. He said, without hesitation:

"Three hundred pounds."

"For the whole land, including the barn?"

"Aye."

I felt my heart pounding.

"Is it freehold?"

"Aye. And there's nobbut two pounds a year tithe on it. Only thing is that the mineral rights belong to the Lord of the Manor."

I laughed.

"That means, I suppose, that if there's a seam of coal anywhere, it wouldn't be mine."

He did not answer. I looked at Dain. She knew that all we had in the bank was just a little over three hundred pounds, out of which we had not only to buy a site, but build our house too. But her eyes were saying "yes". I said to him:

"It's a lot of money for us. It's about all we've got. Will you give us another five minutes to consider it?"

"Aye. But I'll not take a ha'penny less, think on. And you wouldn't get it for that price if it wasn't such a long way from where I live and I wasn't so badly. I tell you what. I'll just ride up and have a look at them bullocks of mine. And then I'll come back. It's three hundred pounds, and I won't stand any waitin' for it. I'll want it settled up within a week."

He rode off up the hill. We were alone. My heart was still pounding. Dain got hold of my arm.

"We've *got* to take it. It's terribly cheap. Just imagine. Forty acres of our very own. A stream of our own. Why the barn alone must be worth nearly three hundred pounds at least. There *is* just room to build here between it and the stream. It wouldn't take long to mend the roof. We might even live inside the barn until we got our house built."

"Build it with what?" I said grimly. "We'll have just nothing if we buy this."

"Oh, we'll get the money somehow or other. We could borrow on the land itself once it was ours."

That, I thought, was possibly true. Freehold land was supposed to be one of the soundest of all securities. That was why so many of the local farms had been bought up by investors. But then, presumably, they had plenty of spare money lying in their banks. We had not. But an idea was already starting to take shape in my mind.

"Let's have a look at the barn," I said.

We stepped in through one of the doorways, into the very place where we had made our fire and sheltered from the storm. It was surprisingly large and this was only one half of the whole building. There was a window space in the wall opposite to the door. We looked out of it down to the wood over the tree tops, and down the valley of the beck to the sea. It was a perfect view. We could see the sky through the roof.

Some of the rafters were worm-eaten and rotten. But the walls were sound and of immense thickness. They were straight, and the flagged floor was level. I paced the floor. It measured twenty feet by twenty, making a length of forty feet for the whole building, and I said, with sudden excitement:

"Gosh! *This* could be our house. We could take off the roof. Build up another storey, and put the roof back. There would be space for a living-room, lounge, bathroom on the ground floor. At least three bedrooms above."

There was a note of disappointment in Dain's voice.

"Do you mean give up the idea of having it as a stable?"

"Yes, my love. We could build a wooden stable, when we needed one, on the small level place outside. If it was wood it needn't have an absolutely level site, and a stable needn't have a view. This place could be marvellous. We've got the water too, and above the level of the house. It wouldn't need pumping. It's almost ideal. It's not so *very* far from the sea either. We can at least see it."

Dain looked happier.

"There's the stream too," she said. "I'd almost forgotten about that. And a wood, all of our own. And the moors. Yes, it would make a wonderful house. There's heaps of room for a stable outside. Let's go and explore the whole place. Won't the children just love it. We'll have to have huge windows in the wall facing the sea. Oh, let's go and tell the old man at once that we'll buy it. We've just got to. I do hope he hasn't changed his mind again."

We moved out, and saw him coming down the hill again. I tried to appear calm and businesslike. He drew up.

"Now then. Have you made up your minds?"

"Yes," I said. "It's not exactly the sort of place we're looking for, but we'll take it."

He looked surprised.

"Oh. You'll have it, eh? And what about the brass?"

"That will be all right. I'll give you a cheque straight away for thirty pounds. That's the usual ten per cent. The rest when we see the deeds. Have you got a lawyer?"

"Aye. I don't have much to do with them beggars as a rule, but you've got to have 'em for a job like this, I reckon. But I'm not goin' to pay owt for what *they* charge. I'll be in Burnharbour tomorrow."

"If I give you a cheque, and write out a receipt, will you sign it now?"

Again he looked suspicious.

"Aye. But I'll need to see all of the brass before I sign owt else. You wouldn't like to buy them bullocks while you're at it?"

I did not look at Dain.

I said no, and I felt in my pocket for my chequebook.

4

THE LIFE of a writer is traditionally precarious. Our banking account was like the temperature chart of a fever case, up and down, with the downs unfortunately not signifying that things were going well. But it's better to be born lucky than rich. We were lucky!

None of my books so far had made much money directly. But I had sold the film rights of one, producing the present record high. One had produced a lady fan who lived in a castle in the Hebrides, who had made us periodic gifts of salmon, grouse and venison. Soon after the publication of my first book I had received an extraordinary letter. It was from a young man who was living by himself in a caravan. He congratulated me on the reviews the book had got and on the fact that, as claimed in the publisher's advertisements, it was doing so well and looked like being a best-seller. What he liked about the book, however, was that it showed that I must have a distinct leaning towards Communism.

He was a Communist himself. His parents had been rich, and he had recently been left half of a large fortune. He had given it all away for conscientious reasons, and now he was living like a hermit and feeling much happier for doing so. The letter vexed me, for I was not a Communist, and could think of nothing in the book to suggest that I was. True, it had gone into a second edition within a week of publication, but the first printing had been only 1000 copies. We had already spent the fifty-pound advance on royalties. We were particularly hard up at the time and it was just before Amelia was born.

I had written back telling him of our circumstances, and denied that I was a Communist, and I had expanded on a subject I was then feeling rather strongly about. A Labour Government, with a 'near' Communist Prime Minister, Ramsay MacDonald, was ruling our country. Economically the country was in a mess. Three-quarters of the British mercantile fleet was laid up. In our own port there were scores of idle ships. Millions of British workmen were on the dole. And yet MacDonald himself had just launched a public appeal for a fund of £100,000 to buy the *Codex Sinaiticus* from the Bolsheviks. It was not the original manuscript of the Bible anyway, and what better off would our country be for having it?

I had ended that letter (which I nearly tore up, for the man seemed a crank) with a postscript. What a pity, I said, that he hadn't read my book before he had given away his fortune. By return of post came a letter from him containing a cheque, which, until I had read the letter, I dared not look at. He had been deeply moved by my letter, it said, so much so that he had shown it to his sister who still lived in the family mansion. She had shared the family inheritance but did not as yet share his Communistic views. She hadn't read my book, but she had been most impressed with my letter, especially by my remarks about Ramsay MacDonald and the *Codex*. She was a member of the Church of England, and as the

Church had backed the *Codex* appeal, she had been just about to send a cheque for twenty-five pounds to the fund. On reading my letter she had decided to send it to us, and it was enclosed.

We were worried about that cheque. It was almost like sacrilege taking it; like robbing the poor box of a church. We felt that we ought to send at least five pounds of it to the Society for the Propagation of the Gospel, or the Home for Aged Clergymen, or some similar religious charity. We compromised by sending two pounds ten to a fund for the relief of the local unemployed. The balance just covered the maternity fees of our firstborn.

Always, we had found, something would turn up when we were in a jam; things like serial rights, and foreign publication rights, commissions for articles for newspapers or magazines. I had written another book too, which was to be published in the spring and this *might* prove to be a real bestseller. The fact that we would have less than twenty pounds left in the bank when the purchase of Adder Howe was completed, and that we had no regular income except my small war disability pension, did not seriously worry us. Quite apart from having found and acquired a site for our home with the house itself already half-built, there was no doubt that we had made a great financial bargain.

This was confirmed by the friendly Burnharbour lawyer with whom I discussed the matter next morning. If old Isaac's title to the estate was sound, and there was no reason to suppose it was not, the price was exceptionally low even in these days of agricultural depression. The tide would turn. In a few years, and especially if there was another war, its value might easily double or even treble. It should not be difficult to get a building society to advance the cost of converting the barn into a dwelling house, although owing to its isolated situation we might have to pay a little more than the usual rate of interest. It would take a week or two to investigate, draw up the conveyance and complete the purchase. In the meantime we should make up our minds as to what sort of a house we were going to build, go into the matter of cost with an architect or builder, get plans drawn. As soon as we had done that we could discuss the matter of a loan.

We set off for Adder Howe after lunch. The bus service along the moorland road was a more convenient link with Butcher's Folly than the railway was with Browe Beck Cove. The lawyer had loaned us a six-inch ordnance map which showed the boundaries of the property and every field (or once field) with its acreage. This in itself was an exciting document, like the plan of a treasure island, and although we were both fairly familiar with the main features of the place, it was as though we were exploring it for the first time. The map showed that on the moor, quite close to our boundary, were several tumuli. The massive stone wall that enclosed the wood below the barn was marked as an ancient monument. I remembered that the little squire maintained that this wall, which continued along the other side of the valley, had been built by the monks of Burnharbour Priory and had enclosed a deer park. He had a theory too that the monks had some sort of a chapel near Adder Howe.

The wood ended about fifty yards up-beck from the gateway. The wall was broken by the beck itself and then continued up the opposite bank at right angles to the beck and the boundary became a thorn fence running parallel to the beck at a distance of about ten yards, clearly indicating that both banks belonged to Adder Howe. Alongside the beck, crossing it and re-crossing it, was an overgrown path, the one that had brought us from the moor and the trout mere the evening of the storm. As in the wood, the beck was clear and there were a few trout in it. They were small, for most of the bed of the beck consisted of hard sandstone.

The beck itself was beautiful. It fell in a series of little waterfalls, each with a pool. The vegetation on the banks was not so luxuriant as in the shaded wood, but there were tall ferns at the water's edge, and if there were no tall trees there were alders, rowans and birches, and several stunted oaks, reminding us of those which grew near our Cornish creek. About a hundred yards up from where the wall ended the valley turned and widened into a sort of glade, with a patch of almost level ground. There was a rocky mound in the middle of the patch round where the beck divided, making a miniature island. There was grass on the patch, cropped short as a lawn by rabbits. And by the beck was a patch of clean sand. We must have seen this place dozens of times in the past, alone or together, without noting anything special about it. But now Dain cried enthusiastically.

"What a wonderful place for the children to play in. Look, there's everything. There's grass, and sand, and a pool, where they can paddle and bathe in summer. It's almost as good as the seashore. There's a real island for them, and stones to build a little castle. It's ideal. Let's call this place the island."

It certainly *was* an ideal place for children. The pool just above the mound was small, but if it were dammed its length could be increased to about thirty feet, without making any part of it more than a foot deep. There was also, close to the grassy part, a gnarled oak with a branch perfectly shaped to hold the ropes of a swing.

I could not help noticing, however, that the place offered another exciting possibility. The valley immediately down beck was narrow, with naked rock on each side. It would, I thought, require only about twenty feet of stone or concrete wall, about eight feet high in the middle, to dam the stream and make a pool of considerable size. Such a wall would check the scouring action of the stream, especially during spates, and would soon result in an accumulation of gravel and sand and mud on the bottom. Plants would root in this and snails and insect larvae would establish themselves and multiply for the benefit of the trout. It was the same beck, which, lower down near to the sea, ran into the mill dam I had fished in as a boy, and which had first inspired my ambition to own a dam and breed trout. It could be almost as big, and deep. There was no reason why it should not drive a waterwheel powerful enough to generate electricity.

It *was* indeed an exciting possibility. It was not, I recognised at once, anything more than that. The building of the wall would be expensive. It would need expert designing, and would have to be very strong to withstand flood water. A waterwheel was not likely to be cheap, even if we could get one second hand. It would need foundations, and probably a lengthy sluice. Besides it would mean that almost the whole of the level area, including the mound and the sand, and even the trunk of the oak tree, would be submerged. A pool deep enough to breed and fatten trout, to ensure enough water to keep a wheel going in periods of drought, would be dangerous for small children. In all things the children must come first. And the first and most urgent thing was to build the house itself.

We had thought that, in the light of the experience of our Cornish home, we knew just what we wanted in our new and permanent one. We were not architects however. We knew our limitations. Once we had got our site, it had been our intention to employ an architect to draw the plans, provided we could find one who could do it at a figure we could afford, and would be willing to put our own ideas into practical shape, and not intrude his own too strongly. This had been on the assumption that we were going to start from scratch, that we should decide even the shape of the foundations. These, and the overall dimensions of the house, had been decided for us by the original builders of the barn. We could not extend or alter the shape without destroying one of the stout stone walls. We could not afford an architect. We'd have to draw the plan ourselves, then find a builder willing to collaborate with us, tell us if our ideas were feasible, tell us what the cost would be.

We wanted nothing pretentious. It was to be a house to live in: warm, light, labour-saving. But it must be agreeable to look at from the outside. As it stood the barn was not offensive, except for its slate roof, and this we would replace with one of pantiles provided we could get them of the right shape and colour. We were not going to do without any of the good things of modern house construction, just for the sake of looks.

The main room in the house, the chief centre of family activities, should be the one where food was cooked and eaten: the kitchen-living-room.

This room, we agreed, should be square or rectangular, with windows in two opposite walls, one window facing southwards and commanding the best view. The dining-table should be the same length as this window, and for most occasions should fit flush up to it, but should be within a stride or two of the stove. The stove should be in the middle of the partition wall, and not in the main wall of the room, its flue, like all other flues, going up the middle of the house to conserve warmth. The stove should be of the flat-topped, smokeless-fuel, constant-burning type, with a back boiler for hot water to bath, lavatory and sink, and it should be of the sort to give an open fire if needed.

The sink, unfortunately, would have to be in the wall facing north, but it would extend under a window from which there should be at least a pleasant aspect. In the same wall should be a doorway into a larder which itself would extend outside the main wall, so as to give adequate ventilation. On the left side of the sink should be a fixed flat table with a tiled or linoleum-covered top, big enough to hold all the soiled crockery of an ordinary family meal, and on the right of the sink a conventional sloping draining-board. There should be a built-in dresser with cupboards, shelves and hooks on the wall facing the stove. Saucepans should be on racks on each side of the stove.

In preparing a meal everything you needed would be in easy reach, and by having the table flush with the wall there would be no need to walk round it. Chairs could fit under it until needed and they might be of the folding wood and canvas type. The table itself would have a linoleum-covered top, and for most occasions mugs were better than cups and saucers. In washing up you would work from left to right. The crockery, when dried, would be put back on the hooks and shelves of the dresser. It was important that the sink should be of the right height for a normal person, so that he or she should not have to bend over it.

In our Cornish kitchen-living-room we had been a long way from achieving this ideal. The stove was in the wrong place, and because of the wooden roof and partitions could not have been placed anywhere else. The sink had to be placed under the window that offered the only view (across the vegetable garden) because of the drainage; our dining-table, a fixture, had to be on one of the windowless transverse partitions because of the sloping floor. Our dresser had to be on the sink wall, and as its shelves had to be level they were several inches from being parallel with the floor and looked quite crazy. The barn, both in shape and size, seemed just right for the creation of a near perfect kitchen-living-room. After much thought we evolved a plan for the ground floor.

It was fairly simple, we thought, and should present

63

no problems to our builder. It was when we started to plan the upstairs rooms that we came up against a snag. How were we to reach them? Where should the staircase go?

"It must be a wide one," argued Dain. "It ought to be straight and have low steps because of the children."

"Yes. But the lower the steps, the more we shall need, and that will mean more horizontal space. If we have it going up from the living-room the kitchen stove and the sink will have to be moved round. If it goes up from the lounge it will spoil the shape of the room, and it won't be so cosy. What a waste of space a staircase is, anyway. That was one big advantage of our Cornish hut."

"We couldn't have it like that, could we, all on one floor?"

"Not unless we built new outer walls, the same size as the barn. And that would be losing the big advantage the barn gives us. Our house is already half-built."

"It would look wrong, anyway, being a bungalow. What a nuisance a staircase is. I hadn't realised what a lot of space it uses up. And all we really need is a ladder to get upstairs or down. But that wouldn't do for the children." And then she said: "I know what we need. An outside staircase, like they have in lots of Scottish houses and farms, and sometimes in English farms or, at any rate, farm buildings for granaries. It could be covered in, of course, not like the stone steps of a granary."

It was, I saw at once the solution to our problem. It meant an extra building, as high as the eaves, and the horizontal length of the staircase, yet only as wide as the actual steps. It could be built of timber, and we could combine it with the entrance porch which might be enlarged into a small hall from which the stairs could rise. We should need a narrow landing on the first floor, but that would be better than a staircase well, and it would give us four good-sized bedrooms.

We were very pleased with it, until the disquieting thought struck us: what was it going to cost? Having done all the repairs and alterations to our hut ourselves, with existing material, and what our landlord had given us, and dunnage, and planks washed up on the shore, we had only the vaguest idea about building costs. Timber, brick, cement, ironwork like stoves and gutters, baths, sinks, lavatory bowls, water-piping, tiles and slates had been scarce and expensive during the war (the Kaiser's war) and in the early post-war years. But prices must have come down during the current slump. The cost of labour, both skilled and unskilled, presumably was low, seeing that so many workers were unemployed, and we'd have been hypocrites if we'd pretended we were unwilling to take advantage of this in view of our own financial resources.

Studying advertisements of houses for sale, and auction prices as recorded in local newspapers, we had believed that we could get an entirely new house built for under five hundred pounds plus the cost of our site. A building society (according to their folders) would advance up to four-fifths of the value of the house, and you paid this back in instalments over a period of as much as ten years, plus interest. That meant we should have to put down only about a hundred pounds, even if it *did* come to as much as five hundred pounds. And surely, with the foundations and at least half of the main walls already built, it would not cost that.

When I was a boy, the head woodman and carpenter the little squire employed on his estate was Joe Stainforth. He was a fine craftsman and although I did not know him well, I remembered that he had a kind and jolly disposition. Every Christmastide the squire used to have quantities of holly, and a certain number of Christmas trees, cut and piled up at the lodge gates of the Hall, and it was Joe's job to superintend their distribution to any of the villagers who wanted them. The squire's idea in doing this was to stop people going into his woods and plantations and helping themselves. Anyone could have holly. The Christmas trees were reserved for regular church-goers. Joe knew that I was chapel and also a foreigner, but on the one occasion I went up to the lodge he gave me a tree almost too big for me to carry, and he also gave me an apple and a handful of walnuts that must have come from the squire's garden.

Joe lived in a cottage close to the Hall and he had a large family of sons and daughters, all of them now grown up. After the death of the squire and the breaking up of the estate he had gone to live in Burnharbour. I discovered that his youngest son Will, having served an apprenticeship with a local firm of builders and joiners had launched out on his own. He was still only in his twenties, but he had managed to get enough financial support to start a private company and acquire a disused shipyard at Burnharbour and equip it with saws and other woodworking machinery, and despite the general slump was doing well, and making quite a name for himself.

I had a telephone talk with him. I liked his voice and his manner. He knew Adder Howe. He had been born not more than two miles away from it. He knew the barn quite well. He and his brothers bad often been in it, looking for swallows' nests. Often an owl bred in it too. It was in a nice position. It should be quite suitable for conversion into a dwelling house. He had a car. If we liked, he would call for us, and drive us out, and discuss the business on the spot.

I liked Will Stainforth even more when we met him. He was full of self-confidence, but there was nothing bumptious about him, as there might well have been with a young man who had made such a rapid rise in business. He had a strong, facial resemblance to his father (as I had remembered him): fair, with broad features, strong white teeth, and a charming smile. I was eager to hear the story of his rise.

He modestly disclaimed that there was anything wonderful about it. He had been lucky in having a father who had taught him the rudiments of carpentry and joinery and encouraged his earliest ambition to become a builder. He had learnt a lot from the local firm to which he had been apprenticed, but it was an old-fashioned, stick-in-the-mud one, quite content to build a pair of semi-detached villas and a garage or two in a year. It had been a bit of luck finding this disused shipyard at Burnharbour going cheap. It was one of the original shipyards of the port that had fallen derelict when wood ships had been supplanted by iron ones, but during the war the Admiralty had taken it over for the repairing of small craft, giving it up at the war's end. Apart from the obsolete slips there was a large workshop. Much of the machinery he had installed had been ex-government too: saw-benches, lathes, moulding and planing machines, mortar and concrete mixers. He'd had to borrow the money for all this, but there had been a post-war housing shortage in the district and, having built a few houses to order, his company had started building on "spec", and every house had been sold before completion. He was now hopeful of winning the contract for a new council housing estate at Burnharbour: a matter of fifty houses, as well as road and drainage.

He was all for modern machinery, and all for the modern type of house too: built-in cupboards, steel windows, labour-saving devices. He was married, and had two children about the same age as our own. At present he was living in a terrace house in Burnharbour, using two rooms as the company's office. As soon as he'd got time and money to spare he was going to build a house for himself. He and his wife had already worked out the plans for it. It would be modern in every respect and all-electric. It would be light, warm, labour-saving. The kitchen would have a stainless steel sink. There would be a refrigerator, a washing and ironing machine, perhaps one for washing and drying dishes, and lots of other gadgets. The bathroom would be panelled with one of these new plastic materials, and have rubber floor covering and there would be a shower as well as an ordinary bath, all plumbing chromium-plated.

His car (he was obviously very proud of it) was a Chrysler. As he drove us at seventy-five miles an hour up the moorland road I thought it advisable to warn him that although we, too, were modern in our ideas about houses, we hadn't much money, and that we could not at present go in for any frills. The job had to be done as cheaply as possible, compatible with good design and sound material and workmanship. He appreciated that, he said. His own house was still a dream, and it might be a long time before he made the money to build it. All profits at present were being ploughed back into the firm.

We reached the highest point of Low Moor. The highway dipped down towards the valley of our beck. The top fields of Adder Howe were in sight, and as we neared the point where the track joined the road I started to feel anxious as to what he would think of our lines of communication. The heatwave had ended, as usual with thunderstorms, and although the weather was fine again there had been some heavy rains, and there were at least two boggy patches between the road and gate. The track itself was little more than a path between the clumps of heather. I suggested that we should pull up and proceed by foot across the moor, but he laughed.

"There's no point in walking when we can drive. You don't know this car of mine. So long as there's no deep bog we can make it."

There was no ditch to the highroad. He changed into low gear where the track began, and turned on to it. We bumped and swayed over the clumps of heather, and when we came to the boggy patches he accelerated and splashed through. We reached the boundary fence and the gateway. There was no need to get out, for the gate was open and hanging only on one hinge. I had tied it with wire to the post on our last visit, and there flashed through my mind a suspicion that someone, perhaps our neighbour Jimmy, had deliberately opened it, but I was feeling too pleased at the way we had negotiated the moor to worry about that now. We passed through and continued in second gear along the almost level bit of field towards the top of our valley. From there to the barn itself the gradient was steep, but the distance was short. I said to Will:

"Would there be any difficulty in getting building material to the place?

"Good gracious, no! I had to build a cow house on a farm up the dales, and compared with the road to that, this is a promenade. All you may need is a few railway sleepers over the soft spots on the moor. I've got a couple of five-ton trucks. They'd make a road for you if they ran over it once or twice . . . Well, you've got a view and no mistake. I'd forgotten what a lot you could see from here. And there's the barn!"

We'd come to the start of the steep bit.

"We'd better stop here," I cautioned. He smiled and carried on down the hill, and brought up practically opposite the barn doorways. As when we had seen it first there were sheep with lambs (now almost fully grown) grazing round the bog. We got out, and Dain said:

"Well, I never thought we'd be able to drive up, or rather down, in a car to our front door. I don't think we'll be able to do it with a pony and trap, though. Least not up."

"So you're going in for a pony?" Will said. "Too slow for me. You'll certainly have plenty of grazing for it. It's a long time since I saw the old barn. It certainly looks a bit the worse for wear. What are you proposing to do? Have you made any sort of plan yet?"

We had made, on squared paper, a scale drawing of the building itself, and our proposed alterations and extensions, including the exterior hall and staircase. I handed it to him with the diffidence of the amateur showing his work to the expert, and I exchanged apprehensive glances with Dain as he examined it. To our relief, however, he seemed to be most favourably impressed.

"I like the look of it," he said. "And I like the idea of having the staircase outside. That's going to give a lot of extra room. You've given the stairs an easy rise too. That's important when you've got children. I think my wife would agree with that. Where we're living at present the staircase is almost as steep as a ladder."

"It was my wife who suggested it," I said. "An easy rise and no turns. But all that outside part would be of timber, not stonework. That would cost less, wouldn't it?"

"Of course. Very much less, and it wouldn't look bad. And your idea is to use the existing main walls, and build up another storey with stone, using the same roof with the same pitch? We could save most of those slates when we pulled the roof off, but we'd need a few more, of course."

"Oh, no!" Dain put in quickly. "We *must* have a red roof. It would look awful with slates."

"I was hoping," I said, "that we might get some tiles, second hand, from some place that had been pulled down. The older the better, for the colour improves with age."

I sensed the first signs of a contrary wind. Will was looking worried.

"They're not so easy to get hold of. There aren't many firms making those sort of tiles these days. In fact, I don't know of one. They've gone out of fashion. Builders are going in for composition tiles, tinted ones. If you take my advice, you'll stick to slates. They'll not look bad, and you'll save a lot of money. Your timbering for tiles would have to be a lot stronger. But it's up to you."

I saw a strong disapproval in Dain's eyes, and I said:

"Well, can we leave that for the time being, and work out later what the difference in cost would be?"

He smiled, but I had the impression that it was "the customer is always right" sort of smile.

"All right. I like the idea of having the bathroom downstairs. My wife would agree about that for the children."

"Another of my wife's ideas," I said.

"What about the water supply?"

"I'll show you that. Quite a good spring."

"Is it going to be high enough for your service tank?"

"I believe so, but you'll have to check the level. You'll find the walls of the barn pretty sound, and straight. I think the foundations must go down to the living rock. And in spite of so many slates being off the walls are dry."

I was not an expert, but I made these assertions with complete conviction that they could not be challenged. I had closely examined every square foot of the main walls, and in several places I had removed the soil, and bared the solid sandstone rock beneath the foundations.

The walls were two feet six inches thick. Inside they were made of sandstone rubble and mortar but on the face they were of dressed blocks, with the courses varying from six to twelve inches in height. At intervals the blocks were what dry-stone wallers called 'throughs'. They extended through the width of the wall, forming a bond with the rubble. The joints between the facing blocks were not pointed. Here and there the mortar had weathered out, leaving small cavities, and some of the stones themselves were pitted with the action of wind and rain, but they were all sound, and in four walls there was not a single crack or bulge.

But all Will said was a non-commital: "Okay. We'll have a look at them."

We made a tour of the building, inside and out. I showed him the places where I had bared the rock, and he laconically confirmed that my assumption about the foundations was right. He had brought a tape measure, and I held it for him while he checked my own measurements, which I had made with a two-foot rule. At each corner of the house he stood and squinted along the walls. I knew by his expression that he was satisfied that there was no deviation from the vertical. He examined the ground at our proposed bathroom end of the house, and he said:

"There's going to be a difficulty here. I'm taking it you're going to have a septic tank for sanitation. The local council is very particular. It's got to be at least twenty-five yards from the house, and with a good fall for the pipes. It should be excavated in the soil, but it looks like rock here, and we may have to go a long way down. Still,

I think we can get over that. You know that these days you can't just build a house where and how you like. There are all sorts of rules and regulations. And don't forget that before you can start building your plans have got to go before the council, and the site has got to be inspected and okayed by the sanitary officer. Let's have a look at the spring. They're very particular indeed about a place having a proper water supply."

We had spent an hour or so one evening clearing the mud and sedges round the spring itself. There had been several orifices, but we had dug into the bank and found that they originated in one crevice in the underlying rock, and it was now bubbling up, crystal clear. We had hidden a small enamel mug close by, and Will sampled the water.

"Not much wrong with that," was his verdict. Then, with a glance back towards the barn, he said: "You'll have a good head too. Thirty feet at a guess, well above your ridge, as you've got it on your plan. The council would pass this all right."

"What a fuss they seem to make," said Dain. And then taking the words out of my mouth: "How long will it take them to decide about the plans and everything?"

"They have a meeting once a month. They'll pass it straight away if the sanitary officer has okayed it, and the town and country planning officer has raised no objection. *He's* got to see that your building is not going to interfere with the building of any new roads or other developments, and that if it's in a rural area and a beauty spot it's not going to look offensive."

"Good lord!" I cried in alarm. "Does that mean that he

can veto anything that doesn't fit in with his ideas of beauty? This is a beauty spot, of course. The whole district is. That's one reason why we want to live in it. We wouldn't dream of building anything offensive."

"That's why we want a red-tiled roof," Dain put in.

Will laughed.

"He's not a dictator. I've found him quite reasonable. There's nothing in your plan *he* would object to, and while he might suggest that a red roof might look better than a slate roof, and I don't think it would myself, he wouldn't insist on it being red. No, the real dictator is the sanitary inspector. He's a nice chap, and I get on with him well, but he won't pass a thing that's not strictly according to the regulations. That's why you've got to be certain of everything before putting in your plans. Or they'll come back for alteration, and that will mean another month's delay. But there's something troubling me far more than the colour of your roof. Shall we walk back to the barn?"

I couldn't guess what he meant, but there was something very ominous in the way he said it. As we moved back he took a measurement of the distance, and made a note of it.

"Fifty yards. That won't be a big job anyway. It had better be a lead pipe. Galvanised pipes would come out cheaper, but if the water is acid it might corrode and cost more in the long run. You'll not want to spoil the ship for a penn'orth of tar?"

"No," I said apprehensively. "But what is it that *is* troubling you? Let's face it."

He had put his tape away, and he was looking, low

down, at the walls.

"I'd like to do this job for you," he said. "I'd do it well, and I'd do it at a reasonable price, and I'd not try to persuade you into spending more money than you can afford. I know myself how tight money is these days, particularly when you've got a family. But when first you told me that this was a conversion job I was bothered. I thought, however, I'd best see the place, before I said anything. I wasn't quite certain that it hadn't once been a cottage, and actually lived in. Then on the plans it could have been called just 'extensions to a dwelling house', and we might possibly have got round the big snag.

"But this was built as an agricultural building. The snag is, and it's no use beating about the bush, that according to the county bye-laws every building for human habitation, new or conversion, has to have a damp course. In an entirely new building you just take it for granted. When you've got your foundation rising at least six inches above the ground you put a layer of waterproof felt or, if you can afford it, a layer of sheet lead. That insulates your walls from any water rising from the ground."

"But why should water rise from the ground?" asked Dain. "I thought that water always went downwards. Doesn't water always find its own level?"

Remembering my physics, I did know that there was a significant exception to this rule. It was called capillary action, and if Will did not give it its name, he understood it all right. He said:

"No. No matter how dry you think the ground is, even solid rock, it's always got water in it, and if you lay anything dry above it, it sucks it out just like a sponge. You can prove that by putting a coat or a blanket on the ground. Leave it a bit, and it's quite damp underneath. The drier a house gets, with living in it and having fires, the more it will tend to suck the damp up the walls if there's nothing to stop it. And apart from being unhealthy, damp is the number one cause of dry rot in floors. That's why in addition to having a damp course you have ventilators called air bricks between the damp course and the joists of your ground floor. And it's also a good thing to have a space between your outer and inner wall. That stops the moisture from driving rain from getting inside."

"But surely," I said, "your inspector is not going to condemn walls like these, two and a half feet thick, straight as a die, and without a crack in them. It's as strong as a castle."

"He'd pass them for strength all right. He wouldn't condemn them because of them being solid. But if they had no damp course I'm afraid he would. In fact I'm certain of it."

"And is there no way of putting in a damp course?"

"There is. It has been done. And I've been considering if it could be done here. You take out the lowest course a bit at a time, and you insert slates where the mortar was and put the stones back. Slates of course are waterproof and as good as felt or lead. But they'd have to go the whole way through the wall. By the time you'd done you could have rebuilt the whole wall twice over. I wouldn't recommend it."

"Then what do you recommend?"

"There's only one thing to do. And no builder, if he was honest, could tell you anything different. The whole thing will have to come down to its foundations."

I gasped. Dain said:

"How awful! If we've got to do that, it would be better to build an entirely new house, and keep the barn as it is. After all, we shall need a stable." But she quickly added, without bringing any comfort to my mind: "But the barn really is the best place for the house, isn't it? If we built a new house just this side of it, where I thought we could have at least a small stable, the barn would block out all the view."

"The barn is on an ideal site," said Will. "It couldn't be improved. You've got room for wooden outbuildings here, but no more, or you'll be in that boggy bit. I wish I could see some way round the law, but I can't. That's how it is."

I was recovering from the shock. I said:

"Well, supposing we have it pulled down. Could it be built up exactly as it is, with the same stones, and just as strong?"

"I wouldn't say it would be exactly the same, unless you numbered every stone, but I could guarantee it would be *better*. Annoying though it is about the damp course it's a good thing to have one. There's not a bigger curse than damp in a house. I wouldn't have the inside rubble either. I'd do it with brick and have a cavity. The inspector would approve of that. As it is at present we'd have to cut the walls for doors and windows, and put in lintels and sills—a tricky job with a rubble wall. Starting from foundations all that would be easier, and look better when it was finished."

I saw the sense of that. None of the existing doorways or windows could have been used in our projected plan. They would have had to be filled up, and new orifices cut. Obviously it would be simpler in new walls. Our biggest problem remained however. I summoned up courage, and I said.

"Well, can you give us just a rough idea of what the whole thing would cost, including pulling it down. I don't expect an estimate, but just a rough figure."

He smiled.

"Yes, it would have to be rough. It would take me a day or two to work out a definite price."

He looked at our plan.

"It's quite a substantial house this. A big cut above the usual estate house. Those are usually built semi-detached, which saves one main wall. Your lounge and living-room are both on the big side. You've got four bedrooms as well as the downstairs nursery, which could be called another reception room. An estate house, too, would be built of brick. Stone is always more expensive, even when you've got the stone. It needs stone-masons, and they're difficult to find these days. Bricks are easier and quicker to lay. You'll need almost twice the stones you've got to build up another storey. Don't forget it's got to be eight feet from floors to ceilings, bedrooms too. I might get some second-hand stones, but each one would have to be re-dressed. I don't know what's in your mind about a figure, but at a rough guess this would cost between seven and eight hundred pounds."

I looked at Dain. We were both dismayed. It seemed

for the moment that it was the end of our dream. With all our other expenses, with all the other things we wanted, we should never be able to afford a sum like that just for the house alone. We had brought little furniture from our Cornish home. We had no linoleum, no carpets or curtains. It would mean, if we could get a building society loan, putting down at least two hundred pounds, and then having to pay off the loan with interest. I found no comfort in the belief that he was being absolutely honest. I said:

"I'm afraid we could not afford anything like that figure. It's just impossible."

"Would it," said Dain, "make it cheaper, if we gave up the idea of the tile roof and used the slates?"

"Yes, it would. I should say at least fifty pounds. Mind, it's only a rough figure I've given you. But it's no good me trying to lead you up the garden path about costs. As you've planned it, it would be a very nice house indeed. Whatever you spent on it you'd get it back if ever you wanted to sell it."

"We should never do that," Dain protested. "We want it too much ourselves!" And she added: "Really, I don't think that slates would look so bad. Those on the barn are a very nice colour. They harmonise quite well with the stone. Slates looked all right in Cornwall. And there aren't any other red roofs in sight for them to clash with."

Strange that before the present economic crisis had arisen, neither of us had considered the possibility of using slates. They would have seemed as incongruous as a corrugated iron roof, or the ornamental gables, or the stained glass of Butcher's Folly. Now I looked at the roof of the barn, and made two discoveries, one of them distinctly Freudian in its significance. My prejudice against slates was not just aesthetic; it dated back from my childhood when I attended the village school, where, except on special occasions, all our writing and sums had to be done on slates and with slate pencils. To clean them it was the custom to use moisture from your own mouth, and, had I used the hygienic sponge and small bottle of water my mother hopefully supplied me with, I'd have got into trouble with the other boys for swanking. It was possible to obtain very soft pencils, which were a delight to write with. But the ones in general use were hard (they were thin sticks of slate) and they squeaked, like scratching a knife edge on a plate, and sent shivers down your spine. The slates themselves were dark purple in colour, and it had seemed to me that most slates used for roofs were the same, dingy and monotonous. I saw now that the slates that we had proposed to discard were, as Dain had observed, intrinsically of a pleasing colour. They were more grey than purple and were varied in their tints. They had not the smooth surface of the ordinary slate, and they *did* harmonise with the greys and light browns of the sandstone blocks. In our seaward vista there were no other buildings.

"You're right," I said. "You're both right. Let's have a slate roof. Does that mean that it's now between six hundred and fifty and seven hundred and fifty pounds?"

"At a guess," Will answered. "It might be more, it might be less, and you mustn't take anything I say yet as definite."

"Of course. That's understood."

81

It was still, even at his lowest guess, a formidable figure. We simply could not afford anything like the sum. But the prospect of abandoning the whole scheme, or putting it off until we made a lot of money, living, it might be for years, in Butcher's Folly, was appalling. Was there any way out?

I thought of our Cornish hut as we had found it: completely derelict, and how, with practically no capital and no furniture at all, we'd just taken possession and had soon made an agreeable home of it, without any help from builders. Could we do anything like that again?

It was a futile comparison. The only thing there was in common between the situation then and the situation now was our lack of money. We had no children then. The hut was made of wood. As it had already been used for human habitation there was no sanitary officer to worry about. We could not squat here, even if we'd had no children. The first thing, apparently, was that the building itself had to be demolished, and, to build it again, not only had we to satisfy the authorities, it had to be a proposition that would justify a loan. But an idea came to me. I said to Will, but not very hopefully:

"I don't know whether I've made it clear that we don't want any frills. All we really need is the roof over our heads and the shell of the house. We could do quite a lot of the inside carpentry ourselves. Partitions for example. Doors. Not plumbing, of course. I don't think I've made it clear that we don't want any plastering, and we'd do all the decoration We'd have wall boards for ceilings and partitions. Wouldn't that make it much cheaper?"

He smiled, but this time rather grimly.

"I'd been reckoning on wall boards for ceilings and partitions. Inside decorations are usually regarded as an extra. You wouldn't save very much by making your own doors, I'm afraid. As a matter of fact I was thinking that, if you weren't too particular, I've got a number of second-hand doors that would have helped you out."

"Before you made your guess at the total cost?"

"Yes."

My last hope was dashed. Then he said:

"Well, it's no use beating about the bush. I want to help you. How much do you think you can afford? What did you think it would cost?"

"Ours was a guess too," I answered. "Obviously a too optimistic one. About five hundred pounds. That, however, was assuming that we were going to use the existing walls."

"And also the red pantiles," put in Dain. "We're saving there, anyway."

He made no immediate comment. He was looking at the plan. Then at last he said:

" It just couldn't be done, anywhere near that figure. You can get another builder to look at it, of course. I tell you again that my figure is a guess, but I do know without any guessing that you won't get any builder to do this job for five hundred. Not as you've got it."

"Well, can you suggest any way of modifying the plan, that's reasonable?"

"That will depend on what you will call reasonable. Can you do with a smaller number of rooms?"

I looked at Dain. She shook her head, but she said:

"We might do with one less bedroom at present,

provided we could partition one of the rooms later to make it into two."

"That would save a bit," said Will. "But not so much. You can't make any of the main rooms smaller, without having a smaller foundation. I was reckoning on using the foundations as they are." He was silent a moment. Then he said: "I've got an idea, though. It's just come to me. What's going to make your plan expensive is the second storey. As I've explained, there's nothing these days so expensive as stonework. You could cut all that out by having what they call a mansard roof. You've agreed to having slates. Well, in a mansard roof you wouldn't have walls from your first floor. You'd start the roof there, that is from the eaves of the barn as it is at present. But it goes up at a steep pitch, almost vertical to ceiling height of your first floor. Then it goes at a gentler pitch to the roof. You've got practically the same accommodation upstairs, but you cut out eight feet of walling."

Again I was staggered.

"You mean having two-thirds of the house just slate?"

"Yes. It amounts to that. Except that your end walls would have to be stone. But there's enough stone in the present partition to build up those."

"But wouldn't it be very cold in the bedrooms, having only slates for a wall?"

"It wouldn't make that much difference. You'd have match-boarding, or thick wall boarding, under your slates, and roofing felt between the boards and the slates themselves. I'm afraid though, you'd have to give up your outside staircase idea, much as I like it, but that in

84

itself would be a big saving. You could have the staircase rising from the lounge. You could give it just the same rise, and you'd have only the underneath part of half of it showing below the ceiling of the living-room. There'd be a handy cupboard under it alongside your cooking range . . . I'm thinking," he added, with a quick look at Dain, "how we can cut down the cost."

"*I* don't mind so much about the staircase," she said, "so long as it's going to have a gentle rise. But isn't the whole place going to look funny? I don't quite understand what you are proposing to do."

He made a quick but lucid pencil sketch alongside our plan. It did not look so good as the original, but it didn't look bad. My spirits began to rise. I had never heard the name mansard but the shape of it was familiar. It was the same principle as that of the war-time Nissen hut except that it rose from a vertical lower wall and was in two planes instead of one curve.

"Would this sort of roof pass the sanitary inspector and the town planner?" I asked.

"It's a conventional design, and neither of them could jib at it in my opinion. I've never built a mansard myself, but I can show you several in the Burnharbour district."

"I don't think it would look at all bad," put in Dain. "In fact, once you get used to the idea, I quite like it. And I *do* like the colour of the slates. I don't like giving up our staircase. That's nothing if it's going to be cheaper, and we'll be able to build it, without having to wait."

"Will the difference in cost be so much?" I dared to ask.

Will smiled again.

"I'm not going to give you a quotation now. You've said you can't go beyond five hundred. I've got the measurements. I've got your plan, and I'll work it out, perhaps tonight, and see if it can be done about that figure. If I took on the job I'd want to start it soon, and get it finished to leave myself clear for this big estate contract. There's a council meeting in about a fortnight. We might get the plans passed and make a start within three weeks from now, if all went well."

"How long will it take to build it?" Dain asked eagerly.

"That depends on the weather. If we have a fine summer you might be able to move in by the middle of September."

It looked as though our problems were solved. I saw no need to tell Will that we had at present no money. I was confident that, at this figure, the lawyer would be able to arrange the necessary loan. But I had a moment of misgiving. Was this, after all, what we wanted? We'd wanted our home to be close to the sea, with all the advantages, and none of the snags of our Cornish home. We'd wanted red tiles, stone walls, all the way up, not this sort of roof which had made the proposition financially possible. It was definitely a "come down". But you can't have everything, I reflected again. I looked at Dain. She was excited and happy, and I suddenly felt happy myself. Will opened the doors of his car. Then we heard the sound of a horse again, and we saw our neighbour Jimmy riding down our track. He pulled up and, smiling, wished us good evening.

"I saw the top gate open so I rode down to see if my sheep had got in again. And there they are, the beggars.

I've heard tell you've bought Adder Howe from awd Isaac. Is it true?"

"Yes," I said.

"And is it true you're going to make a house out of the awd barn, and come and live here?"

I couldn't help liking him, and I felt no resentment at his curiosity.

"We're hoping to."

"Are you going to start farming?"

"No. But we'll be having a garden, and perhaps an orchard. I hope," I added pointedly, "we'll be able to keep the sheep from doing any damage."

He was still smiling.

"Aye. Of course. I'll have to see that them fences is properly fettled. You'll need a new gate too. Well, if I can help you in any way you let me know. If ever you're short of anything or want to borrow anything you've only got to ask."

Was this just good neighbourliness, or good business? I recalled what Isaac had said about Jimmy, and I was on my guard. I thanked him, and said I'd keep that in mind. Will was anxious to be off. As we moved to get in Jimmy said, perhaps as an afterthought:

"Do you know your other neighbours, Sam Briggs and Matt Pashby?"

I said that I didn't but that Isaac had mentioned their names.

"Aye. Isaac *would* mention them," he said sarcastically. "I wouldn't say anything against either of them myself, mind you. We're all neighbours, and we try to help each other. Only Sam's a foreigner and a bit of a know-all. Matt's as close as they make 'em. If you borrowed a dose or two of sheep medicine from him he'd expect it back next day, even if you had to go into Burnharbour to fetch it. And Sam's not much better. As for his missus, well, you'll find out for yourselves, I've no doubt."

We were moving.

"Leave the top gate open," he shouted after us. "I'll be driving these sheep out that way. And I'll fasten it so that they won't get in that way again."

5

OUR LUCK was in. Everything went well. With the mansard roof, with an inside staircase, with second-hand doors, and a second-hand, but practically unused kitchen range, the quotation Will gave us was just a little above £500. It included the making of the water cistern, the laying of a lead supply pipe, and the installation of a septic tank. We were to do all the inside painting and decorations ourselves, and build all cupboards. He would remove all debris from the site when building was completed and leave it clean and tidy. Apart from the staircase, and the slightly reduced size of the bedrooms resulting from the design of the roof, the inside accommodation was just as we had originally planned it.

He had helped us with the preparation of the plans

and other documents which had to be submitted to the authorities. He had taken the sanitary inspector to visit the site. It appeared that neither he nor the planning officer had raised any objection. The plans had been passed. Duplicates of them had been submitted by the lawyer to a building society. They were willing to grant a mortgage on the security of the whole estate provided I could produce a guarantor, and that interest payable should be half per cent above the rate charged on a more conventional proposition. A family friend had agreed to be guarantor, and to make things even brighter there had come to us an utterly unexpected cheque from an American publisher which would keep the wolf from the door for several months to come.

The job began on a Monday in mid-July. I had explained to Will that I wished to see the whole thing done from start to finish, not because I had any doubts about it being done properly, but because any sort of construction had a fascination for me, and the building of what was to be our own home particularly so. He said that it would be all right so long as I refrained from criticising any workmen. They were all skilled, and like most Yorkshiremen independent, and a bit touchy. If I had any suggestions to make I must make them to the foreman, Harry Knaggs, and I must be particularly tactful even with him.

I caught the first moorland bus that morning, and was in time to meet the firm's laden lorry at the junction of our track with the high road. I had already done some clearing of the track. For most of the distance between the high road and our gate, the ground was quite hard and stony under the heather turf, which was easily removed with a spade. In the two boggy patches I had dug shallow ditches on each side, for there was evidence that in a really rainy spell they would have streams coursing through them. There were seven men on the lorry including the driver. With one exception they were all young and brawny. I didn't know any of them, but the face of the one elderly man, who was sitting next to the driver, was vaguely familiar. He was short with a wrinkled humorous face and a grey, ragged moustache.

They were a happy, eager-looking company, and I knew that I was going to get on with them all right. On the lorry, in addition to scaffold poles and boards, ladders, trestles, wheelbarrows, picks, shovels and crowbars, was a score or so of old but sound railway sleepers. These were offloaded at the first bog and, although the driver protested that he could have got through without them, they were laid to form a low bridge, and there were enough left to do likewise at the second bog. The gate, which Jimmy had promised to fix properly, had by now fallen to bits, and I had not bothered to try to repair it, for Will was making a new one. The sheep at present could do no harm. I had no doubt that I could solve that difficulty later on, and that I should find Jimmy himself quite amenable.

The last bit of gradient did not deter the driver. The lorry pulled up where Will's car had done. The men jumped off and started to unload. I found myself standing near the elderly man who was staring at the barn with keen interest. I had already guessed that he was Harry Knaggs, the foreman, and I now realised why his face was familiar. He had been one of the employees of the little squire, a contemporary of old Joe Stainforth. I asked him if this was so.

"Aye. I was his foreman mason. There was four of us working for him regular at one time or another. He was a queerish chap, and hard to please too. You'd lay a bit of walling, and it might have been a week's work, and he'd look at it, and look at it, and hum and haw, and then he'd say, No, I don't like this Knaggs, or I don't like that, and it would all have to come down again. It's not up to standard, he'd say, and he'd start telling you about how monasteries and abbeys was built hundreds of years ago for the Glory of God, and that he expected us to work with the same idea, even if it was nobbut a cowshed we were building.

"He had me working on a doorway for nearly six weeks before he was satisfied, and I don't know how many good blocks of freestone we wasted. Still, he was a good master as masters went in them days, although there was one chap he took on told him straight that *he* wasn't going to rive *his* guts out building cowsheds for the Glory of God, and only a bob an hour. He was one of them bloody Socialists. He got the sack, of course."

He broke off to direct the workmen to put ladders up to the eaves of the barn, and a roof ladder to the ridge. Then he went on:

"This spot belonged to him, of course. I remember I had to come up with him one day to have a look at it. Some slates had come off in a gale o' wind. He told me that he believed there used to be a sort of chapel round here that belonged to Burnharbour Priory. One of the fields was called Chapel Garth in an old map he'd got. This barn had been built by his grandfather but he hadn't been able to find out if there'd been any ruins on the spot, but there might have been, and this might have been the very spot where the old chapel stood, and if it was, it was consecrated ground. If he could prove that, he said, he might someday pull down the barn and rebuild it as a chapel, and have it re-consecrated, and he asked me what I thought of his notion.

"Well, I thought it was daft. There was always plenty of room in t' parish church even when the bishop came for a confirmation, and he wouldn't get many folks coming up all this way to a service, especially in wintertime, and if it was called a chapel folks wouldn't know whether it was Church or Wesleyan or Congregational. But I knew better than tell him so, and he never mentioned it again to me. It was just one of his notions."

I recalled a legend of the once existence of a Saxon chapel in this district. Our boundary wall was authentic evidence of a monastic deer park. I was fascinated. Had the eccentric little squire got a hunch? Would we find signs of an ancient building under the foundations of the present one when it was demolished? We might, I thought, letting my imagination soar, even find treasure, Saxon coins, silver chalices . . . But Harry, having fired me, was watching the men who had now got their ladders in position.

"Coping stones off first," he shouted, "and don't break any of 'em fetching 'em down. They've all got to be used again. And don't break any of them slates, either. Carry 'em all down and we'll stack 'em where they'll be handy."

The coping stones were sandstone blocks about two feet in length, and nine inches wide, dressed convex at the top and concave underneath, and they were set in mortar along the ridge to cover the ends of the top courses of slates. They were easily moved. When the first of them came down, Harry himself carried it clear of the building. The lorry was already on its way up the hill, and from among the gear that had been offloaded from it he took a bag of tools. There were several hammers, mallets and a variety of steel chisels, some with toothed edges. Using a hammer with a chisel point, he cleared the old mortar from the stone.

"First stone down," he said. "And it will be the last to go up when the roof's on and the slating's done. And here's the next 'un."

One of the young men brought him another. Lest my close presence might embarrass him I moved away, and I became aware for the first time that a woman was standing at the far end of the building, where the path fell away down to the mill wood. She was watching the men with interest, but she saw me and approached with an amiable smile. She was middle-aged, buxom, a typical Yorkshire country woman. She wore a cotton dress, with a sack for an apron, no hat, and heavy boots. She at once released a torrent of words.

"Now then. You won't know me, but I know you and your missus well enough by sight. I'm Mrs Briggs from Howe Beck Mill, just down in t' wood. You've been living away in Cornwall, haven't you? And haven't you got two little bairns? Ee! Time flies, doesn't it? It seems only yesterday since your missus was a young lass tearing about on a pony.

"I've heard tell you've bought Adder Howe, and that you're going to build a house and come and live here. Well, as I was telling our Sam, that's my husband, it's a nice place in summer, but wild in winter and lonely too. Folks that live round here aren't much cop, only don't let on to any of 'em that I've told you so. They keep themselves to themselves except when they want to borrow summat from you like Jimmy Bond, who's always after summat, but never thinks of bringing it back. He's had a saddle of Sam's for nigh on a twelvemonth, and when Sam asks for it he always says he'll let him have it back next day but he never does, and him and our Sam aren't on speaking terms at present, so he's got to borrow from Matt Pashby, although it's little he'll get out of him. He's over stingy, and his wife's not much better. I could tell you a lot about her if I had a mind to, but I really came up to ask you if your missus would be wanting milk and eggs and things when you get settled in. We've got a good herd of milkers and we're never short of eggs, and we churn once a week and you can always be certain of cream and butter. And we've got a vegetable garden too, although Jimmy's sheep got in and et half our cabbage plants a while back although, of course, he said they were Matt Pashby's that did it. Next time it happens, Sam's going to catch them and tie 'em up, and let him come and fetch them and pay for the damage, and that'll larn him."

She stopped at last. I was amused, but also alarmed. We wanted from the first to be on friendly terms with all

94

our neighbours, and not get involved in any quarrels or feuds. I liked Jimmy, and on first impressions I rather liked Mrs Briggs. Probably everything she had said about Jimmy was true, and probably the dark hint he had uttered about her was justified. I was not going to take sides nor commit myself about the milk and I told her this as tactfully as I could. My wife, I said, would have to decide things like that. She seemed satisfied, and as she turned to go, she said:

"Well, you tell her not to be afraid of walking in to our spot any time she likes, and if she wants owt she's only to ask. We're always glad of a bit of company. So long for now. I've got a boiler full of washing I've got to get out on to the line. Come down and have a cup of tea with us whenever you like. Kettle's always on the hob, and it's no trouble at all."

I thanked her.

The last coping stone was down, and the men had already started removing the top courses of slates. I itched to give them a hand, but I feared that my motives might be misinterpreted and resented. I could not remain idle, however. We had decided to have our vegetable garden on the bank opposite the barn, and starting just a few feet up from what was still the sheep-trampled bog made by the spring. It was not too steep. It faced south and was protected from the prevalent winds of the coast. Rising up the bank on the north side was one of the few dry stone walls which had remained standing and this, if heightened, would give extra protection, although to make it sheep-proof it would need poles reaching above it, and at least two strands of barbed wire. I was confident that I could beat those sheep.

We had reckoned that, for the first year, a garden measuring about twenty-five yards each way would be enough for us. We could extend it later as far as we liked. The ideal thing would be to have high stone walls for all its boundaries, but for the present we should have to do with posts and wire-netting with barbed wire along the top. The first thing was the soil itself, which looked as though it was virgin land.

On successive evenings we had brought out various tools, and made a cache of them in the bushes near the barn. They were all tools we had used in Cornwall for our gardening and making paths. I could start work at once, and still be able to watch the demolition.

We had learned all our gardening in Cornwall, getting our knowledge from books and gardening journals and from practical experience of successes and failures. There we'd had to deal with an existing garden, however, one that had gone back to nature through neglect. There was a deep natural loam which unfortunately was highly favourable for the growth of docks, giant nettles and many other weeds, and in our initial enthusiasm we had improved conditions for the weeds by digging deeper and overloading the soil with manure, for in addition to the dry goat muck under the hut we'd had an unlimited supply of seaweed on the shores of the cove.

Here, I guessed, we were not going to find an excessive fertility. The chosen site had growing on it a few thick clumps of whins, some brambles (already laden with immature berries) in the lee of the wall, and a patch or two of bracken, but mostly it was covered with coarse grass that had been closely cropped by the sheep and rabbits. Their droppings must have contributed some fertility to the soil, but not on the same scale as the goats of that early tenant of our hut had done. The most encouraging thing was that there were neither docks nor nettles, and only an occasional thistle.

First, I paced out what were to be the boundaries, driving a stick into the soil at the four corners. Then I started on the whins and brambles. For this I used a hedging slasher, an instrument with a short, moderately heavy blade shaped like a cut-throat razor, with a hickory shaft about four feet long. Using both hands and swinging it down like an axe you could cut through the toughest whin with one blow if you made a downward slanting stroke close to the roots. For the roots I had a kind of double-bladed mattock, a combination of pick-axe, chopper, adze and hoe, known in Cornwall as a visgy. Both blades were broad and flat, at right angles to each other. You cleared the soil with the horizontal blade, chopped the root stems either with that or the vertical one, and so long as it was sharp it was a most satisfying tool to use.

I worked, however, with one eye as it were on my own job, and one on the barn. The men were working on both sides of the roof easing the nailed slates from the narrow battens which ran horizontally across the rafters, carefully handing them down to the ground, where the foreman was as carefully examining them and then packing them on edge.

At ten o'clock they knocked off for what appeared to

be a customary short breather. They climbed from the roof, sat down on the bank, and opened their bait tins and thermos flasks. I thought it would be a good chance to have a closer look at the building. By then about one-quarter of the slates had been removed from each side. I strolled down to where the men were sitting.

"You're getting on well," I said.

The foreman grinned.

"Aye. We ought to have all them slates and most of the timbering off before knocking off time tonight. Are you going to make a garden where you're clearing the whins?"

"Yes. That's going to be the vegetable garden and we'll be planting a few fruit trees."

"You'll need a good fence to keep the rabbits and sheep out."

"Yes. I thought the roof rafters might do for posts."

"A good idea. They're over twelve feet long, so each of 'em will make a couple of posts. If you take my advice, when we pull the walls down you'll save all the mortar, and put it on your ground. It's all lime and sand, and you can't beat that for a garden. Will you have a sup of tea and a bite of summat?"

At once there was a chorus of offers of drink and buns and sandwiches from the other men. But I had brought my own refreshments, and I said no. I took the opportunity, however, of making a short speech.

"I hope," I said, "that none of you chaps think I'm here to spy on you, or to find fault or anything like that. It's just that I'm interested in seeing how a house is built, especially as I'm going to live in it, and for that matter seeing an old building pulled down. It's an old place this, and we might find things. It does sometimes happen. Even treasure," I added ironically.

The men laughed, and the foreman said dryly:

"I've helped to pull down a lot of buildings in my time, but I never found any treasure. But I did once find a newspaper stuck behind the plaster in a farmhouse we were retiling. It was over a hundred years awd. It gave the latest news of Napoleon's retreat from Moscow, when the Russians were after him. The report had taken over six weeks to come from the front, and it must have come on hossback and sailing ship and hosses again. There was an account, too, of how some smugglers had had a fight with excise men when they'd been trying to land a cargo, somewhere round here."

"That's the sort of thing I mean," I said enviously. "Don't throw away any bits of paper you may find."

"Why," one of the young workmen put in. "When they were doing some alterations to a house down by the fish quay at Burnharbour only a while back, they found a secret cellar that had been walled up, and there was a keg of brandy in it. That must have belonged to smugglers."

"We're wasting our time drinking tea," laughed another. "Let's get them walls down and see if there's any kegs of brandy there. But that reminds me," he added seriously. "I saw summat queer stuck under the rafters just where I left off. It looked like some sort of weapon. I'll have a look at it."

He was a big, fair-haired youth, with fine teeth and a merry smile.

"Wait till you've finished your meal," I protested, as, with a half-eaten sandwich in his hand, he got up. He laughed, and strode towards the nearest ladder. He climbed to the roof, and up to where the rafters were showing, then put his hand under the rafters, and started to jerk at something.

"Why," he shouted. "It's a great spade. Get underneath one of you, and give us a hand. Nay. Look out! I can't hold it."

There was a clatter on the flags inside the barn. I rushed in and saw it. It was a spade, but certainly not an ordinary one. It had a thick wood shaft about eight feet long, with a curved piece of wood like the top of a crutch at one end, and about two feet down, a short cross-piece. The rusty blade had the real spade shape, coming to a rounded point. But the cutting edge was curved up on each side, plough fashion. The men gathered round it, deeply interested and puzzled. But Harry with one glance at it, said:

"Why—haven't any of you ever seen a thing like this afore? It's a turf spade, for cutting turves on the moor for burning. Every farm round here had one when I was a lad. But they've got too lazy to use 'em. It's hard work, mind you. The blade's rusty and it will be blunt. It ought to be sharp as a scythe. But I'll show you how it works."

He carried it out to the grassy bank where they had been sitting.

"Of course," he said, "it should be moor turf, where the heather top has been burnt off, leaving nowt but the roots where they're matted together. That's the stuff that burns. You mustn't have any soil in your turves. They should be almost as light as straw when they're dry."

He chose a fairly level patch of grass, put the crutch part of the shaft in the pit of his stomach, and grasped the cross piece with a hand at each side. The shaft was oblique to the ground. He pushed the point of the blade in a few inches, then at a lower angle to the ground, he pushed the spade forward for about a foot, then jerked it up and sideways, throwing up a thin sod, as neatly as if it had been ploughed.

I was deeply impressed. Isaac had told me that we had the right to cut turf on the moor. Apart from saving coal, it would be delightful to have a turf fire in our lounge. There were some burnt patches on the moor quite close to our boundary wall. I would cut a good supply of turves, and we'd have a stack close by the house for winter burning.

I itched to try the thing, but the youth who had found it had taken it from Harry, and was now attempting to repeat his performance. He dug the point in, leaned his weight forward on the shaft and pushed. There was a crack, the shaft snapped, and he fell headlong on to the ground. I was not worried about the spade. The shaft was worm-eaten. It would be easy to make a new one, but I jealously picked up the broken halves so that they would not get mislaid. Harry had pulled out his watch.

"Came on, lads! Let's be at it again."

"Aye!" one of the young men shouted. "Let's be finding one of them kegs of brandy."

But there were no more treasures in the roof, nor did I expect that any would be found in the very solid-looking walls of the barn, although there was the exciting possibility of finding traces of the Saxon chapel in the foundations. Least of all did I expect to find anything in the patch I was clearing.

I had just started on the root of the second clump of whins when I had left off for the "ten o'clock", having slashed off all the stems, and I returned to the task of digging a trench all round the stump in order to expose the roots. I was pleased to find that here at least the soil was deep and that judging by its colour and smell it was rich in humus. That, however, might have been due to the shedding of the whins, the rotting down of fallen blossoms and foliation, and to the fact that both rabbits and sheep would tend to concentrate their traffic at the bushes for food and shelter.

I was using the hoe-shaped blade of the visgy. I soon struck one of the main side roots, about six inches below the surface. I tried to get the blade of the visgy under it, and lever it up, but something was obstructing it and I reversed the tool to the other blade and swung it down hard. There was a metallic ring; the unmistakable sound of metal striking metal. I dropped the visgy, bent on to my knees, and scratched out the soil where the blade had struck. I saw part of the root bleeding sap, and then what looked like the gleam of silver.

The discoverer of an Egyptian royal treasure house could not have been more excited than I was then. The object was thin, rounded like the rim of a plate buried on edge. I scraped more of the soil away. I was more certain than ever that it *was* silver, that it was a vessel of some sort and that as yet I was seeing only the rim or the handle. It would not move.

I was afraid of using the visgy again. I scratched away with my fingers, and succeeded in getting slightly under it with one finger, proving that it was not a dish, but some sort of handle, for it still would not move. And then I realised that what was holding it was the root itself. I sawed this through near the stump with my knife. I pulled at the loose end. The object moved up a little, and I was able to get a grip of what I still took to be a handle. Then working it gently from side to side, and pulling upwards on the, end of the root, it suddenly came loose from root and soil, and I had it in my hand.

It was not, as I had imagined, a silver plate or chalice, a relic of Saxon or Roman occupation. It was not even silver, but nickel, and by that fact and its design it was, as the archaeologist would say, of recent date. It was a child's stirrup, and it would not have taken a Sherlock Holmes to deduce that someone, at a date that must certainly have been farther back in years than the age of the root that had grown through it, had been walking a pony (probably at the end of a hunt) up the hill. The stirrup had been dangling from its leather, the buckle of which had been loose, and had caught in a branch of whin or bramble. It had been trampled into the soft ground perhaps by other ponies or horses or cattle. Nature had done the rest.

It was an anti-climax. Stirrups, like the rowlocks of boats, or gloves go in pairs, and what can be more exasperating than losing (or finding) just one of a pair of gloves? There would be no sense in looking for its mate, for even I, with my slight experience of riding, knew that such things were secured to the saddle independently.

No one would lose both stirrups at the same time and in the same place.

The thing was valueless. And yet, I thought, it would be of interest to Dain, and I wished that she had been here with me to help in its discovery. I laid it on the wall, with the broken halves of the turf spade, thinking that she would certainly be amused when I showed it to her, and told her how I had found it. Then, rather ruefully, I got on with the job of digging out the stump of the whin. Neither of us, even if we'd possessed the inventive genius of Conan Doyle, could have guessed what the upshot of the finding of that old stirrup was to be.

6

ALTHOUGH THE aunt was still staying with us at Butcher's Folly it was impracticable for Dain to share my self-imposed occupation of watching the building of our house and the pioneer work on the vegetable garden. It was only in the evenings, when the children were in bed, that she felt free of maternal responsibility, and it was not until the Friday of that first week that she was able to see the progress that had been made. I had stayed on after the men had packed up, and I met her bus at our road end.

She was surprised by what had been done. The entire building had been demolished down to the first foundation course of stones. All the dressed stones had been cleaned of mortar and piled in convenient heaps ready for rebuilding. The slates were neatly piled, the rubble was in another heap ready to be taken up by lorry on to our moor road to help fill in the soft sections of it, and the old mortar was in another heap close by the garden.

The foundation course of stones was to stay. It had been cleaned and rendered smooth with new cement mortar so as to give a dead level surface. On it, the foreman had explained, would be laid a continuous strip of bituminous felt, the precious damp course which the law demanded, and on this the new building would begin, but not until Monday. Saturday, being a short day, only the lorries would be coming out, bringing loads of bricks and mortar.

The flags on the original floors had been taken up and preserved for making footways outside the house. I had carefully examined the thin sandy soil beneath them, but had found no sign of the squire's Saxon chapel. Dain shared my disappointment and yet I felt that nothing short of a treasure trove could have excited her more than the stirrup had done. She had cleaned and polished it until it shone like new, and had shown it to Amelia, explaining what it was for. She regarded its discovery as symbolic and prophetic. It was a sign that we were going to get a pony for Amelia.

"I wish," she said, "that we could find the other one. I must see the exact place where you dug it out."

We walked over to the garden. I had finished the first digging of the patch, not going too deep, and leaving the soil in clumps to break down with the winter frosts. I had started to dig the holes for the fencing posts. Dain complimented me on what I had done but I could see that her mind was on the stirrup and she looked with great interest at the place where I had found it. She had agreed with my theory (a purely masculine and logical one) as to how it had come to be lost, and that there was no chance of finding its mate, but with that feminine intuitiveness which so often confounds masculine common sense she wasn't going to let it stop at that.

"The other one is bound to be somewhere," she said. "It must have been a child who lost it, and probably it was a little girl, and if it had been a hunt there would have been someone with her, her father or mother. They'd have noticed it was missing when they came to mount again, and looked for it, in vain, but they wouldn't have thrown the other one away. I think it's quite possible that someone still has it, hanging on a nail in a stable or harness-room if they're real hunting people. It would be fun to find it. I think we ought to ask all the farmers in the district if they can remember a child riding a pony and losing a stirrup."

"We could certainly ask Jimmy," I said, not very hopefully. "And we might write a letter to the local paper, saying how we had found it. But it must have been lost years ago judging by the thickness of the root that had grown through it. The child who lost it must be grown up by now."

"Yes. She, and I'm certain it *was* a girl, may have children of her own, and probably they are just as keen on ponies! You must write that letter. If we don't get the other stirrup it would be just as exciting for the person who has it to get ours."

Dain had brought a picnic supper for us both. I had my billycan for coffee and we soon had a fire going close by the garden wall, where with timber from the house I had rigged up a temporary shelter in case there was rain. There had been no rain, however, throughout the week, and it had been another fine day, with a moderately fresh westerly wind, which, with the sun getting low, had almost completely dropped. The air was warm, scented with new-mown hay and heather. We sat down, facing the seaward view. The hill behind us shaded us from the setting sun, but its rays were still shining on the sea, which close in to the shore had fallen to a dead calm.

"Isn't it a wonderful view," Dain cried happily. "Isn't it exciting to think that this is where we are going to live."

I was happy too, but I could not help saying:

"Yes. But it is a pity the sea is such a long way away. It would be a grand evening for fishing. Not to mention having a swim."

"Well, it isn't so far, really, and it will be nothing when we have a pony. Let's walk down now, the way we came up from Browe Beck Cove the day we met old Isaac. If we hurried, we could get the last train back. Or do you want us to get on with the garden? I think you ought to have a change from digging. You have got on well, though."

I did not feel that I wanted to do any more gardening at present. But, alluring as Dain's suggestion was, I thought and I said that it was too late in the evening to go so far. It would be tantalising to get down to the beach

107

and then have to rush back to the station to catch the last train. We didn't know the time of the trains, anyway.

"Well, let's have a walk over the moors then," she said. "Let's walk down to the island, and follow our stream up to the boundary and then get the path we followed the evening we were caught in the storm. *I* know! Let's go and look at the trout mere itself, and see if there are any fish jumping."

I was startled. I had not forgotten about the trout mere, but I had done my best not to think about it as a place where I might ever fish again. We were now landowners, with a stream of our own—a trout stream— even if the fish were no bigger than sardines. Also, there were rabbits, and presumably more interesting species of game on our property, which I myself would have to protect against possible poachers if we were to enjoy the hunting and the eating of them. It would never do for me to be caught poaching . . . Yet the proposal was attractive, if only for the memories it evoked of that exciting experience. I had no fishing gear. The moor itself was a common, and we now had rights on it. It would be most interesting to see if there were any trout left in the mere. Unless it had been stocked by the present owner, the chances were that we would see no sign of fish at all, for the dam wall had been too high to allow migration from the beck below it. I hoped in a way that it would be so. Then there would be no temptation.

We hurriedly finished our meal, and set off down the path to our beck and the island. Here at the island it was Dain who wanted to loiter, to clear some old leaves and dead twigs from the sand where Amelia was to play. But

I pointed out that if we were going to see the mere we must not delay, for the last bus passed our road end at half-past eight, and it was now nearly half-past seven. The wood of small oaks extended beyond our boundary on each side of the beck, but the well-remembered path soon left the beck and led out of the wood into a small field which extended to the high road. On the other side of the high road lay the open moor. The field was a hayfield that had recently been mown, and a solitary man was engaged turning the swathes with a pitchfork.

"I know *him,*" said Dain. "His name's Pashby."

I knew him myself by sight. He was one of the old-timers of whom I had been so scared as a boy. He had been tall then, but now he was bent and wizened, and his movements with the pitchfork were slow. We left the path and went up to him and I wished him good evening. He stuck the tines of his fork in the ground, and with his gnarled hands clenched on the handle he leaned against it and answered quite affably:

"Now then. I don't know you, do I?"

I told him who we were and that we were coming to live at Adder Howe. He didn't seem in any way surprised. He said:

"Nay. I can't call either of you to mind. But Jimmy Bond told me Isaac had sold the spot to someone or other. And I see you've begun pulling the barn down. But you'll not be starting farming, will you?"

"No."

"Then you're wise. There's nowt in it these days but hard work and no profit. There's no one to give you a hand. Jimmy promised to give me a help with this hay,

109

but he's never turned up."

"Can *we* give you a hand?"

"Well, that's very kind of you, but I've just about finished."

He was staring at Dain. Suddenly he said:

"Now I do call *you* to mind. You once had a black gallower and you used to ride to hounds. Have you still got it?"

Dain told him that it was dead, and then she said:

"I wonder if you remember a child riding to hounds, or anyway, riding round here, many years ago, and losing a stirrup? It might have been a boy or a girl, but I think it was a girl."

The old man shook his head.

"Nay. I never heard of anyone losing a stirrup. But there was often a youngster or two hunting on small gallowers. I never heard of one of 'em losing a stirrup. Why—have you found one?"

We told him about our find. He pondered for a while, and then he said:

"Well, now I come to think of it there was a man and his wife used to ride regular to hounds and they had a little lass with a small gallower. He was a major in the army, and he lived down at Skerry Hall, just this side of Burnharbour. I can't think what his name was, though, but I think he was killed in the war, and she and her little lass flitted to somewhere else. She was a good rider, that little lass, and used to win prizes at Burnharbour Foal Show. But I can't remember their name. It's a long time ago. And I never heard of 'em losing a stirrup. But they were quality folk, with plenty o' brass. It wouldn't have

110

bothered 'em much."

There was a gleam of triumph in Dain's eyes, as though the mystery of the old stirrup was already solved.

"I'm sure that must be the one who lost it," she cried.

"Skerry Hall is quite close to us. We'll soon find out the name of the people who lived there."

We said goodbye to our third neighbour. We crossed the high road with its still busy stream of holiday motor traffic, and were soon striding over the real moor towards the valley of the beck and the mere.

The sun had almost set. The clouds in the west were tinted red and orange. The wind had dropped to a complete calm. The air was still warm, but not so close as it had been on that last exciting occasion. There was no definite path here. In places we followed the tracks made by the sheep. Where they twisted we had to plunge through the thick heather, and we put up several coveys of young grouse which reminded me that this *was* sporting land, and that it was probably patrolled by a gamekeeper. We were out of sound of the motor traffic. The land was sloping gradually towards the edge of the valley of the beck. Soon we would see the mere, and Dain said:

"I wonder if we're going to see them jumping like we did before. What a pity you haven't got your rod and line."

I said, virtuously:

"It's just as well I haven't. And I rather hope we're not going to see any fish."

We came in sight of it suddenly, just as we reached the ridge of the hill. It lay beneath us, about fifty feet down, with another heather-clad hill rising on the other side. But it was not as we had seen it first. The water was still there, and apparently it was still as deep, but, except for one small patch in the middle, its surface was entirely grown over with bright green weed.

Dain gave a cry of disappointment.

"Why, it's all choked up. It looks like a bog. There don't seem to be any fish at all."

We stood looking for a while. It seemed that she was right. Even from where we stood we could see clouds of insects hovering near its surface. There was not the slightest sign of a fish rising at them.

"They've gone," I said. "Perhaps we caught the last ones ourselves."

"What a pity! And yet it's very lovely here. Wait, though. What's that splashing among the rushes? I believe it's a fish."

There were certainly ripples and a faint splashing sound among the sedges at the shallow end of the mere.

"Let's creep down nearer," whispered Dain. "I'm certain it's a fish."

I didn't think it was, and I was right, for as we moved stealthily down through the heather, we saw emerge from the rushes a tiny dark fluffy object, then another and another until there were at least half a dozen moorhen chicks scurrying to and fro, and now and again leaping with flapping wings almost out of the water as they chased the insects. Behind them, swimming more sedately, and clucking encouragement, came the mother bird. We stopped and crouched down in the heather so as not to scare them. It was a pretty and a fascinating, and, I thought ironically, a very innocent sight. No squire, or lord of the manor, or gamekeeper seeing us now could have suspected us of any illegal intent. We watched two of the chicks make a frantic effort to catch a large green dragonfly, which circled with tantalising nearness, just over their heads. Then there was a sudden strident clucking from the hen, and she marshalled the whole brood back into the rushes. A sparrow-hawk had swooped down over the mere. But the chicks were safe.

I remembered the time.

"Come on," I said. "We'll have to fly or we'll miss that bus."

We started up the bank, and at the top we paused for one last look at the mere. On the whole, I *was* feeling happy about it. If the trout had been jumping, as they had been on the last occasion, I knew that it would have been impossible for me to have resisted the temptation to come again, and with fishing gear. I felt that I had laid a ghost. But I was wrong: for, as we looked, there was a sudden commotion in the clear patch of water out in the middle of the mere. A fish shot up into the air and fell down again with a splash that resounded across the mere, that sent waves curling among the weeds, as though impelled by a sudden gust of wind. It was a trout, the biggest trout I had ever seen in my life!

Satan himself could not have done it better.

7

THINKING IT over in the bus, which we caught by the skin of our teeth, and later on at home, when we went into their room for a peep at our sleeping innocent children, I decided that I must take no further action about that trout. I was now a parent, with a parent's responsibility, and it would never do to get landed in a police court on a charge of poaching, just as we had come to resettle in the district. The fact that, if caught, the trout might prove to be a record would in itself be embarrassing. It would be hard to keep quiet about it. No one was going to believe that it had been caught in our own beck.

The chances were that I should not be able to catch it if I did try. One could not use fly on the part of the mere that was covered with weed. The clear patch, where it had jumped, was a long way out of fly-casting range. The weed would have made impracticable the use of a spinner. Again, while it was big as trout went, I had caught cod weighing up to three times its size, just fishing from the beach in autumn. But we could find out, tactfully, to whom the mere now belonged. If the person who owned it was a keen angler himself, then that was an end to the matter. If he were not, and he was unaware that the fish was there, there might be some way of getting permission to try. Dain had agreed with this argument.

"Still," she had said, "there would be no harm in walking to the mere again one evening. And when we've got into the house, we must take the children there. We shouldn't need a pony for that. What a pity the moorhen chicks will be grown up by then."

I thought, but I did not say it, that for the time being, at least, we had better leave the mere alone; but I was determined that Dain and Amelia, at least, should not miss the start of the building of our new home.

I rang Will up on the Sunday night. He was himself coming out in the morning to give the site a look over before building started. If we liked he would call for us and run us out, and bring my wife and Amelia back. At Dain's request, I asked him if he knew the name of the army major who had lived at Skerry Hall some twenty or thirty years ago—a man and his wife and child who used to hunt. He did not, but he said he would try to find out. The Hall had had so many owners. The present one was an ex-army officer too, a colonel. He believed that he actually rented the shooting on the moors round our land, but again was not sure.

We were all ready when he called for us at eight next morning, Amelia wildly excited at the prospect of a trip in a motor car. It was another fine day. The first thing he told us, when we got under way, was that he had found out that the name of the major who had lived at Skerry Hall was Allen, and that he had been killed in the early days of the war, but he had moved from the Hall some years before the war and was running a stud farm near a village about half-way to York. So far as he could learn, his widow and the daughter, whose name was Rosemary, had carried on the stud farm, but the daughter was now married and living in Canada. Mrs Allen was running the farm on her own, or at least had been up to a year or two ago. He mentioned the name of the village. Dain was delighted, and told Will about the stirrup. She was certain that it had belonged to Rosemary. She would write to Mrs Allen and find out. Amelia remarked (showing that she, too, was not lacking in intuition):

"I *do* want a pony!"

"Wouldn't you, darling," I said, "like a big motor car too, like this?"

She thought this out, missing the irony of it.

"Yes. But I want a pony, because a pony is alive, and a motor car isn't alive. It's dead."

Will laughed.

"I like that. Seeing that she can do ninety."

We were already doing sixty and had turned on to the moorland road. He said, when we reached the beginning of the moor, that he had been right about the colonel renting the shooting right on the moors round Adder Howe.

"Oh, yes." I tried to appear not too interested. "I suppose he's one of the usual sporting type, hunting, shooting and fishing."

"Well, I don't think he does much of anything these days. He's old and doesn't get about much except in his car. He owns some farms up country from Burnharbour. I've only once seen him out with a shooting party on this

116

moor. He doesn't ride. I've never heard of him being keen on fishing, but I don't really know much about him. His sort are finished, in my opinion. In spite of his Rolls-Royce, I don't think he's got much money. It's a 1913 model, anyway. I don't think he's even got a full-time gamekeeper, not for this moor, anyway."

I made no comment on this rather significant piece of information and the subject dropped. It was then that Will gave us the news that he must have been bursting to impart from the first. He had landed the housing estate contract. It was a very big thing. It meant more than a year's work for his firm. It meant that he would be able to take on many more workmen from the large local pool of unemployed. He only wished (and wasn't his wife pestering him about it) he could make a start with the building of his own house.

The lorry had just finished off-loading another cargo of bricks when we arrived. To the foreman and the men, Will expressed his satisfaction at the neat job they had made of the demolition, and it was easy to see that they appreciated his praise, and that he was a well-liked employer. There were two extra men this morning; one of them, he said, a mason. He had brought with him a large-scale plan of the house, pasted on to a piece of plywood. This, it seemed, for the foreman's guidance. With a clean straight board and a spirit level, he checked the whole length of the mortared foundations, and then, with two boards nailed together at right angles, like an oversized joiner's square, he checked the four corners, to make certain that these were exact right angles. Meanwhile, one of the workmen was preparing one of several rolls of bituminised felt. It looked like a heavy grade of ordinary roofing-felt, and it was the same width as the original walls, two feet six. Starting at the right-hand corner of the wall nearest to the little stream, he unrolled it so that it covered the now hard mortar. Will watched him, and then he said:

"Right-o! And now let's get the first corner stone laid. You take charge, Harry. Is it all ready? You know we really ought to have a gold trowel for this job."

I had not told Dain what was expected of her, nor that at my request Will had brought out with him a dozen bottles of beer. There was laughter when he told one of the men to fetch these from the car. Close by the corner was one large stone, and on a board a heap of wet mortar. Harry gave this a quick turn over with a shovel, then handed a trowel to Dain.

"Slap it on," he said, "and then spread it out, just like butter on bread, only a bit thicker. Eh—and let the little lass put some on too." He gave Amelia a smaller trowel. She, well-practised in the making of mud pies, did not hesitate. A patch of the felt, just bigger than the base of the stone, was covered, and Harry gave it an expert smoothing off.

"Now then," he said. "Let's have some money in it for luck. If you chaps have spent up your last week's wages already, or your wives have been through your pockets, ha'pennies will do. But no brass buttons or owt like that, or it'll bring bad luck on the house."

He had taken a sixpence from his own pocket, and he stuck this into the mortar. All the other men followed with coins of some sort, and Will made his contribution.

Amelia looked bewildered.

"What are they doing that for?"

"For luck," I said, handing her a coin. "To propitiate the gods. So that we'll all be happy when we come to live here, and perhaps make enough money to buy a pony."

"Oh! Then we ought to put in a lot more pennies than this."

There was more laughter, and one of the men said:

"What about this? This ought to bring you a pony. Shall we stick it in? It's a bit big, though."

It was an old, rusty, well-worn, cart-horse shoe which had been lying on the ground.

Harry examined it.

"A horseshoe, if it's to be lucky, should be fixed with its ends up, or all your luck runs out. We can't do that in mortar. But I suppose it's all right if it's laid flat."

He passed it to Amelia, and she pushed it into the mortar along with her coin. Again he gave the mortar a smoothing over. Then he signed to me to get hold of one end of the corner stone. We lifted it up, lowered it on to the mortar, and he asked Dain to tap it with the handle of the trowel.

"Now, then. You've got to say, 'I declare this stone well and truly laid,' and the job's done."

She spoke the traditional words. We all cheered and the beer was handed round, and we drank to the success of our new home, Dain and I holding hands, Amelia smiling up at us as though she knew how happy we were.

Will, with his many affairs, was in a hurry to get back. Dain and Amelia got into the car again and it drove up the hill. The men fell to, and the building of our house began.

Like most writers, I liked to have quiet and freedom from distraction in my working hours, and I knew that I would find neither in the house itself except when the children were asleep. At the foot of the steep bank which fell from the front of the house, and just short of the boundary wall of the wood, was a small quarry from which the stones both of the barn and the ancient wall had been taken. It was cut into the bank, leaving a vertical face about twelve feet in height. From the foot of this to the wall the ground seemed level and quite dry. I had decided to build a small hut on this site.

It would be out of sight and normal sound of the house, yet within hailing distance. It would have no view, which in itself was an advantage, for a view to me *was* a potential distraction, particularly one that embraced the sea. I thought it would be even safer if I had no window at all that I could look through, to build it like a sculptor's studio with the light only in the roof. Will had sent out the timber for this, and it had been carried down to the quarry. As I had completed the pioneer work on the vegetable garden, and it was imperative that I should start another book as soon as we moved in, I thought I had better get on with it at once. I could still watch the building of the house at frequent intervals.

As with gardening, I had acquired all my experience of carpentry and joinery the hard and difficult way in Cornwall. Nearly all the wood we'd had given to us, or had found washed up, was of odd lengths and thicknesses. Dunnage, the boards and timbers used on ships for stowing mixed cargoes, and usually thrown overboard when cargoes like coal or grain or china clay were carried, was, as a rule, poor quality stuff: sap-wood, or cross-grained, split or warped, and some of it was so hard that one could not drive an ordinary nail into it without drilling first.

My tools had mostly been cheap ones, and it had taken me a long time to learn that saws have to be sharpened and re-set at frequent intervals if they are to cut easily and straight along a pencilled line; that the blades of planes and chisels must be kept razor sharp; that even the cutting edges of bits must be re-sharpened if they are to drill holes without one having to press and crank the brace until the wood smoulders like a savage making fire.

One of the things we'd both had to learn was to repress our desire to get a thing done quickly to see how it looked, especially with a piece of furniture. Hard woods, like the oak and teak and elm we wrested from the hulks of the derelict ships in our creek, we had prized because of their sentimental interest, and because, when planed and sandpapered and waxed they were, when made into furniture, so beautiful to look at. But what a job it had been, particularly with some elm that had been part of the keel of a brig, half-sunk in the mud at least fifty years. It had been hewn from a log which must have been at least three feet in thickness, and we'd had to knock the great iron bolts out of it before getting it ripped into boards at our landlord's shipyard.

We had made a table, and a linen chest, and two

stools from the keel of that ancient brig, and we had plugged the holes where the spikes had been with oak pegs that had been used for her planking. From some teak planks we had found in the cuddy of another derelict sailing ship we had made a cot for Amelia which was now being used for Jane.

The timber I had got for my new hut was all softwood, brand new from the timber yard: tongue and groove one-inch planks for the floor, three-quarter inch for the roof, which, like our Cornish hut, would be covered with felt; three-quarter inch feathered weather boards for the exterior walls; lengths of three by two for the floor joists and rafters; two by two for the frames.

There was, Will had told me, no need to submit plans for a wood building, provided that it was not of a greater cubic capacity than one thousand cubic feet. I only wanted room for a table, chair, shelves for books and documents, and a heating stove; and if I made it twelve feet by eight, with a height to the ridge of seven feet six, I was well within the prescribed cubic capacity, with plenty of room for all my furniture. As it would be almost completely hidden between the quarry cliff and the wood it wouldn't matter-how it looked from outside.

How different my job promised to be from anything I had tackled before. With all the wood the right thickness for each part, and sawn accurately, so that a piece of two by two did measure two inches on each of its four sides, it was almost like building with a child's constructional set, for all I had to do was to cut the lengths to the required size and nail them together. My plan was to make the floor first, laying the joists on bricks to keep them clear of the ground. Remembering Will's lecture on rising moisture, that bricks are porous, I would take the precaution of laying a piece of felt between brick and joist.

The making of the floor, however, was not so simple as I had imagined. The ground, and it was almost bare sandstone, which had *looked* level, proved to be like a mountain range in miniature when I came to lay the bricks for the first joist. There was a hump in the middle. There was a difference of nearly a foot between one end of the site and the other, but the slope was not a constant one, either in degree or direction. I had a spirit level. I was surprised and disconcerted by the difficulty of coaxing a single brick to sit on the ground so that the bubble came central along its length and breadth, and when it came to levelling a joist between a pair of brick supports the task was doubly difficult. What I needed was mortar, and more bricks, which at least gave me an excuse for going up to the house and seeing how things were progressing.

Once there I found it hard to tear myself away. Although scarcely an hour had passed since the laying of the first corner stone, felt had been unrolled along the whole of the foundations, the three other corner stones had been laid, and next to the first one Harry had got several stones set along the wall nearest the garden. Inside of these one of the men was laying a wall of bricks, and had almost reached the other corner stone.

This wall was two bricks wide, extending to the inner edge of the damp course, leaving a space between bricks and the rough undressed inner faces of the stone. A glance at the plan showed me that this inner brick wall would have only one more course of double bricks. After this for the whole height of the wall it would be single, and the purpose of having the greater width below was to form a ledge to hold the ends of the floor joists, above the damp course. Both Harry and the bricklayer had cords, stretched from corner-stone to corner-stone to guide them.

I noticed another thing: that at four equidistant places, one opposite to the last stone, the bricklayer had left a space, the length of a brick, and that Harry himself was preparing to set the next stone with a gap the same size, and opposite to the one in the brick. He showed me the galvanised iron grid that was to be cemented into this gap, so that air could circulate not only under the joists, but through the vertical cavity in the walls.

I was fascinated. I began to wish that instead of building my hut in wood I was going to do it the same way as the house, in stone and brick, and I thought how exciting it would be to begin at the very beginning, by cutting the stones out of the quarry itself, so conveniently near.

Yet I had only to watch these two men at work to realise the truth of what Will had told us first: that building with stone was slower and therefore more costly than either brick or wood. Harry had to carry the next stone that he was to set from the pile that he had already dressed and sorted, but it needed both his hands; and having put it down close to where it had to go, he checked its height, and discovered that it was a fraction over size. It was soft, and he deftly and swiftly reduced it to the required size with his chisel-pointed hammer, but the whole operation took him at least three minutes. By contrast the bricklayer seemed to be working automatically.

There were boards with heaps of mortar on them placed at convenient intervals along the wall, and piles of bricks too, and they were constantly replenished by another of the workmen. He just slapped one trowel full of the mortar on to the wall, spread it with a stroke which brought enough of the mortar up the end of the last brick to make a joint, pressed the new brick down and gave it a light tap, then reached for more mortar and another brick. Another bricklayer and another mason were similarly engaged on the opposite wall of the house, but the mason there hadn't got as far as Harry had done.

Almost in the middle of the site two other bricklayers had made great progress with the building of a solid wall, about six feet by four, the foundations of the double fireplace and chimney stacks, and another was engaged on the building of small brick pillars, at intervals between the main house walls, that were to give extra support for the floor joists, the very things I was trying to make for the joists of my hut. I saw that he began each one with an ample clod of mortar on the rock itself. I borrowed a bucket of mortar and returned to the quarry, inspired.

Although his sheep were still grazing on our land, I had seen nothing of Jimmy since the day we had first come out with Will; nor had I seen Mrs Briggs again. I guessed that, like our third neighbour of Bog Hall, they were all preoccupied with their hay.

I had felt rather diffident about accepting Mrs Brigg's invitation of hospitality. If there was a feud between her husband and Jimmy it was essential that we should keep out of it, and not antagonise one by appearing too friendly with the other. I didn't want to get up against Jimmy, seeing that he was my closest neighbour. Besides, I liked him. At the same time I must not appear standoffish, and after I'd had my lunch (I'd got my joists fixed, ready for planking), I sauntered down through the wood towards the Mill Farm.

At the ford, which we had crossed with Isaac and Snowball, I kept to the beck side, leaving the main track. As then, there was no sound in the wood except the steady murmur of insect life and running water. There was no wind here. Even the highest sun-dappled leaves of the oaks were still. The bed of the beck was less rocky than it was on our own land, and its gradient was gentler. Some yards below the ford I came to quite a large pool, with an ash tree branching over it.

I approached it warily, using the trunk of the tree as a screen, for I had already heard the plop of a rising fish. Then I saw it, at the head of the pool close up to a tiny waterfall made by a largish boulder. Compared with the trout of the mere it was no more than sardine size. Compared with the trout in our own beck it was a beauty. It was at least nine inches long. It was fat, in splendid condition. If there were more like it then this section of the stream certainly would be worth fishing. If Sam Briggs was going to prove as friendly as his wife, he would most likely give me leave. I might bring my fishing gear out tomorrow and have a try. I made a noise, and the fish darted out of sight under the boulder, and it was joined by several smaller ones that had been in the shallows.

I moved on. There was one more pool, and this too contained trout, which if not so big were of catchable size as beck trout went. Beyond the pool was the boundary of the wood, the road and the stone bridge, and I heard the sounds of a farm: of poultry, pigs and a dog. I climbed over the wall on to the road, crossed the bridge, and saw the farm itself.

It stood back from the road and the stream and the ruins of the old mill. Like nearly all the other farms in the district, I'd deliberately avoided it as a boy, and I'd never had reason to go near it since. The house was big, stone built with the usual pantiled roof. There were cow-houses and stable and barn enclosing a stone-paved yard, and with a stackyard on the other side of the house. I noticed one new stack of hay, and another half completed, with a loaded, but horseless, wagon alongside it. I observed too, as I passed through the yard, that all the buildings seemed to be in good repair, and that the yard was clean and tidy. There was an air of efficiency about the place.

The house door was open. From within I heard the sound of men's voices, talking and laughing. I knocked. From a doorway on the left of a long dark passage that evidently opened on the living-room came Mrs Briggs, looking hot and a bit flustered, but just as affable as before.

"Why it's *you*! You've bin a long time getting yourself down. And you haven't brought your missus with you now. Come your way in. The men have almost finished dinner, but I'll soon get you a bite of summat. How are you getting on with your new house? I've been so busy with hay-time I haven't had time to get up."

I protested that I'd had my dinner, but as I followed her in, she said:

"Why, you'll have room for a tart or a bit of cake and a cup of tea. You must have summat!"

I entered a large, low-ceilinged room, with an old-fashioned kitchen range on one side of it, with whitewashed walls, and scrubbed and sandstoned flagged floor, and a large table, still laden with food at which there sat four men, three of them familiar to me. There was Tommy Peck, the country postman, whom I knew very well indeed. We'd been at school together. There was our third neighbour Matt Pashby, and to my astonishment there was Jimmy himself, with a mug of tea in one hand, a piece of cake in the other, the familiar half-mocking smile on his face. Next to him, at the head of the table, was a younger-looking man, with dark hair, a pale clean-shaven face, and very intelligent eyes. He had risen as I entered, and he reached out his hand to me as his wife introduced him as Sam. His speech was broad, but he had good manners.

"You'll know Tommy, our postman, and Mr Pashby of Bog, and Jimmy, here?" he said.

"Aye," Jimmy laughed. "We've met a time or two. I see you've got a start building this morning."

I shook hands with Tommy Peck. He was a big, powerful man, with a red face, good but rather prominent teeth, and a rather big nose. It was his nose that I remembered best about him. Although a year or two my senior, and big for his age even then, he was the one lad in the village that I could always successfully lick in a fight. He had been like myself, an outcast, for his father was a farmer. Nearly all the other boys were the sons of fishermen or sailors; and farmers were regarded as traditional foes.

Tommy and I should have been friends. All my yearnings for friendship, although bitterly unsuccessful, were for the fishermen and sailor lads and it was perhaps as much as anything to win their approval that I so willingly took on Tommy for our first scrap. It was in that scrap that by accident I discovered the extraordinary vulnerability of Tommy's nose. One slight blow on it and it started to bleed, and at the first sight of his own blood, Tommy would start howling surrender.

From that time onwards, for many years, whenever we met, alone on the beach or in one of the village alleys, or in a country lane, we'd set to on each other like a couple of terriers, and although I'd had several black eyes from him, I'd always managed to get in the winning blow. He had been among the first of the local boys to join up in the Kaiser's war, in which he had won a D.C.M. for taking a German pillbox single-handed, and bayoneting its crew. I was glad that in the pressure of hand and in the twinkling of his eyes there was now only friendship.

Yet it was the apparent friendship between my three neighbours that surprised me most. Or was this just the good nature and good manners of Sam and his wife? Sam had pulled up a chair to the table for me. She had poured out a mug of tea, and pushed a cut cake and a plate of tarts in front of me.

"I'm glad you've come down," said Sam, with undoubted sincerity. "If you want owt, you just let us know."

"Same here, of course," said Jimmy. And my once enemy, the postman, said, with a wink: "I hope you're not going to have many heavy parcels sent to you when you live up there. They don't give me a motor car."

The elderly Mr Pashby got up and said:

"Now it's time we were at it again. We've bin lucky with the weather so far, but you can't trust it these days."

The others got up too, and I said to Sam:

"Do you want any help?"

"Nay. Thanks very much, but we've only another load to bring in. You finish your mug of tea."

They moved out, Jimmy last of all, and Mrs Briggs followed him to the door, then came back, shutting the door behind her. Then, after a quick look through the window to make certain that he was out of hearing, she let herself go.

"Well! If that chap Jimmy doesn't beat the band! He hasn't been near here for over three weeks since Sam told him off about that saddle, and he comes down first thing this morning, all smiles, with a hay fork over his shoulder, and he says to Sam, 'Now, Sam. I thought you might like a hand with your hay. A nice crop you've got, too,' he says, buttering Sam up. 'I've never seen a finer crop round here.'

"That's how he always gets round Sam. Buttering him up, telling him what a good farmer he is, which is true enough, without anyone having to tell him, just to get round him. Not a word from Jimmy about that saddle of course, that he's promised to bring back. That's why he walked down instead of riding. He's using that saddle every day, and he didn't want Sam to see it. But Sam couldn't be vexed with him seeing we're so short-handed, for old Matt's not much good, and, anyway, we had to help Matt yesterday, and that's why he's here today.

"He's a cough-drop, is Jimmy, but as I've said before it's no use being vexed with him. It runs off him like water on a duck's back. *I* know why he's turned up to give Sam a hand today. His wagon's broken, and he'll be wanting to borrow Sam's to fetch a load of bracken in from the moor, later on. And I bet he'll need our mare too, and expect Sam to give him a hand. He'll come and try and get a bit of hay out of Sam too, if it's a hard winter, for he hasn't got much of his own, but he'll not get it if Sam listens to me, not until he fetches that saddle back . . . Eh, let me fill your mug up. Try one slice of that cake. Jimmy told me it was the tastiest he'd had for a long time."

I still liked Jimmy, but I liked Mrs Briggs too, and I thought that in all her diatribe against Jimmy there was no spite, that she, too, was susceptible to his blandishments, and that she enjoyed dramatising his behaviour. She was a woman of boundless energy. She spoke quickly, almost torrentially, but all the time she was moving about her spotlessly-clean kitchen, clearing the dishes from the table, giving a poke at the fire, opening and closing the oven, from which came the smell of still more pastry.

I didn't want any more tea, but I tried a small piece of the cake and it was excellent, and I told her that Jimmy hadn't been humbugging about that anyway, and she was pleased. I had to go. I got up, and I mentioned the fishing in the wood. Did she think her husband would mind if I had a try one day?

"Why, of course he wouldn't. He never bothers with owt like that. And come again whenever you like. But don't let on to anyone that I've been saying owt against Jimmy or they may think I'm a mischief maker! So long for now. I must get on with the washing-up, and it's washing day, too. And I've got to make a mash for the hens, and them men will want another meal when they've finished the hay. So long."

8

A WATCHED KETTLE will never boil! To me, in spite that all the men were working full out, that there was no hold up for material, and no interference by the weather during that first week, the building of our house seemed exasperatingly slow.

I would work at my hut as long as two hours at a time in the hope that when I went up I should see some dramatic difference in the height of the walls or chimney stack. There would be a difference, but it was never a big one. It was like waiting and watching for the opening of the bud of a flower, and it was only by visualising the bare foundations as they had been when the cornerstone was laid that I could appreciate the extent of the growth. In this Dain had the advantage over me, for it was not until the Friday evening that she was able to come out again with another picnic supper for us both.

It was apparent to me, as soon as she got off the bus, that she was bursting with excitement.

"Good news, darling," she cried. "Whatever do you think has happened. You just won't believe it."

Our post at Butcher's Folly did not come until long after I had left for Adder Howe. I had a thought that he might have brought this morning another unexpected publisher's or agent's cheque, but I was quickly disabused of such a material hope.

"I've had a letter from Mrs Allen. The stirrup *was* hers, or rather Rosemary's, and she thinks she may have got the other one, and if she can find it she's going to let us have it. Isn't it wonderful? And she's invited us to go over to her place one day next week. It *is* a stud farm she's running and she breeds all sorts of ponies, and although she doesn't say so in her letter, I shouldn't be a bit surprised if she's got one the right size for Amelia."

Although I had a deep respect for feminine intuition I was still incredulous.

"Did she," I asked, "say when and where and how she had lost it?"

"She doesn't remember the exact date, but it was at least twenty years ago, and it was somewhere round here. You were not quite right about how it came to be

133

lost, though, but you were nearly. She was just riding with another grown-up girl, and not hunting. The leather broke, and as they couldn't mend it, Rosemary put it in the pocket of her coat, and it must have just dropped out. Won't it be an extraordinary thing if it leads to us actually getting a pony, and just the right one."

"Yes," I said, still marvelling, and not daring to suggest that she was being over-optimistic, straining her gift for clairvoyance too far.

We came to the view again. Although there was still no sign of a break in the dry weather, there had been a change. The west wind had backed to south and then south-east, and the sea was rough, breaking on the outermost scaurs of the bay, and the air was cooler. There was not the same temptation in its aspect there had been last Friday, to walk to the beach to fish or swim. We hurried down to the site.

I had warned Dain that she wasn't going to see any striking progress. The main walls had risen only by two complete stone courses above the foundations, and were still short of where the window-sills were to be. The only gap was the doorway. The joists of the ground floor had been laid, their ends fixed on narrow boards laid lengthways along the ledges made by the first course of bricks, and supported again by the brick pillars spaced between the walls. And a gangway of loose boards had been thrown across them so that one could walk from one end of the floor to the other.

The chimney stack, too, was up to the height of what was to be the first floor. Its two breasts had been formed, narrowing into the two separate flues. Apart from the chimney stack, which would form part of the main partition, all the partitions would be of timber and wall boards, and the whole place was a long way yet from looking like a house.

Yet enough of the stonework was done for us to appreciate how good it was to look when it got up to the eaves. No two stones were quite alike in tint and grain. Some were brown, the colour of dead bracken. Some were yellowish, some an almost pearly-grey, some had a greenish tinge, and were streaked almost like agates. I held one of the slates against the wall, and while I still felt a bit doubtful as to how the shape of the mansard roof was going to look, there was no doubt that the slates would harmonise perfectly with the stone. Another thing was very clear: the workmanship, and the material were both first class. There was no jerry-building here. The walls of our house at least should last forever. Dain expressed her satisfaction and delight, but she said, rather wistfully:

"They do seem to be making a fine job of it, but it isn't quite so exciting as though we were actually building it ourselves, is it? It will be more fun when we get in and start making the cupboards and things and more furniture, and doing the painting. I hope it's not going to be too grand. It *will* be different from our hut. Fancy having the walls all finished properly, and no holes to be patched up with pieces of sail cloth."

"Yes. And the floor level, and no gale howling through the boards, and a fireplace that doesn't smoke, and water coming through a tap and not to be carried from the well in a bucket."

I said this with conviction, yet I knew she was right that there was more satisfaction in making things ourselves. Even in Cornwall we had been a long way from starting from scratch. If half a dozen skilled men with proper tools and material had only got as far as this in a week how long would it take us to build even the humblest sort of a house? And there was going to be plenty for us to do when the workmen had finished. In a place like this there would be enough to keep us occupied for the rest of our lives.

There was the land itself, our gardens, an orchard, paths, walls, the clearing of the island, the making of a pool for the children, perhaps one day the building of a dam for a waterwheel. We should never want to farm, but one thing we must do was arrest the encroachment of the whins and bracken over the fields that were still tolerably clear, and improve the grazing so that when properly fenced from our neighbour's stock we might possibly let them.

And most sobering of all thoughts, I had to go on writing, probably forever, so that we should be able to buy the things which, because of the complexities of modern civilisation, we could never make or produce ourselves. It bothered me that since the finishing of my last book (although I had written several articles and stories) I had not conceived an idea for another one.

We walked down to my hut. It was nearly finished. I had nailed the last board of the roof just before going up to meet the bus, and all I had to do to the main structure now was put on the felt covering, fix the glass panes, make the door. I would line it inside with the same wall board that was going to be used in the house. My stove would be in one corner, and its pipe would lead by an elbow through one of the walls just under the eaves, to obviate the risk of a leak in the roof.

It had no pretensions to beauty. In spite of the clean material, I had made one or two mistakes in measuring the pieces for the frames and in nailing up one frame I had found that instead of being square it was slightly rhomboid. I had got over this by drawing the nails and inserting small pieces of wood between the joints.

The door jambs, too, suffered from the same defect, and it looked as though I should just have to cut the door to match them, for I had nailed them too well to permit of drawing. Dain was not critical, however. She thought I had made a splendid job of it, although she felt that I might hate not having a window to look through, especially in the wall opposite the wood, and wouldn't the sky itself, seen through, the top lights, prove a distraction? Not, I said, if I used frosted glass, which indeed I was going to do as an extra precaution against just that very thing. A cloud sailing across a blue sky might certainly tempt me to look up from my typewriter and cause my mind to wander.

"Come on," she said. "Let me help you put the felt on. It will be like old times, won't it? Do you remember our first night in the hut when the storm came on and the rain streamed through the roof, and we had to go out and try and patch the felt?"

I did remember, and as I got hold of the first strip of felt to carry it up on to the roof of my new hut there came to my mind most vividly the dramatic happenings of that night.

There was a gale and torrential rain. While trying to secure the torn and flapping pieces of felt, we had remembered that we hadn't properly moored our newly-acquired dinghy, and we had dashed down to the cove just in time to save it and haul it ashore. We had found that the cove itself was full of dunnage and other flotsam and jetsam that apparently had come from a ship we had watched coming into the harbour the same afternoon, and while we were harvesting this we had found a half-drowned kitten. We had resuscitated it with hot milk, and then, giving up our attempts to mend the felt, we had rigged up an old sail inside our kitchen to form a tent. And it had been then, with the storm still raging outside, but both of us and the castaway kitten, too, warm and dry, that I had conceived the idea of my first book about the family of Bramblewick fishermen I had been living and working with before Dain and I had met. I had started the first chapter, writing by the light of a hurricane lamp, which occasionally hissed as a drop of water fell on its top.

I made no comment on Dain's remark. She had taken one end of the piece of felt, and we had stretched it over the first section of the roof, overlapping at the ends and the eaves. I asked her to hold it there while I tacked the first lap. But we were both thinking about Cornwall, and she suddenly said:

"It was an exciting night. That was when you started the book, do you remember? Why don't you write a book about all that? There were lots of other exciting things happened. I mean it was quite exciting going out there the first time, with Joe Hoskins, and then how he let us have the boat and yacht's bath, and how we fixed the place up, and the garden. And all the other extraordinary things that happened, like the ship coming to lay up just below our cove, and our finding out who the mate and his wife were, and how we had to hide from them. It could be quite funny in parts, especially how our dinghy sank in sight of the ship and we tried not to be rescued by them, and then found out how kind they were. It's only an idea of course. I suppose it would be very difficult, really."

Only an idea! I felt a sudden elation as great as that of the night of the storm and the starting of that other book.

I gasped. "Yes—yes! A wonderful idea. I think I could do it. It might be a sort of *Robinson Crusoe*, or *Swiss Family Robinson*."

"Or a *Blue Lagoon*, for we did have a baby. Two, in fact."

I put the hammer down.

"It might," I said, with growing enthusiasm, "be a terrific success. Beat all our other books into a cocked hat."

"It *would* be! It couldn't help! It was all so wonderful. Think of the building of our cruiser, and trying to get that old engine to go, and then not being able to stop it when it started. And how the book came back from one publisher after another, and then the telegram saying it was accepted. That wouldn't be quite *Robinson Crusoe* or the *Blue Lagoon*, but it was exciting, and anyway, finding that the people on the ship knew us was like Robinson Crusoe finding the footprints in the sand."

"Come on, my love," I said. "Let's leave this job. Let's celebrate. What have you brought for supper?"

"Nothing very interesting, I'm afraid. Only sandwiches and cake."

"Then let's go and catch some trout down in the wood. We'll grill them."

"That would be fun. But I do think we ought to finish this job first, now we've started. Especially as this is where you are going to write the new book. I'm so excited about it."

I had written too many books by this time (including some which had never met a publisher's approval) not to know of the difficulties that lie on the way between the coming of the idea itself, and the writing on the final page of that often elusive phrase, THE END.

No matter how good the idea may seem in its first conceptive stage it is nebulous, and you never know until you get down to the job of crystallising it into words and sentences and paragraphs and chapters whether it *is* as good as it seemed in the first raptures of discovery, and even then you never know for certain, for once started the book itself takes charge.

Its substance must spring, or be pumped or squeezed, largely from your subconscious mind, from that store of impressions made by your senses of sight and hearing and smell and taste and touch, which together make memory, and have their own way of getting muddled. Your lodestone may be money, or the possible acclamation of critics or the public, but no matter how you may yearn and strive for these you are limited, thwarted by your own inability to think the right way, to find the right word, often to think at all. But while I knew all this, that I would suffer many agonising hours in this sound- and distraction-proof hut I was making for myself, fighting the devils of self-distrust, I was aware now only of a joy that verged on intoxication.

We didn't talk about it anymore. I didn't want to think about it hard, lest I should see some snag. I didn't want to change the nebulous, glowing character of the idea. We both affected an outward calm, and carried on with the laying of the felt. The panes of glass could wait, for I had no putty, and it was a job that would have to be done very carefully if there was to be no leak. Before we packed up I would lightly tack some felt over the vents in the roof where the panes were to go, in case there was rain.

For convenience's sake I had been having my midday meal down here where I was working and I had been keeping my things inside. My fishing rod was there. Curiously enough I had only used it once since I had brought it out, and only half-heartedly. The big trout (and it wasn't so big, anyway) had proved itself indifferent to the artificial fly I had cast within an inch or two of its nose, and the only fish I had landed were so small that I had put them back in the stream. My reel and fly box were in my rucksack. When the last piece of felt was on, I went in and got the rucksack.

"Come on," I said. "Let's go and fish. They are small, but they'll be very nice, and if we only get a couple they'll make a symbolic feast."

I saw a sudden look in Dain's eyes that alarmed me.

"It *does* seem a pity to catch small trout. Won't they

grow bigger by next year, if they're left alone? Think of that big one in the mere!"

I had guessed what she was leading to.

"I am trying, darling," I said, *"not* to think of it. I've been trying all week not to think of it."

"But how can you help thinking about it when it's there? And no one seems to bother about it. Otherwise, it wouldn't be there, would it? Someone would have caught it. Whoever owns the mere they can't possibly be interested in fishing."

"It would still be poaching, if we tried to fish there. It would still be breaking the law. We've got to wait, and find out definitely who does own it, and then ask permission. If it is the colonel, he might just as easily give us leave as the Briggs have done to fish in the beck."

"But what if he said no? Then it would look twice as bad if you fished there and were caught."

I had already thought of that possibility. And I now thought of another one, which apparently had not occurred to Dain, that some other angler less scrupulous than I was trying to be might discover the existence of the fish. Such persons often stayed in the district during the Easter and summer visiting season and I recalled how, as a boy, with great glee I had once seen the old miller catch one of them fishing in the dam (I had come for the same purpose myself and was hiding in the undergrowth), and not only had he cursed him and ordered him off, but he had warned him that next time he would throw him into the dam. Suddenly I knew that, come what may, I had to do it. If I didn't now, then it was going to hang over me until I did. The chances were all against my catching it, anyway. My gear was cheap and old, for we had never done any trout-fishing in Cornwall. I had even forgotten the name of the few flies I had in my box. I had no landing net either.

Quickly, I lit our fire, and while the coffee was getting hot I tacked the felt over the vents. We ate our supper. Then we went up and had a last look at the house, as though in the excitement about the book we had forgotten it.

"It does look good," said Dain. "Aren't we lucky. Everything seems to be going right for us. We *were* right to leave Cornwall. It's going to be much better having a proper house. The children are going to love it here. I'm certain we're going to get just the pony we need from Mrs Allen. And it's going to be a wonderful book that will make us lots of money. And I'm certain you're going to catch that big trout. Come on. We haven't got much time."

I seized weakly at that last excuse for escape.

"We haven't. By the time we get there, and I get my rod together, it will be practically time to go for the bus. We only just caught it last time. We really ought to come out specially if we're going to do it. Take our time over it. Not rush it."

"It wouldn't matter if we missed the bus. It's only four miles to walk. The children will be all right, and I told Auntie we might be late back. Come on. It's a lovely walk over to the mere, anyway, with the heather starting to flower."

It *was* lovely. The real heather was a long way from being in full bloom. Enough of it was out to give a blush of tender purple to the dark green and browns of the moor. The sea wind had packed the sky with cloud, too even in its structure, too pale and too low to portend rain, and although there would be no visible sunset, the light was strong and the lower air so clear that every detail of the moorland landscape for miles around was optically sharp. The lone pines, the odd groups of sheep, a shepherd's hut, the low hills each surmounted by one or several of the conical mounds that marked the burial place of an ancient Briton. The salty wind was cool but invigorating, and the sun-dried springy turf exuded a warmth. There was a steady droning of bees and you could almost taste honey in the smell of the heather blooms they were plundering.

We came to the edge of the valley of the beck and the mere. The mere lay beneath us, and I felt my heart beating faster at my first sight of it. I had deliberately carried my fishing rod (in its canvas case) like a walking stick, holding it by one end, and Dain had got the rucksack over her shoulders. We sat down in the heather, and we could have still passed as a couple of hikers, resting to admire the view.

I was already satisfied, and my sight was good, that the whole of the moor was deserted of human beings apart from ourselves, that the coast was clear, and my interest was concentrated on the mere itself, with lessening excitement, however, for there was no sign of our fish. It was not, in spite of the rising land on both sides of it, completely sheltered from the wind, but this, as so often happens in a valley, constantly varied in its direction, forming eddies of air that made catspaws on the water. These had made a noticeable difference to the floating surface weed, causing it to thicken around the shores and increase the patch of clear water. There were two clear patches, each more or less the shape of the mere itself, each a long way out from the nearest shore. It looked too, as though the gusts of wind were keeping all airborne insect life away from, the water.

"I don't think it's worthwhile my fixing up my rod," I said, daring to speak quite loudly. "There's not a sign of fly. Perhaps it's too cold. Our trout, if he's still there, is probably feeding on the bottom."

Dain was not discouraged.

"Well, there's plenty of time. We didn't see it before until we were just going. The moorhens aren't there either." She dropped her voice. "Perhaps we shouldn't talk so loud. Anyway, you haven't to *see* fish before you fish for them, have you? And if the big one isn't jumping for flies, perhaps he'd be all the more interested if he *did* see one. Do fix up the rod. We can't go back without at least trying."

I was a practised, if not a very knowledgeable or skilful, freshwater angler. I had never acquired the habit of emotional detachment, the patience, so essential for success. I was usually all right when it came to action, but often at the start of fishing, and especially when the fishing looked good, I would find it very hard to keep cool, to make certain that in assembling my gear the joints of the rod were accurately fitted, the eyes for the line running fair to the tip; that the reel was securely locked, and the line on it free of kinks, and the cast and fly tied with the right knot. I was able to do all this now slowly, and deliberately, with a clear eye and steady fingers, for I was quite convinced that on this occasion, at least, we were going to see no fish; that I was merely going to make a token demonstration. It would be interesting to see if it were possible to cast a fly into one of the clear patches, using the very tricky wind to help me.

My rod was a ten-footer, split cane, quite a cheap one, with simple push-in brass joints. I had once broken the middle section, and had mended it with splints, gluing them and whipping them over with strong thread. I tested this joint, and it seemed strong, but as I had proved before, it detracted from the suppleness of the rod. My line was an ordinary trout line of braided silk, the very one I had used on our first fishing of the mere, but when I tested it now it withstood a fairly powerful jerk. My cast was simply a six-foot length of Jap gut, unknotted, and as thick as ordinary sewing thread. Fortunately, I had packed it in moist flannel after my fishing in the beck and it would soon stretch straight. The only fly in my box that I definitely knew by name was a March Brown, obviously not the choice for an evening in late July. Of the others, some were light, some were dark, and I chose one that was practically black, and it might have been a Black Gnat. It was the one whose hook was the least rusty.

It was Dain now who was getting impatient with my unusually careful preparations.

"Are you ready now? I'm certain the fish will be there, just waiting. Do hurry and start."

"A stitch in time saves nine," I said, wisely and calmly.

I tested the knot I had made on the fly. I got up,

146

holding the rod low, and had a last look round to make certain that we were still alone. Then we moved down to the water's edge opposite the nearer of the two clear patches.

"I don't think there's a hope," I whispered. "Not a hope. It's no good dropping the fly where the weed is. It will just foul, and I'm certain I can't reach the clear water."

This was wet-fly fishing. In dry-fly fishing, which requires much greater skill, the fly and cast are buoyant, and the fly is made to alight and remain floating on the surface, a sitting target for the fish. With the wet technique the fly starts to sink, and you keep it in motion by dragging it in, in a series of jerks which are meant to suggest to the fish that it is either a drowning fly or an amphibious insect. With both types of fishing you use your rod like a stock whip, imparting motion to the line by whipping it to and fro, increasing the length with every stroke. I did this now, not letting the fly drop until I knew that I was at my casting limit. It fell at least twenty feet short of the edge of the clear water, and among the weed. It did not foul but when I drew it up the whole line was stuck with the tiny fronds of duckweed, and I could not cast again. I reeled it in until I had the fly in my hand.

"It's hopeless!" I said. "We'll just have to wait until there's been a gale to blow all the weed to one side of the mere, or try in the early spring before the weed starts growing."

My eyes, however, were still on that tantalisingly clear patch of water, and I was wondering if, supposing the fish did rise there, it would be possible to reach it. What was the depth in between? At the actual shore, where we stood, the water, although peat-stained to the colour of tea, was clear, and by stirring the scum of weed I could see the bottom. It was shallow, not more than a few inches, but the bottom shelved quickly outwards. What we needed was some sort of a boat or raft.

"It's no good," I said. "We may as well pack up while there's time to catch the bus."

And it was then that we both saw something moving under the weed, close to the edge of the farthest clear patch. I thought for a moment it was an otter, for it was making a considerable bow wave, and yet it was not travelling fast. I expected that shortly we should see its head break the surface, but it went on, still underwater, and keeping near the margin of the clear patch. And then it turned, and there was a swirl in the water, and among the weed I caught a glimpse of a dark dorsal fin.

"It's the fish!" I gasped.

Dain seized my arm.

"It is—it *is!* Hurry—before it swims farther away."

"I can't possibly cast as far as that. And then it's no good unless I can get beyond the weed. Oh, for a boat! There's only one thing to do. One chance. Take the rod a moment. I'll have to wade in."

I took off my jacket, whipped off my shoes and socks, and rolled up the legs of my flannel trousers as far as they would go. I took the rod and stepped into the water. There was peaty mud on the bottom but under it at first was a firm footing. There were stones, and the half-rotten twigs of the heather that had been drowned when the mere had been made.

But the proportion of mud to hard ground increased

with every careful stride I made from the shore. I was soon well over my knees. Then I discovered that the hard ground was giving way to pure peat: a thick spongy mass which must have made the bed of the original valley before it was flooded. I needn't have troubled to roll up my trouser legs. My feet sank into the peat. The water was soon almost waist deep.

I knew the technique of bog and mud walking, however. No matter how deep it is, and how soft, there is a point at which it compresses sufficiently to give temporary support for your feet, and so long as you keep moving, you will not sink beyond this point. What bothered me was that when I did get within range of the clear patch I would *have* to stop, and stay put if I were to use my rod.

It was hard work. With every stride I had to extricate one foot from the peat against a powerful suction, leaning my body forward on the other leg to do so. Yet I was making progress. Another half-dozen strides and I would be near enough to cast. I struggled on, the edge of the clear patch at last not more than twelve feet away. And then fortune favoured me. My foremost foot encountered something hard, only a few inches under the peat. I explored it with my toes, and found that it was a boulder well buried in the peat, but broad enough and flat enough to give me, when I got my other foot on to it, secure support.

All this time, I had seen no sign of the fish. I had not dared to shout to Dain to ask her if she could see it from her higher vantage point on the bank. Even now with my feet firmly planted on that providential rock, I kept my body crouched, and my rod low as I surveyed the surface of the mere around me.

I could see nothing. I turned to look at Dain, waved to her questioningly. She shook her head. The water now was just above my knees. I dared to stand up straight, although I did this slowly, for nothing startles a fish more than movement. I concentrated my attention on the clear patch. The wind was still blowing in gusts, and its surface was furrowed, but not continuously. There were moments of complete calm, and it was in one of them that I saw, some twenty feet away, close to the edge of the weed, a slight movement that was not caused by the wind.

Another gust came. Another calm. It was still there, something moving, just under the surface, moving slowly. Was it the fish? It was within range. My knees were already trembling with the cold. But it wasn't just cold that made both my hands shake as I prepared to make my first cast. I took a deep breath and prayed for that calmness of mind, that perfect control over nerves and muscle, which in battle makes a hero of a man.

I did not feel any sudden access of either quality. In lifting the rod, I got the fly fast in the cuff of my sleeve, and I had to lower the rod into the water and use both hands to disengage the hook. I knew that in my present condition I was bound to make a mess of my first cast. If the fly did not fall clean, and the gut hit the water first, the fish would probably be scared and shoot off. I thought I had better make a practice cast well to the farther side of the patch, and I waited for a favourable gust. It came and I shot it out, three times forward and back and then let it drop. It dropped clean, and a little

150

more of my confidence returned. I jerked it, as though I were definitely fishing, then whipped it out, and made one more practice cast. Again I was successful, and this time as I jerked it back I looked at the spot where the movement had been.

Another gust had come. I could see nothing but the ripples it made, but I let go and landed certainly not a foot away from where I thought I had last seen the fish. It began to sink. I gave it a gentle jerk. There was a sudden swirl in the water. I gave a gentle flick to the rod. And it was as though an electric current had passed through it from the fish to me. I *felt* the fish. The miracle had happened. It had taken the fly. It was hooked. I gave a wild whoop to Dain. But I dare not look at her. The battle was on.

I knew that with a trout even a quarter the size of this one, that neither my line nor rod would withstand its full and direct weight and strength. In that first striking flick there had been little force. I braced myself for what was coming next, which was another swirling movement, dangerous because it slackened the line. I took in the slack by lifting the rod top, and then struck again, a little harder to make sure the hook was well home, relaxing at once, but ready for the rush. It came. The line tightened like a fiddle string and I let it go from the reel, checking it with my finger, praying that the rush would end before all the line was paid out. I heard Dain shout:

"Have you really got it?"

I did not answer. The fish was aiming straight down the mere towards the dam well, and the deepest part. I looked at my reel. There was very little of the line left.

The terrifying thought came to me, that in my careful preparations I had not looked at the knot which fastened the end of the line to the reel itself. I dare not risk letting the last coils go out. I raised the rod, checked the reel hard, and again prayed. The line tightened. The rod bent. I felt the prodigious power of the fish, and I heard the line *singing,* in itself a terrifying sound, and I knew it was going to break unless I eased the strain.

I did the only thing possible. I stepped off my rock back to the peat, the longest stride I could take. But I knew as soon as my feet sank in that I could not follow the fish. I would have to keep moving, but it must be in the direction of the nearest shore. My stride had given me only a moment's grace. The line tightened again. I just hung on. And then suddenly the strain went completely. The line went slack, the rod straight.

"It's gone!" I shouted. "I've lost it!"

I heard Dain's disappointed "Oh!"

I started to reel in the slack line, taking my first difficult stride towards the shore. And then I saw the line suddenly tighten, and just in time I raised the rod, to take the strain of another rush, not from the dam end of the lake, but from the opposite shore.

"You've still got it. You've still got it," Dain shouted excitedly. "Oh, I do hope you catch it."

It was not rushing directly away from me now, but swinging round parallel to the farther shore. It was still taking out line. I dared to check it. Again the line sang. The strain was not so great, and I attempted another stride towards the home shore. It had to be a backward stride, and neither in bog nor mud had I ever attempted

152

this method of progression. It was twice as difficult to extract a foot from the peat, to balance on the other when it was free and move it.

I daren't for a moment turn my attention from the line. I still had not seen the fish itself. It was keeping near the surface, making a wave clearly distinguishable from the ripples of the wind. It had turned again for the dam end of the mere, and although I gave it line, I kept some pressure on it in order to prevent another full check, to rein it as one would do with a horse charging for a dangerous looking obstacle. It answered by coming back again on the same course as before, enabling me to gain a little line and take one more stride shorewards. If it would go on doing this, travelling obliquely, I could gradually diminish the lengths of its sweeps, shorten line, and work it homewards.

Its next sweep nearly beat me. It charged straight up the line to where I stood so that the whole of it went slack again, and then, before I could reel in the slack, swung round in the opposite direction, and when the line tightened I just had to hang on, with the rod flat with the water, and extended as far as I could reach without losing my balance.

It seemed to know that it had got me in a tight place. It kicked, and for the first time I saw its tail out of the water, and the size of that tail gave me a fright. I'd never get the brute ashore. It went on kicking. I just hung on, waiting for the line to break. Then it quietened. I gently raised the rod, found that the fish was coming towards me, without any resistance at all except its own weight. I reeled in. I risked another backwards stride, then another. Dain shouted:

"Can I help you?"

I daren't look round, but I shouted:

"Yes. I've got to try and work it in to shallow water. Clear a space of weed if you can, so that I'll be able to see it. But don't stir up the mud."

"All right! It's still on, isn't it? I can't see it."

I couldn't either, just then. But I could feel the weight, and I was still gingerly winding in. Had it completely exhausted itself in its frantic kicking? I managed another stride. I was still several strides from the hard bottom near the bank, and as I attempted the next one I felt a sharp pain in the leg I was extricating from the peat. It was a spasm of swimmer's cramp, due to the unusual muscular strain of my method of progression. I had to stop and lean the other way to relieve it, but when I tried again it got worse, and I knew that I'd have to turn round and move *forwards* the remaining distance to the shore.

In this the fish itself helped me, for it had a sudden access of energy. It made another violent sweep round to my left, towards the shore itself, passing within a few feet of where Dain herself, with her shoes off, was standing in the water brushing away the weed with a clump of heather. She gave a shout, and again with the line completely slack I thought that it had broken me. But in the excitement I had overcome the pain in my leg. I moved forward, reeling in desperately. I felt the first touch of hard ground, and I got the weight of the fish again just as it swung out, and I knew that not only was it still fast, but that it was tiring. I was still about fifteen feet from the bank. I turned round, checked its outward rush, and brought it to a halt. I moved shorewards, pulling on it gently. I shouted to Dain:

"Have you cleared the weed? Can you see the bottom?"

"Yes. It's all clear. I saw the fish. It's enormous, enormous. *Don't* let it get off!"

"It *may* get off," I said. "I can't guarantee it. We haven't a landing-net. We haven't a gaff. I've got to get hold of it somehow. Keep on clearing the weed, in case the wind blows it back."

I was relatively calm by now. The fish tried kicking again, but I had got its measure, and with plenty of line on the reel I could afford to give it its head. I still could not see it, but in the shallower water the waves and eddies it made gave me its exact position. It quietened, and I dragged it closer in. It made another outward swing. The pressure I put on the line brought it round again quickly, and I was now within twelve feet of the shore.

Dain was still in the water, less than knee-deep. I saw the clear patch she had made. I moved to the leeward end of it, and stopped. The fish seemed completely quiet, making no muscular resistance at all. I reeled in very slowly, ready, I hoped, for any last-minute rush. I held my rod well down. I saw the knot of my cast above the surface of the water, just at the edge of the weed. Then I slowly raised the rod till the cast was halfway out of the water, and I saw the fish itself moving along the bottom towards my feet, its tail moving very slowly.

I had never in my life seen a trout so big, nor had I ever been confronted with such a problem. It was undoubtedly the fish we had seen the evening a week ago, the single survivor of those that had been trapped in the mere when the dam had been built. It would be a cannibal trout, devouring even its own progeny (if it ever had any) in the struggle for existence. It was well over two feet in length, its weight at least seven pounds. Even if it had been dead, the weight alone would have broken the line if I had tried to lift it straight out of the water on to the bank. And it wasn't dead. I took two strides nearer to the bank, pulling at it very gently. It was almost within touching distance. I could see its great eyes, its quivering pectoral fins, the dilating gill apertures.

I said to Dain, in a hoarse, shaking whisper:

"It's now or never. You take the rod. If it panics, just let the line run out, then pass the rod back. I've got to try and get hold of it with my hands."

She took the rod, with the knot of the cast almost up to the tip, and the cast itself running like a halter to the trout's mouth, and slack. The fish itself was still. I moved round until I was behind it, and then closed on it until it was in reach of my hands. I bent down, lowered both my hands into the water, one on each side of the fish at its tail end, between the root of the tail and the short second dorsal fin.

A sudden gust of wind flurried the surface, and I had to wait till it calmed. Then with my fingers extended, and curved like the talons of a hawk about to grasp its prey, I moved my hands deeper and nearer until I was almost touching. Perhaps I did touch, for the tail jerked. What happened next was completely reflexive. I closed my hands, gripped fiercely, heaved, swung round, with the fish out of the water, kicking madly. I got one foot on the bank, slipped and stumbled, but as I did so I swung the fish up and round, on to dry land, and as it dropped I flung myself on top of it. It was still kicking. It was still only a few feet away from the water. I gripped the tail with one hand, and got my other hand into a gill aperture, and then I rushed up the bank at least twice the jumping range even of a salmon. Even then I did not immediately relax my grip until Dain, still holding the rod, came panting to my side.

Neither of us could speak at first. We just stood staring at our prize. With my hand in its gills, I dared to hold it up. It was only then that I noticed that the top part of the rod was lying in the heather close by, that it was only the bottom half that Dain was holding.

"You said, hang on, darling," she said. "And I did. But I didn't think it was going to rush this way. Oh, isn't it a beauty! Won't Amelia be excited when she sees it? What *are* we going to do with it? It ought to be skinned and stuffed, and put in a glass case. It's the biggest trout *I've* ever seen."

I had a knife in my watery trouser pocket, and I quickly gave the fish its *coup de grâce*. What *were* we going to do with it? I did not know what the record trout for the district was, but if a bigger one than this had been caught I had never heard of it. But could one claim a record for a poached fish, no matter how fairly it had been caught? I had a sudden twinge of conscience.

"You know what we really ought to do is to take it to the man who owns the mere. The Colonel, if he is the owner."

"But he'd just be furious, wouldn't he? It *would* be silly!"

"Perhaps," I said. "But it really is his property. Although probably he didn't know he'd got it. We could make a cast of it first. We've got plenty of candles in the house. We could melt them, and make a mould tonight when we get back, and then just take it to him tomorrow."

"And not eat it ourselves, when you've caught it? It would be silly! And it's only an accident it belongs to someone else. Isn't it just the last of the trout that were in the beck when the dam was made? I've got an idea. If this is the last fish why shouldn't we put some little ones from our stream into this mere? Carry them in a bucket. Then they'd grow as big as this in time. And really that would be more than paying him back. We could put in quite a lot."

I gasped.

"It's a brilliant idea! Brilliant! And wouldn't it be funny if he or his gamekeeper caught us doing it? Poaching in reverse. Come on. We've got to watch out we're not caught now, with this. I think it's too big for the rucksack, but we can tie some heather round the part that sticks out. It's just as well we're walking home, and that it's getting dark."

"I'll fetch it and your jacket and your shoes. Oh—you must be cold."

I *was* cold. I started to wring the water out of my trousers. My knees were shaking, but I looked at the trout and I didn't mind, and I thought of our house that was being built, and the new book, and of how excited Dain had been about her letter from Mrs Allen, and of our walk back in the gloaming along the moorland road to our temporary home (carrying the precious trout) and then stealing in and having a look at our children, and I thought this surely was one of the happiest days of my life, and I felt that Dain was feeling the same, the way she looked as she climbed up through the heather with the things, although she was pretending to be cross. What did I think she had found at the bottom of the rucksack? The boiler suit she had given me at the beginning of the week, which I had promised to wear while I was working so as not to get my clothes in such a mess. I'd never apparently worn it once.

"I was keeping it for a special occasion," I said. "And here it is. I'll change. And we can wrap the trout up in my wet trousers and put it in the rucksack."

She smiled.

"All right. I suppose they'll wash."

9

SLOWLY BUT surely the walls of our house rose, although the higher they grew the less one could see of the house because of the scaffolding. The spaces for the windows were formed, and when the long lintels (of reinforced concrete) were in position one could look through them and appreciate the view, and it was like putting a frame on a picture, or rather several pictures for even those that faced the sea were slightly different from each other. The lounge-to-be, with its two windows, one in the front and one in the end wall, gave both the sea view and the moor view, and it was hard to tell which was the more beautiful, although the sea, because of the traffic on it, would always have more variety.

I had calculated that from our height of five hundred feet there would be a visibility range of more than twenty miles directly seawards. The coastal traffic lane lay much closer in than this, and in clear weather no ship could pass either to the north or south without it being in sight, although from the shore, or even from the cliffs of the middle part of the bay (where we had originally planned to build our home), it might have been below the horizon.

That site certainly would have had many advantages, just like Cornwall had, but it was best not to think about them. There could be no doubt that, taking everything into consideration, this was the best place for us all. If only the workmen would hurry up and finish the job, so that we could move in and get on with the hundred and one other things we wished to do ourselves, and could only be done when they were out of the way. I knew that they could not have worked harder or faster, however, without skimping the job, and this neither Will nor the foreman would have allowed them to do.

I had finished my hut but for the installation of the stove, and there was no immediate hurry for that. I could not possibly settle down to writing until we had moved in, and while I kept on thinking about the new book, the whole idea was still nebulous. It had no definite pattern, and the thing would have to go on fermenting in my subconscious mind before the pattern would start to emerge. Like the building of the house, hurrying might result in skimping. Anyway, I had plenty of jobs to do, and if they were more pleasant than sitting at my typewriter in my sound- and view-proof hut, that couldn't be helped.

One of them was to beat the sheep, for while it was going to be fairly simple to keep them out of the vegetable garden with a wire netting and barbed fence, we didn't want to have to fence the immediate surroundings of the house and the little stream where we were to make our flower garden.

In spite of his protests of good neighbourliness, Jimmy so far had done nothing to his own fence to stop them straying; I could scarcely blame him for this so long as they could get through our own moorland gateway. The new gate had arrived and the fixing of this was of first importance.

Fortunately the two posts, which were oak, were quite sound and firmly fixed in the ground. The heavy wrought-iron hinges on the old gate, although rusted, also were sound, and all I had to do was remove them and re-bolt them to the new gate which Will had had made exactly to the dimensions of the original. I could also use the original spring hasp, the type fitted all gates in the district, which had a long shaft rising above the top bar so that a horseman could move it without dismounting. This, however, and I was thinking of Jimmy, could be supplemented with a heavy chain and padlock, and, for our own ordinary use so that the gate need only be opened for cars or vans coming to the house, I would build a tall narrow foot-stile in the fence close by the gate, too narrow for a sheep to pass over it.

It was an easy, pleasant job, and I was amused by the thought that this gate was a symbol of our ownership and privacy, and that what I was doing was an unmistakable assertion to my neighbour of my legal rights.

It seemed that Jimmy spent a considerable part, if not most, of his time just riding about the moor. Those of his sheep which appeared to have taken up permanent residence on our land were only a small proportion of his flock, which I was to learn later numbered more than a hundred and fifty breeding ewes, most of which did keep to the open moor.

I could not think why he should give them such unremitting attention. I was to discover in the course of time that he had a sort of Biblical affection for them, that he knew every member of his flock as a father would know his own children, knew their faces, which all looked alike to me, the shape of their horns, their gait, even the varying pitches of their bleats. I had not been working very long before I spotted Jimmy on his chestnut mare away over the moor, and he must have seen me, for he crossed the high road, and trotted along our track, pulling up but not dismounting.

He greeted me with his charming smile and usual affability.

"Now then. So you're getting that gate fixed up, are you? A brand-new one, eh? It's a nice-looking gate. It'll be a great improvement, but if I were you I'd nail a strand of barbed wire along the top bar. They're rare leppers is moor-sheep, and dammit an awd ewe would climb over a house if it got separated from its lamb. There's nowt will stop 'em when they're urgent, and I don't want any o' my sheep doing damage to your garden when you get it made."

This sounded like the good neighbour again, but I was not completely convinced of its sincerity.

"No," I said firmly, yet deliberately using the plural. "We've got to keep them out, and I'll have that barbed wire on the gate and put a padlock on it too, in case anyone should leave it open by accident."

"A very good idea!" he said. "Some of 'em will be in now, I reckon. It's another queer thing about sheep that when they take a fancy to a spot they'll not budge away from it unless they're driven. You see, Isaac never troubled about his fences. You couldn't blame him with him being so awd and lame, and having such a long way

163

to come from where he lives, and them odd twenty ewes o' mine with their lambs took fancy to that bit down by the barn, and no matter how often I've driven 'em out, they've found their way back. Still, you say, we've got to stop 'em now."

"Isn't it the law," I asked gently, "that a farmer has got to keep his own stock from straying?"

He laughed.

"Aye. That's the law for ordinary stock, for cattle and hosses, and ordinary sheep. But it's different for moor-sheep. They're in a different class. There was a case only a while back about that. It was in the papers. Some moor-sheep had got into a field of oats, and the chap who owned it sued for damages in the County Court, but the judge said that as they were moor-sheep, chap who owned them couldn't be held responsible. They were in a special class."

I looked hard at my neighbour. I wondered whether he was trying to take advantage of my ignorance, bluffing me. 1 thought of what Isaac had said about him from the first, and what Mrs Briggs had said. He *was* a coughdrop, a humbug, but he was no fool, and 1 was still liking him. I noticed the saddle, that here and there the stuffing was coming out, and I wondered if this was Sam's saddle, that he had borrowed, and wouldn't give back. I said:

"I didn't know that."

He laughed again.

"Nay. Neither did the chap who's oatfield it was. But anyway, I'll see that them sheep won't bother you. Have you made up your mind yet what you're going to do with

164

your land? If you're not going to farm, there's about eighteen acres up here that'll be going idle. You'll not want to garden here, will you?"

"No."

"You don't want to sell it, do you?"

"No," I said quite definitely.

Even if I had wanted to, I could not have done so, because the land was the security for our building loan. He was still smiling.

"Well, of course you couldn't expect to get much for it if you did sell. It's all rough stuff. It would never plough up. There's too many rocks. It's never been looked after. If it was mine, I'd give it a heavy dressing of lime, and then a ton or two of slag, or superphosphate to bring heart back into it. It's a pity to see it going to waste. Would you think of letting it off?"

Was he being serious?

"I might," I said guardedly. "Part of it, anyway. But it would need another fence, wouldn't it?"

He was certainly serious now, but I had a suspicion that he was being crafty.

"Now I've been thinking of that. And I've been thinking the best way of keeping them sheep away from your house and where you're going to make your gardens. I don't want them to be a nuisance. It's only these top fields that would be of use to me, them that join on to my land. Best thing to stop sheep is wire netting, with barbed wire along the top of it, and if you ran a fence from just inside your gate along where the land starts to fall away to where your house is, it would parcel it off nicely, and it wouldn't cost so much brass as fencing the whole of your land. It would save you a lot of brass. Mind, I couldn't pay much rent for it. All of us farmers are having a struggle to make a living at all these days. It would chiefly be a benefit to you. You don't want to get your garden nicely planted and then have them sheep come in and snap everything up. It's not only what they eat, you know. They trample about. I know what it is with our own garden."

I was getting Jimmy's measure. I was sure that he was not in the least worried about the damage his sheep might do; that he was only concerned about getting the grazing for them as cheaply as possible, that he was trying to jockey me into a bargain. Yet these top fields were of no use to us. If we got a pony there was more than enough grazing on the land that would remain on our own side of the proposed new fence, and, if this fence was made as he suggested, it would certainly save having to render sheep-proof the existing one along the whole boundary. If he would pay for the fence, and in addition improve the land with lime and fertilisers, we should be killing more than two birds with one stone. I could afford to be generous and not charge any rent at all, at least not for a year or two. I was, I felt, calling his bluff.

Would a netting fence, with wire on top, really stop his sheep from straying, I asked him—even the "urgent" ones?

"Aye. So long as you have plenty of posts, and you leave no spots under it for a lamb to get through. It's the lambs that does it. Mother love, you know. You can't blame the ewes for not wanting to be separated. That's

166

what makes 'em urgent."

"What would a fence cost?"

"Now I've been having a look at it. There's about two hundred yards altogether. With posts and nets it could be done for about twelve pounds."

"Would you pay for it?"

He laughed.

"Well, you could hardly expect me to do that. It would be your fence, on your land. I'd give you a help setting it, of course."

I felt that he was winning again.

"Well, how much rent would you pay?"

He gave me a very shrewd look.

"Why now, it would have to be a fair price for both of us. You can get grazing round these parts for ten bob an acre, but that's on good pasture. This is only rough, and it's not worth half of that. But I tell you what I'll do. I'll give you five quid a year, and that's more than you'd get from anyone else. In fact there's no one else would want it. It's too far away. Only it's handy for me."

"And would you lime it, and put on some fertilisers?"

"Aye, of course. I'd soon get some nourishment into it, and I'd graze some bullocks on it, too. That would help. *I'm* not the sort to neglect land."

I'd had no opportunity yet of seeing anything of Jimmy's own land, and I saw no reason for doubting his statement. It was a blow about the fence, for we were likely to be hard up for a long time yet, and twelve pounds was a biggish item. I thought a while, and then I said:

"It seems a pretty low rent for nearly eighteen acres of

167

land, but I'm willing if you'll go halves with the fence, and call that one year's rent. And it would be only the grazing. I've got to keep the sporting rights over the whole land, and I may want to do a bit of digging to see if there are any flint implements, like arrow and spear heads."

He looked interested.

"Aye? I've heard that there's lots of things like that on the moor, but I've never found one, but then I've never looked. Are they worth any brass?"

"No. They're only of interest to people who are interested in that sort of thing, and they never have any money."

"Oh. But we're all like that these days. Well, I suppose I'll have to agree about the fence, but only five quid towards it, remember. It's a biggish rent for land like this. In fact three quid would be nearer what it's worth. But I said five quid, didn't I?"

"You did," I said firmly.

"All right then. It's a bargain. Now square mesh is for the netting, and you can get it at Baxter's in Burnharbour. And they're doing some timber felling in a wood over near Maybecks, and I've an idea you'd get some nice oak posts there very reasonable, but see that they're all heartwood. If you'll get the posts and the net, I'll settle up with you and, of course, I'll be giving you a hand with fixing it. It's got to be done proper. We'll need a wire strainer for the job, and a heavy wood mell. I've an idea that Sam Briggs has a strainer, and if you tell him what it's for he'll lend it to you, and he's bound to have a mell. Well, I've got a lot to do, so I'll be getting on. I'm glad we've fixed things up, but I still think we ought to make it less than five quid. What about splitting the difference and calling it four?"

"No," 1 said. "We'll stick to five."

He laughed.

"All right then. Well, so long."

He turned the head of his mare round, and away he went, over the moor. I watched him for a while, wondering again what it was exactly that kept him so busy on the moor, for it seemed that he did nothing but just ride, and ride and ride. He was an extraordinary man. I had an uneasy feeling that he had bested me in this deal about the land, yet, like Mrs Briggs had said, you just couldn't feel angry with him. I got on with my job, and it occurred to me that while he had told me what a good gate it was, and what an improvement it would be, he had never apparently thought of dismounting and offering to give me a hand. And still I liked him.

We hadn't told anyone about the trout, whose weight had proved just one ounce short of seven pounds. On getting home I had made a shallow box, half-filled this with wet clay from the garden, and laid the fish in it, moulding the clay round under half of the body, and pinning out the tail and dorsal fins to make them lifelike. Fortunately, there had been plenty of candles in the house. We had melted these in a saucepan, extracted the wicks, and poured the liquid wax into the box so that it was at least half an inch thick over the highest part of the fish's body. As soon as the wax had started to set, I had immersed the whole contraption in the kitchen sink, filled with cold water.

In the morning, it was set hard, and it had come cleanly away from the fish, which was no worse for the heating it had received and made us a splendid lunch. I had asked Will if he could send me out some plaster of Paris with the workmen, and the next night we had taken the cast, and it had been a great success, and looked so good in dead white that we decided not to paint it in imitation of the original. In asking for the plaster I had resisted the temptation to tell Will what I needed it for. I had told him, however, about the letter Dain had received from Mrs Allen about the stirrup, and he had promptly suggested that he would drive us out to see the lady, as he had business in York at an early date.

I felt rather uneasy about this expedition. Both Dain and our daughter were completely convinced that she had a suitable pony for sale, and that we were going to buy it. It was, for Dain at least, the logical climax to our detective story, which had begun with the finding of the lost stirrup.

But this was feminine logic. It just wouldn't happen like that, I protested, to which she made the feminine retort that she had been right about the trout, as she would also be right about the new book being a huge success when it was written and published. We should probably have enough money then to own several ponies (hadn't we got enough land?) and perhaps start breeding them, and even make more money out of doing so. To this I had no answer.

I wished, though, that I could share her enthusiasm for riding and ponies, as she had shared mine for sailing and boats. The truth was that although I had experienced the joy and exhilaration of riding, I knew nothing about the animals themselves. I thought privately that, of the three quadrupeds that man has adapted and trained for close companionship with himself, the horse, the dog and the cat, the horse is the least interesting, for it is the most enslaved, and the most strictly utilitarian.

All you could do with a horse was ride it or drive it. It seemed to me to have a very low order of intelligence to submit with such docility to being strapped to a cart or plough, half-blinded with blinkers, holding an uncomfortable piece of metal in its mouth and being steered by the pull on this to the right or left, straining with all its power to move the thing behind at a speed convenient to its human master; or, with a less complicated and perhaps less uncomfortable contraption of metal and straps and padded leather, to take the weight of a human being on its back, and trot or canter or gallop or leap over ditches or fences; or in the company of many others of its species, gallop full out along a race track lined with a shrieking mob of human beings, perhaps to win a fortune for its owner, and lose one for someone else, but earning for itself at best a pat on its steaming flanks, a drink of water, a bucket of oats and a pleasant rest.

The dog, if it could be bred to the necessary size and strength, might be trained to do all these things, but it would do them for a different motive: a simple and stupid and whole-hearted devotion to its human master. A cat, *never*, unless it could see something in it to its own exclusive advantage.

But these heretical views I kept to myself. I was more practically concerned by the fact that ponies were expensive; so, I believed, was riding equipment, a bridle, a saddle, not to mention the trap that Dain seemed to have set her mind on, for which, of course, we should need harness. If it also meant building a stable, it would probably cost us at least fifty pounds before we had finished, and for the present we simply could not afford it.

Mrs Allen had invited us to lunch. Will's business in York (it concerned his big house contract) would keep him until three o'clock and he would collect us on his way back. He had left us at the gates of a handsome Queen Anne manor house, with well-kept flower garden and lawn, and behind it a coach-house, stables, cottages and the usual complements of a country residence.

To my own relief Mrs Allen was not an aggressively-horsy woman. She'd be about sixty, with grey hair, but a handsome kindly face, and a fascinating smile. She was conventionally-dressed in a linen coat and skirt, but hatless. She and Amelia took to each other from the start, and, holding Amelia's hand, she led the way into a hall which contained some fine Queen Anne furniture, and what were clearly two ancestral portraits. There were also many prints of horses, several mounted foxes' brushes and there were riding-crops on a small table near the entrance door. Mrs Allen offered us drinks (sherry, and orange squash for Amelia) and made us sit down, and Amelia dramatically handed over the stirrup.

It was Rosemary's, all right. Mrs Allen had found its mate and she fetched it and placed the two together.

They were identical. I had to retell the story of how I had found it, and our hostess said that really it was one of the most extraordinary things that had ever happened. She remembered quite well the day of the ride, and that she'd been cross with her daughter about it, for she and her friend had gone out for a short ride, and they'd been very late getting back. Rosemary would be so interested when she heard the whole story. It was a Shetland pony she was riding, Mary Jane. Mary Jane was now dead, but she had left behind her many sons and daughters. One of the daughters, Annabella, she would show us after lunch. It was the very spit and image of Mary: a four-year-old, and such a darling.

I saw a gleam in Dain's eyes. Mrs Allen insisted that we have another sherry. Lunch would be a few minutes yet. She wanted to hear more about the house we were building. She knew Adder Howe. But it was a long time since she had been in the district, although an old friend of the family, Colonel Brighouse, was always pressing her to go and stay at Skerry Hall. Did we know him? He was awfully nice. He had a sense of humour too. He would be most interested in, and amused by, the story of the stirrup. We *must* meet him.

The sherry was dry, but I still had my wits about me. If the story of the stirrup would be of interest and amusement to Colonel Brighouse, would he react as favourably to the story of our trout if he ever heard it? It was ironic to think that if we had only waited we might, through Mrs Allen, have procured his leave to fish in the mere. But would it have been so exciting? I exchanged glances with Dain and I said, with calm hypocrisy, that although we knew *of* Colonel Brighouse we had not met him, although we would like to very much. I believed that he either owned or rented the sporting rights of the moor adjoining Adder Howe. Lunch was ready. To my relief Mrs Allen made no further reference to him. There was to come a stiffer test of my capacity to steer out of a difficult situation, for after we had taken soup the maid brought in a dish of grilled trout, setting it down in front of our hostess, who beamed at Amelia, and said:

"I hope you like trout, Amelia. These were specially caught for us by the gardener in our stream last night. You have a trout stream on your land, haven't you? Are there any as big as these? Not that they're very big, of course."

There were about a dozen moderately-sized trout on the dish, and I knew that Amelia, as she looked at them, must have been thinking of the single trout which had filled a larger dish on our own table only a few days ago, and that she must have been making a comparison. I didn't give her a chance to answer.

"These *are* beauties! Ours are very small, of course. The stream's too swift. We're hoping, by the way, to fix up a waterwheel in it eventually, and make our own electricity."

I gave Amelia a look, entreating her, telepathically, not to say a word about our own trout, and I daren't look at Dain at all until the course was finished, and the maid brought dessert. By that time the conversation had travelled from waterwheels and electricity supply for country houses back to the subject of riding and ponies, in which I could be securely silent.

Lunch over, Mrs Allen first of all showed us round the house itself. It was very lovely, with its period furniture and numerous objects of art, and everything arranged without ostentation so that what was old seemed in no way incongruous with what was sensibly new like the thick carpets and bright curtains and cushion covers, the distempered walls of the bedrooms, the luxurious-looking comfort of the beds, easy chairs and divans. The place was on public supply for electricity. Every room had heating and power points. The bathrooms were all electric. The house was empty at present, she explained, because she was taking a holiday from entertaining. Usually, and always in the hunting season, it was full of her relations and friends.

Amelia was deeply impressed, and I felt a tinge of envy, for while Adder Howe would be a big rise above the ugliness and discomfort of Butcher's Folly, we should never be able to achieve anything comparable to this, although we scored in situation and view. Here there was neither sea nor moors. The country was almost dead flat, and the trout stream, just visible from the bedroom windows, looked sluggish as a canal. In a large pasture, bordering the stream, were a large number of horses and ponies, many of them with foals, and I noticed Dain looking towards that field with deep interest.

But our hostess, like a good showman, was not to be hurried. She took us into a large walled fruit and vegetable and nursery garden behind the house. There were hothouses with peach trees laden with fruit. She gave us one each to sample, and told us she would give us a basket of them to take home with us as well as some muscatels.

A wicket-gate in the wall brought us out into a paved courtyard and the stables. There were two main buildings. We entered one. It was as bright and clean as a hospital ward. There were at least ten stalls on each side. Each had a board over it giving the name of a horse or pony, and nearly every one had also the cards showing that its occupant had won prizes at shows or gymkhanas. Now the entire building was empty. All the occupants were out at grass.

We passed into the saddle-room, an annexe to the stables. There was no one in it, but there was a big coal stove, chairs, and a table, and it was evident that in this department alone there must be constant employment for at least one man keeping clean and in order the scores and scores of saddles and bridles. Most of the staff, Mrs Allen said, were on holiday today, as there was a fair at the local market town. She took from a rack a small saddle and bridle, and now (I had taken the saddle from her) she led the way from the stables along a short lane to the gate of the big pasture we had seen from the bedroom windows. Most of the horses, ponies and foals were at the farther end of the field, grazing or lying down, but as Mrs Allen opened the gate one of the ponies cocked its ears, looked in our direction, shook itself, whinnied and started to come towards us at a brisk walk. Mrs Allen had made no sound or gesture. It came right up, stopped and extended its muzzle to the hand that held the bridle, as though asking her to put it on.

"This," Mrs Allen said, "is Annabella."

"Isn't she beautiful?" Dain cried ecstatically.

Frankly I did not think she was. She was the size of a large donkey and about the same colour, but much heavier of build. She had a long mane and a long flowing tail, and it seemed to me that from a strictly aesthetic point of view her head was too big for her body, and that the shape of her muzzle seen in profile had no grace of line, such as even I had noticed in some breeds of the equine tribe. What Annabella undoubtedly did possess was character, a good nature, a prepossessing likeability. My instant fear was not that I was going to be persuaded into buying something which at present we could not afford, which would involve us in further expenses, but that Mrs Allen would have no inclination to sell.

She slipped the bridle on, and then the saddle. The stirrups were almost identical with the one I had found, but the leathers had to be adjusted. Amelia was speechless. She allowed herself to be lifted up into the saddle, to have her feet guided into the stirrups, and Mrs Allen showed her how to hold the reins. I opened the gate, and we set off up the lane, and I closed the gate.

It was Amelia's first ride and there was a look of complete happiness on her face, and I noticed Mrs Allen watching her, and perhaps she was thinking of the time when she had given her own daughter her first ride long ago. It was a short ride, and wisely Mrs Allen did not try to make Annabella do anything but walk. We returned to the gate. I realised that the time was getting on, remembered that we had promised Will that we would not keep him waiting. Mrs Allen, too, had told us that she had an engagement in the afternoon. We had stopped with Amelia still on the pony. The situation suddenly had become embarrassing. I knew that we just had to have Annabella, if it were possible; that Dain was thinking the same thing, and I didn't know what to say, how to begin asking, nor apparently did Dain. Mrs Allen solved the difficulty for us. She was looking at Amelia.

"Do you like Annabella?" she said quietly.

Our daughter smiled.

"Yes. I just love her."

"Would you like her for your very own?"

Not altogether to my surprise, Amelia didn't answer at all, except with a gasp of delight. Mrs Alien, being a woman understanding, did not wait for a formal "yes".

"Then she's yours," she said. "You can have her just as soon as your new house is finished and you go to live at Adder Howe. We'll send her over in a van. You can have the saddle and bridle too, but I'm afraid the saddle's very old and worn, and of course you'll have to have the other stirrups. The one your Daddy found and its mate."

It was our own turn to gasp, and we both protested. We wanted a pony for Amelia very much indeed, and Annabella would just be ideal, but we did expect to buy it.

Mrs Allen smiled.

"Nonsense. It would just spoil the whole story if you bought her. And I wouldn't sell, anyway. She's too much one of the family, and I know she'll have a good home, and that you'll be kind to her. Down you come, Amelia. We must let Annabella go, and hurry and pack those peaches and grapes."

She put her arms round Amelia to lift her to the ground. Amelia was smiling blissfully.

10

ON THE whole it was a fine summer. There was no heat-wave after the break of the one in June. But there were no continuous spells of rainy or cold weather, and so far as temperature and sunshine were concerned there was little noticeable difference between summer here and any of the four summers we had spent in Cornwall, nothing to make us yearn violently for what we had left behind, although I often thought of our boats and the deep clear water of the coves, the fishing and swimming, and the sun-warmed rocks.

When our house was finished and we got settled down, and found the time for it, we'd get something almost as good down on the shores of the bay. Next summer it would be much simpler and easier, with our second born no longer in arms, and consequently more mobile. Certainly Annabella would be a godsend in this respect. Mrs Allen had told us before we left that she had been broken in to harness and was quite capable of pulling a fair-sized trap. We should be able to get both harness and trap second-hand quite cheaply.

The main thing that was good about the weather was that it enabled the building of our house to go on almost without interruption. There were only two days towards the end of August when heavy rain brought work to a full stop, and even then it was only because the rain was accompanied by strong squally winds. A calm was essential for the laying on of the felt, which as a precaution against sweating, was to be spread over the rafters, before the battens, and then the slates were nailed on.

By this time the main walls were finished, the windows, although not glazed, were fixed, the chimney stack was up to the ridge, and it needed only the slates and the coping stones and gutters to complete the external work and give absolute protection against the weather. The laying of the floors, the building of the partitions, the fixing of the staircase had to wait for this, for rain would have swelled and warped the planking.

We were indeed lucky that the period of rain and strong wind was so short, that towards the end of the first week in September the slating was completed and the first of the coping stones, that had been carefully carried down from the old barn, was carried up by Harry himself and mortared into its place at the end of the ridge, that our house was finally roofed in. Even then it was not until the scaffolding was removed that one could really see it.

I had looked forward with repressed excitement to this moment, as a woman might look forward to the trying on of a dress she had designed and made. I was glad that Dain was not with me, for I had an unpleasant shock.

I was in the garden, close to where I had found the stirrup, when the last of the scaffold poles came down; slightly higher than the actual foundations of the house, yet lower than the eaves. My view was practically broadside on, and of what an architect would call the front elevation, except that it was of course the back. I could not see either of the end walls.

What offended my eyes so much was the relatively enormous expanse of slated roof compared with the vertical stone wall. The slates themselves were a pleasing colour; they did undoubtedly harmonise with the colour of the stone, but they were darker, heavier in tone, and they gave at least the optical illusion that the building was top heavy, an effect that was increased by the fact that there was no window, no break in either of the two planes of the mansard roof from gable to gable on this side of the house. And in the wall, too, there was only the single kitchen window, and the doorway (at present without its porch) for the staircase, descending into the lounge, had made it impossible for us to have a third window in the lounge itself.

I stood surveying it with growing dislike, and Harry, seeing what I was at, came up and joined me.

"Now then," he said, "what do you make of it, now that the scaffolding's down? You don't look over-pleased."

I had to laugh.

"I don't quite know what to say. It certainly looks well built. You've made a good job of it. But I don't think I like the looks of the mansard roof."

"Nay, neither do I, if it comes to that, and I've thought so from the first, but it's saved you a lot of brass, and looks isn't everything, remember. That was what was wrong with the squire, he put looks above sense very often. You mustn't be like him, and want to start pulling a thing down just because it doesn't *look* quite right. Anyway, this is the back view, isn't it? There's no one yet invented a house that looks pretty both back and front."

A dress could be altered, an artist's drawing rubbed out, an unsatisfactory manuscript revised, or even consigned to the flames, but only a squire, and a mad one at that, could afford to take down a roof that didn't please his eye, and have it built again. Besides, how could it look right unless we reverted to our original plan and took the walls up another story, and had only a single span of slates ?

I took no comfort from Harry's reminder that this was the back view, or from the reflection that even Mrs Allen's house which had looked so good from the front was a muddle behind, for it was clear, without going round to look, that it was impossible to see the front aspect of our house at all except from the opposite side of the valley that contained the wood, and at a distance of at least half a mile. There was only a space of four feet between the front wall and the steep bank that fell down to the quarry and my hut. You had to stand back from a large object to see it properly. There was just nothing to stand *on*. Only the birds, or an airman, would be able to get the real perspective of our front view.

But when we walked round so that we could look at the end of the house nearest to the moor, I felt better. This wall did go the whole way up to the ridge; at least the middle part of it did. The roof was foreshortened, so that the proportion of visible slate to stone was very small. The wall was broken by the lounge and bedroom windows, and the stonework itself looked beautiful, and Harry, as though reading my thoughts, said:

"Say what you like, you can't beat stone for house-building. It looks twice as good as brick. I've enjoyed doing this job. I'm sorry it's about over. There's only that fireplace to do, and I'll be packing my tools, and leaving the carpenters and plumbers to finish off. And they ought to be finished in another fortnight, and you'll be able to move in. It's a nice house. I only wish we were going to build more like it. I care nowt about them council houses we're going to build at Burnharbour—all brick and concrete. Give me stone. Now what about that fireplace? You'll want that done in stone, won't you? Didn't you say you were just going to burn turf and wood on it? We'd better go in and have a look at it."

I was feeling better. It *was* a nice house. It was well built, of the right material, well-planned, and it was in the right place. Did it matter that the mansard roof made it look top-heavy and rather ugly from the back? Apart from the saving in cost, it had considerably shortened the building time. It was exciting to hear that we might be moving in within a fortnight. Anyway, the main purpose of a house was to be lived *in*, not looked at from the outside.

We moved round to the entrance. The ground immediately in front of it had been levelled off, and paved with the flags that had formed the original floors of the barn. Under the flags, well below frost level, had been laid the lead supply pipe from the spring, and this had been taken into the house under the kitchen window, where the plumber was now engaged fitting the sink.

There were no partitions yet, but the carpenters, there were four in all, had nearly completed the laying of the ground floor. There was an ear-splitting sound of hammering, sawing, the clattering of boards, and an exciting smell of shavings and sawdust. There was nothing for Harry to do with the kitchen fireplace. It was simply a recess into which the stove (a completely independent unit) had already been placed. An iron sheet had been fixed horizontally to cover the entrance to the flue, and this had been pierced to take the vertical smoke pipe from the stove. It was the plumber's job to connect the water pipes to its boiler. The lounge fireplace was a similar recess, about eighteen inches deep, four feet across and four feet from the floor to its arch.

Dain and I had thought a great deal about the design of this fireplace, which was in the very place where we had made our fire when we'd sheltered in the barn the night of the storm. Its chief function would be the provision of heat, especially in the long winter evenings when we could expect some very cold spells. But the main fireplace of a house should provide something more than heat, which could be done far more efficiently with steam pipes and radiators. It should be a substitute for the living sun, warming the heart as well as the body, something that you could look at with perpetual enjoyment as well as feel, and there should be nothing about it that could detract from this enjoyment.

It had been on this principle that we had designed and built the fireplace in the big room of our hut, and, on the rare occasions always in warm weather when it had burnt vigorously and without smoking, it had convinced us that our principles were mainly right. It must have been the chimney that was wrong.

One of its most pleasing features had been the lintel. For this we had used a thick oak beam, a section of one of the sailing ship's timbers we'd found half-buried in the mud. It had just the right amount of curve on it to form a shallow arch, and what made it particularly interesting to look at was that it had been partly bored by ship worm. We had planed it down to expose sections of these borings, and the pattern they made suggested primitive carvings. Unknown to Harry as yet, a piece of this very timber, which I'd included among the things we'd brought with our furniture from Cornwall, was now lying on the ground outside. I'd had it sent out from Butcher's Folly by the railway van, carrying it myself down from the road end.

I felt a little diffident when it came to explaining to Harry how I wanted the fireplace to be built. First of all, I knew that it would look wrong if it were made in the stone blocks of the main building. They were too big, too solid for supporting what would only be a mantelshelf. They'd look cold. Dare I tell him, after what he had recently said, that it must be done in brick—the same bricks of which the breast was built? They were common bricks, rather rough, but they had a warm glowing colour, and they had just as much variety of tint of red as the stones had of grey and brown. I drew a rough sketch of what was actually our original Cornish fireplace. He stared at it, and then at the existing cavity. He gave a nod of approval.

"There's nowt wrong with this. It'll bum wood and turf all right, and you'll want firebrick for that, and firebrick at the sides too, and at the back, and you'll want the back canted forward a bit to throw the heat out and not let it go up the chimney." Then he relieved my mind further by saying: "Stone will be no good for this job, though. It'll all have to be built with bricks, although only firebricks where it will be hot. What about the lintel ? Are you having it wood?"

I told him about the precious oak beam I had brought from Cornwall, that it was lying outside. One of the labourers who was gathering up the scaffold poles pushed it through the window. It was about six feet in length, five inches wide across the slight curve, four inches thick. Harry examined it.

"I don't like this," he said emphatically. "Why, it's all worm-eaten, although I've never seen worm holes so big!"

I explained that the cavities were not really wormholes, but that they had been made by a marine shellfish, and that apart from the holes the wood was hard as iron, as he would find out when he tried to cut it to the right length. He believed me when he tested it with the blade of his pocketknife, but I knew that I would never convince him that the holes themselves were decorative.

"Aye," he said reluctantly. "It seems hard enough. But I wouldn't use a timber like this. I'd rather have a new bit sawn. Still, I suppose you could fill them holes with putty, and stain 'em same colour as the wood. We'll make a start, anyway. We'll have some bricks and mortar in. I noticed there's some firebricks have been sent out. We'll make a start, and when we get up to the lintel we can see how it looks."

In spite of his disdain for the art of bricklaying it was soon evident that Harry was an expert at it, and he worked with incredible speed. He formed the entire hearth foundations of the breast which were level with the now planked floor. Then he began on the jambs, each a brick length square, but with another two courses of firebrick inside them to form a hob on each side of what was to be the actual fireplace. He laid the bricks so that on successive courses they went lengthways and endways, stretcher and header.

I watched him; completely fascinated, oblivious to the other activities that were going on in the house: the hammering, the the roar of the plumber's blow lamp as he wiped a joint (an operation which interested me deeply, for it was a thing I longed to be able to do for myself). I was even oblivious to the views from the two windows of the lounge, although I knew that they must be particularly lovely for it was a perfect September day, windless and cloudless, with a pale mist making more beautiful than ever the shapes and colours of the fields and cliffs and sea, and the moors, which, although the heather was dying, were still purple.

Harry was using neither line nor plumb. He was working entirely by sight, just tapping each brick down perfectly level and square, slapping on another trowel of mortar, another brick. It had taken us, I remember, nearly two months to build our original fireplace, counting the time it had taken us to collect and prepare our material, to correct our mistakes, including the shoring up of the floor when it started to subside with the growing weight of stone and concrete. And even then, although it had looked so good, it had been a failure. It took Harry little more than an hour to carry up the jambs to where the lintel should bridge them. He borrowed a saw from one of the carpenters, measured the gap, and cut off both ends of the beam. I helped him to put it in position. Then he stood back and surveyed it as a painter might survey a canvas.

"It doesn't look so bad," he said, "except for all them worm-holes. I still think you'd better ask the boss to get a new lintel cut at the mill. We could bring it out tomorrow."

"No," I said firmly. "I like it as it is, and so will my wife. Do you think it's at the right height? Will there be any danger having it so near the fire?"

He measured the height with his rule, and took a measurement from it to the back of the fireplace, allowing for the firebricks that were to go there.

"It's safe enough. Even if you burn dry wood or ling, the flames will lick up the flue well away from it, but it would be safer still if you nailed a bit of zinc along underneath and behind. I'll get a bit from the plumber."

We took the beam down, and he sheathed the under section of it and the back with metal, and we put it back, so that none of the metal was visible from the front, and then without another word he carried on with his bricklaying, shaping each brick of the first complete course to fit the slight convexity of the beam, and using half-bricks at each end to close the ends into the jambs.

It was shortly after the dinner break when he had

started the job. It was just on four when he laid the last course of bricks which would form the mantelshelf, and these he had bevelled and set out from the face for a couple of inches as a coping. He did not stop then, but, using firebricks only, started to form the back, staggering each course so that as it rose it leaned forward. Finally, he covered the floor of the fireplace, and the job was finished.

Again he stood back and surveyed it, artist fashion.

"It doesn't look too bad," he said. "Even that beam of yours. You don't notice the holes so much now! It'll look all right on a cold winter's night when you've got a good pile of turves on it, and a couple of nice dry ash or oak logs. Don't forget that with turf you must never rake all the ash out. When you leave it at night, put the turves on flat and press 'em down. They'll go on smouldering and in the morning all you need do is poke the top ones up on edge and they'll soon blaze. Are you satisfied with it?"

I was. It was better than anything I had imagined. The hearth was dead level. The jambs dead plumb. The bricks looked much better than the stones we had used in our original fireplace and yet the pattern was the same, including the ship's beam, and it was exciting to think that it would always be there to look at, to remind us of our creek, and the mud and the bones of the old sailing ships which had found their last moorings there. But would it serve its most important function as a fireplace? I asked Harry if we dare try it, to test the draught.

"Why," he said, " I was just thinking of that. By rights we should give it a few days for the mortar to dry out, but it will do no harm to set fire to a few shavings in it.

We mustn't let it get really hot, though."

I helped him to gather some shavings and a few board ends the carpenters had left on the floor. He made them into a small heap on the hearth. But as he struck a match I held back his hand, and said:

"No. We'll leave it. I'm certain it will work all right. But I'd rather not try it now."

We were, I had suddenly realised, anticipating a ceremony: the final act of house-warming in which Dain and the family should share and I explained this as well as I could to Harry. He smiled and instead of lighting the kindling, put the match to his pipe.

"Aye. I understand. And the mortar will be better for waiting. But you needn't worry about the draught. Look!"

He puffed a mouthful of smoke into the fireplace. It curved up under the lintel out of sight.

11

WHAT A vast number of manual operations must be performed inside a house after the roof has been finished, before the place becomes habitable, the things you take for granted once you are in. You open and close a door. You don't, unless you saw the empty space in the original partition that door now fills, realise the thought and the time and the labour that was involved in putting it there.

Including the main entrance door, but not including the cupboard doors that we were to make ourselves, there were to be ten doors in all. They were second-hand, and some had original hinges and latches on them. This was no advantage, for we wanted all hinges and latches to be of the same type, and in particular it was important to have the latches low because of the children. Not only had these to be removed, but the old recesses and screw holes had to be filled in, and new ones. made for the new hinges and latches, a multiple operation requiring forethought, measurement, several sorts of tools. The same applied to the frames in which the doors were to be hung. The doors had to fit into them snugly so that there should be no gaps to cause a draught, yet it was just as important that they should not jam, and that when opened they should rise slightly to clear linoleum or carpet.

There were six large windows (each with nine panes) and four smaller ones. The panes were standard size, each one had to be carefully puttied into its frame, and the putty faired off for subsequent painting. Each window had to have an interior window board fitted to it, the depth of the double wall and projecting slightly over the wall board lining. Wall boards (they were made of compressed wood fibre five-eighths of an inch thick, and measuring eight feet by four feet) had an immense advantage over plaster in the matter of time and labour-saving, but the frames for the partitions had to be very carefully planned and built so that the edges of the boards fitted evenly for nailing, dead in the centre of the vertical or horizontal members of the frame.

The partitions had to be lined on both sides. In fixing the boards to the main walls wood plugs had to be driven into the mortar of the brickwork flush with the wall. To these plugs were nailed upright and horizontal battens, to which the boards in turn were nailed, and the joints between the edges of the boards were finally hidden with narrow bevelled laths.

The ceilings of the bedrooms had to be done in the same way. We were having no ceilings to the ground floor rooms for the joists of the bedroom floor were of a beautifully-figured Columbian pine, but leaving them bare entailed panelling the under part of the floorboards showing between with strips of wallboard, and there was certainly no saving in time or labour.

I never tired of watching these men at work, and it was always with reluctance that I left them to get on with my own jobs. One of these jobs was the cutting of the turf.

I had made a new shaft for the turf spade, scrubbed all the rust from the blade and filed its cutting edge as sharp as a knife. I had found a wide path of burnt heather close to our track. It hadn't taken me long to get the knack of turf cutting. It consisted of shaving the top three inches of the turf, which was composed of a mat of roots, and it had to be done in furrows the width of the spade. But every two feet or so you had to give the blade an upwards and a sideways tilt which cut a single turf free, and turned it upside down. After cutting, you took them in pairs and leaned them edge to edge like the first operation of building a pagoda with playing cards. When thoroughly dry they had to be made into stacks about four feet high, laying them shingle fashion, and narrowing the top layers to a point.

The actual cutting was exhausting work, far more so than ordinary digging, and I had to do it in daily spells. It struck me as strange that not once during these spells had Jimmy come up to me to see what I was doing and give me advice, as he had done about the gate. Indeed, although there was never a day I did not see him riding over the moor, he had not approached within speaking distance since we had struck our bargain about the letting of the land and the fence. The rolls of netting and the posts for this had been delivered and were actually lying just inside the long-since finished gate. I had paid for them too. Was he deliberately avoiding me? Was he going to stick to the bargain we had made?

I felt diffident about calling on him. He must have been aware that the wire and posts had arrived. Although I knew I would have great difficulty in putting up the fence myself it was imperative that it should be fixed before Annabella arrived, and, anyway, his sheep were still on our land. I thought that the best way of attracting his attention to the matter would be for me to make at least a start putting up the posts. But it was Sam Briggs, and not Jimmy, whose attention was attracted. He had been to Burnharbour, and had left the bus at our road end. I was just starting to dig a hole for the first post when he came up to me.

"I hope you don't mind us coming down over your land from the moor road," he said. "I know there's not a right of way, but it saves us nearly a mile for getting the bus."

I laughed, but I appreciated his gesture.

"Seeing that I've been fishing in your beck and using your road through the wood it would be funny if I did mind. Of course I don't."

I told him what I was doing, and I thought there would be no harm in telling him of the arrangement I had come to with Jimmy: that I was letting him have the grazing of the top fields. I did not say how much rent he was going to pay. I did mention what he had said about the land needing lime and fertiliser, and that he was going to attend to that himself, as a condition of our deal.

I was alarmed by an expression of ironic amusement in Sam's eyes.

"Did he tell you that, and that *he'd* be paying for it?"

I answered uneasily:

"Yes. Don't you believe he will?"

Sam smiled.

"You don't know Jimmy," he said quietly, and I was

sure without any malice or even resentment towards our neighbour. "You don't know Jimmy. He talks easy enough of what he's going to do, but when it comes to doing it, why that's another matter. It would be a surprise to me if he put any dressing on your land—lime, or owt else that costs brass, and a bit of work. In all the time we've lived here I'll lay he's never put a shovel full of owt on his own pastures, let alone someone else's.

"You see, Jimmy's not a real farmer. His only interest is moor-sheep, and they get their living on the moor, and all he grows for them are a few swedes or mangolds, to help 'em out in hard weather. He's only got a couple of old cows for his own milk and butter, and to feed a calf or two. He has to buy all his hay for them. He's got a few hens and ducks, but he's got no food to keep pigs. This land of yours would be of use to him, of course, although he's been using it free these last few years, or at least his sheep have. He'll be afraid of your fencing it off to stop his sheep from straying on it, and that's why he wants to rent it. *I* know Jimmy. He's a very nice chap. He's a good talker. He means well too. But when it comes to doing anything he's worse than hopeless."

I felt discouraged.

"He said he'd give me a hand putting up this fence," I said. I refrained from saying that he had also agreed to pay half the cost.

"Aye. And I bet he hasn't been near hand since. And I'll make another bet. He told you to come and borrow my wire strainer to do the job."

I laughed.

"Yes. And what he called a mell. I suppose that's a

195

wooden hammer."

"Aye. Last time he borrowed them from me I had to go and fetch them back myself. He'd left the strainer in his fence, and even then he hadn't finished the job he'd borrowed it for, and he'd had it for weeks. As my missus often says, he's a coughdrop is Jimmy. Well, I'll lend you the strainer. But don't expect Jimmy to come and help you. I'll come and give you a hand myself."

This was indeed a friendly gesture, and I had no doubt about its sincerity. I hesitated, however. I had an uncomfortable feeling that everything that Sam had said was true, that, even as I had suspected when we had made the bargain, Jimmy had got the better of me. He had seemed just a little too glib in his assurances about improving the land, in insisting on what an advantage it was to me to have him as a tenant.

Yet, the fence *was* an advantage. It was the cheapest and surest way of keeping out his sheep, even if he did not pay his share, or as seemed likely, the rent. And I still could not feel angry with him, least of all did I want to have a quarrel with him. Wouldn't he consider it a slight if he saw Sam doing the job he had offered to do himself? I told Sam of my fears. He laughed dryly.

"You needn't let that worry you. It would take summat different to make Jimmy vexed. In fact, you never can vex him. That's where he's always got you. And I'll make another bet. When it's finished he'll just ride up and tell you what a job you've made of it. But it's a pity in a way you've gone and let him have this land at all. I won't say that he'll do it any harm, but he won't do it any good. It isn't bad land, you know. It's better than a lot of mine was when I bought it. It's all fairly level, and it's well drained. Let's have a look at it, and then I'll go down and get changed, and I'll bring the mell up and a crowbar, and we'll get your posts up, anyway."

We had only to walk a short distance to have a view of all the top fields. There were four of them in all. Apart from the moor fences all the other fences were mere vestiges, heaps of stone, a few gnarled thorn bushes. Sam bent down and examined the turf then tried to pull up a handful of the coarse grass, but it defeated him.

"Why—it's too tough even for moor sheep to eat, this. They'll only nibble round it getting the new blades. It's all muck, and it's all matted so that the air can't get into the soil. It would be a waste of time and money spreading lime or fertiliser on this as it stands. I know what *I'd* do with it if it was mine. I'd plough it up, bury all this top stuff. I'd dig all round those rocks that are sticking out of the ground, and blow them up with gelignite. Get a quarry man to do the job. I'd fill in the holes, then get it all ploughed up, and then after a winter's frost, I'd lime it, and give it a dressing of slag or superphosphate. Come spring I'd sow it with oats and an undercrop of good grass seed which would come up in the stubble after harvesting, and I'd make a good pasture out of it in a couple of years, or I'd get some good hay off it. Did you notice that hay we were leading when you first came down to our spot? That was from a field that was in poorer shape than this when I first started on it, except that it hadn't any big rocks like this. It was half-covered in whins and brambles and bracken. I got a fine crop of oats from it first harvest."

197

He talked with an infectious enthusiasm. Why, I thought, had I been such a fool as to let the land go to Jimmy when perhaps Sam himself would have taken it. As though reading my thoughts he went on:

"If this land hadn't been on the wrong side of the valley, I'd have been tempted into making an offer for it myself. But it's too far away, and anyway, clearing those rocks would be a problem. It wouldn't be so bad if they were just soft sandstone. But they look to me like flint."

We strode over to one of them. It was an irregularly-shaped slab, about eight feet across its wider part, and elevated about two feet above the grass. Geology had been one of my passions as a boy, but my interest in it had been chiefly confined to fossils found in the liassic beds that formed the cliffs and scars of the bay, and the formations that lay above the lias, and extended over the moors, had few fossils in them. They were principally sandstone, yielding the freestone of which our own barn had been built.

This rock was not sandstone. It was greyish white in colour, close-grained without any stratification lines. It certainly looked as hard as flint. Had I been a trained all-round geologist, or a mining engineer, I would have at least suspected that it was gannister or silica rock, the basis of a fire-resisting cement used for the lining of furnaces, and of definite commercial value, but my present interest arose only from what Sam had said about the land that it was fouling. There were, from where we stood, at least a score of visible rocks. There would undoubtedly be more under the turf although it did not occur to me then that they were outcrops of one underlying bed.

"Aye, it's tough stuff, this," Sam went on. "And there's so many of them. Even when you got them blown up you'd have to lead the bits away, and it would be no good ploughing unless all the land was clean. It wouldn't be so bad if farming really paid."

"And it doesn't?"

He laughed.

"It just about keeps you from starvation, if you go hard at it. You'd earn more money being a grocer, or a bricklayer, or a bus driver. It suits me all right, though. I wouldn't like to do owt else. And if I owned this land I couldn't bear letting it go to waste. I'd have to do summat about it."

"You wouldn't," I said, "consider taking it on if Jimmy didn't stick to his agreement?"

"No. It's in the wrong spot. But if ever you want to do it yourself I'll give you all the help I can. I'm hoping to get a tractor one day. When I do I'll have to take on other work, for my farm's too small to keep it going and pay for it. Of course, I may be wrong about Jimmy."

How right he was. It took us an afternoon to get all the posts of the fence fixed, and the netting strained tight and fixed at the main posts, so that all I had to do was to staple it to the intervening posts. It was the next morning when I was engaged on this simple operation that Jimmy rode up just as Sam said he would, and he said, with his usual smile:

"By! You've been quick with this. I was coming to give you a hand but I saw that you'd got Sam helping you. You've made a very good job of it. I'm glad you took my advice and got that square mesh. That'll stop them ewes of mine, especially as I've got rid of their lambs. I'll have a ride round now and see if any of 'em are on your side."

He did not mention the money he had agreed to pay towards the cost of the fence. Nor did I. If he did not pay, our agreement was null and void, and I had made up my mind that one day, when it suited my own convenience—and pocket—I'd see these fields as Sam had so vividly pictured them for me, under a crop of oats, or covered with bright-green grass, full of clover.

12

AT LAST, at the end of the last week in September, our house was technically completed, and officially pronounced habitable. The carpenters and plumbers had packed up their tools on the Friday afternoon. They had swept up the shavings and sawdust from the floors. All the remaining rubble and other debris had been cleared from the surrounds of the house and the surplus building material and apparatus stacked ready to be loaded on the lorry for its last journey.

Will came out before knocking-off time. He made a final survey of the whole building, outside and in. He opened and shut all doors to see that they fitted well, and did the same with the window casements. He examined all the plumbing. The last job the plumbers had done was a "bottle-gas" installation. This was to serve us for lighting until such time as we could solve the problem of producing our own electricity. It had the merit of being fairly cheap and very simple. The gas was supplied in portable steel cylinders which held it under pressure in a liquid state until the pressure was released by turning on the taps. In addition to lighting it supplied two boiling rings fixed near the cooking-stove.

It was only in the bathroom that Will was critical. It would have looked much better, he said, if the whole room had been done with plastic panelling, as he was going to have done in the bathroom of his own house when he got it built. Actually, he envied me this place, he said. He liked the looks of it, both inside and out. It was nice and light, and it ought to be warm and cosy in the coldest winter. He only hoped that we were going to be satisfied with it, and that we were going to be happy living here.

There was nothing formal about this occasion. Apart from the material for my hut and a few other small items Will's account would be settled by the lawyer. The key of the front door was already in my possession. Nor was it an occasion to say farewell, for he had eagerly accepted my invitation to come out rabbit shooting whenever he liked. But I had some beer for the workmen, and when the lorry arrived there was a quick final celebration. I rode up with Will to the road end, and there I got out to wait for Dain's bus, an earlier one than usual.

She got out of it laden with parcels, and there was a sweeping-brush too, and a bucket, a mop and a kettle, so that we could not, as she clearly wanted to, run all the way to the house.

"Is it *really* finished?" she asked, excitedly. "Shall we really be living in it tomorrow?"

"It's really finished, least so far as the masons and carpenter and plumbers are concerned. It's all ours. There's water flowing in the pipes. The gas is laid on. The lorry brought out a bag of coal, too, this morning, but I haven't lit the kitchen stove because I thought you'd like to see that done, and I don't think we should light the lounge fire until tomorrow night when we shall really be at home."

"I do hope that it doesn't smoke. But of course it *won't*. Amelia is as excited as though tomorrow was Christmas Day. Will it be safe for Annabella to arrive next week?"

There was no reason why she should not. The fence was finished, and since then there had been no sign of any sheep on our side of it. So long as our top gate was kept shut there would be no fear of Annabella straying, and as there would be no more traffic of the firm's lorries I could now put the padlock on.

Of the many stages in the evolution of a house none is more dramatic than when the actual building is finished and the workmen have packed up, and the place stands completely empty and silent. There are no curtains, no floor coverings, no furniture, the walls are bare. This can happen only once in its history, for whoever lives in it will make marks on its structure which nothing will ever completely erase, and those marks will as inevitably be evidence of the character and behaviour of the occupants.

Our Cornish hut, although its history was relatively short, was very rich in this respect, for apart from what the goat-keeping and beer and condensed-milk drinking tenants had left, there were many signs that it had been used as a shipwright's workshop and earlier still by soldiery. Originally it had been one of an encampment of huts on Salisbury Plain, housing Australian troops. Some of these had scribbled, and even carved, their names and numbers and home addresses on the walls. Some had scribbled verses, done drawings, some lewd, some even religious.

But here in our new house, apart from the ship's beam in the fireplace, the second-hand cooking-stove, and the individual stones and slates of the old barn, there was as yet no past. It was new, unmarked, exciting in its very emptiness. When I shut the front door behind us we could hear the bang of it echoing through the whole house. Then a dead silence, broken when our feet resounded on the hollow living-room floor as we walked in and stopped by the stove, and, as there was nowhere else, deposited our things. upon it. That silence imposed a silence on us for a while like that of a church.

Then Dain said:

"Oh, darling, I can hardly believe It. We're here at last. And it looks just too wonderful. This room is so big and it's so light, so different from that awful kitchen at Butcher's Folly. What a pity we can't be moving in tonight. Come on, I want to look at every room before we start scrubbing the floors."

"We'll need hot water for that, anyway," I said. "Let's

light the fire first, and see how it works. It's laid. You light it. I'll fill the kettle, and I suggest we have some tea."

I wanted to prove, at least for my own satisfaction, that we had got the right layout for the stove and the sink. I took the kettle from the stove and had only to make one stride, and a half turn to reach the cold water tap of the sink. I filled it, and to complete the demonstration I put it on one of the gas rings, which Dain lit with the same match she had used for the fire. There was a short period of hesitation before the draught took hold, but when it did it roared like a miniature blast furnace. But the draught, both in its force and direction, was controllable by dampers. The heat from the fire could be directed either round the boiler or the oven, or divided between both. Again, although the coal had to be well alight first, the front of the fireplace could be opened up to give a slower burning, but visible, fire.

"Do you know," I said half seriously as I added more coal to the roaring blazing fire, "I think that the only thing we're going to find wrong with this place is that everything's so completely right."

Dain laughed.

"I've been thinking that, but I shan't worry if this stove proves perfect after struggling with the one at Butcher's Folly for three months. I wonder how long it will take for the water to get hot. Not long, I think."

Leaving the fire to roar, and the kettle to boil on the gas, we made a tour of all the rooms. Not one of them had been finished when Dain had seen the place a week ago. Upstairs there had been only the framework of the bedroom partitions. The only thing not finished now was the airing cupboard, which would be my own first job, and I felt a bit scared of it, for while it hadn't mattered very much if one made little mistakes in our Cornish hut, my own carpentry here would have to be in keeping with the high professional standard of the whole building.

"Isn't it good," I said, "having all the floors dead level, and the walls and ceilings smooth and clean, and the doors fitting closely. No patches anywhere. No stains on the walls like there were in our bedroom where the rain came in, even after we'd stopped the leaks."

"Yes. They even showed up again after we had painted them. There was one patch shaped exactly like a giraffe. Still, it was fun, all that, and it's going to make a grand book, remember."

I hadn't forgotten that book, nor in any way lost interest or faith in the idea. It might well be more successful than anything else I had written. It might indeed bring us real wealth, so that we should never have to bother again as to whether we could afford this, that or the other, or worry about bills. It was not, however, going to be an easy book to write. It was still completely nebulous. It might be months before it started to take shape. It might be a year or two years or even three before it was finished. You just didn't know with a book.

I had not lost sight either of the fact that although Will's account for the building of the house was being settled by our friendly lawyer, all this money, plus interest, had to be paid back. The material for my hut was an extra, so was the bottle-gas installation. I'd had to pay the entire cost of the new fence (I was assuming that Jimmy had no intention of sticking to his part of the bargain), and apart from a multitude of small items we needed for the furnishing of the house, pots and pans, crockery, we'd had to buy three chests of drawers and a kitchen dresser, all second-hand but not cheap, and a major expense had been the linoleum which we had decided was a necessity for all floors irrespective of whether they were to have carpets or rugs.

Linoleum was hygienic, and labour-saving. It would have been false economy not to have bought the best quality, but its price had been somewhat of a shock. So had the material for the curtains, which Dain had chosen, but had made up herself. We had to have curtains of course, and they had to look good, and she had pointed out that the extra money they were costing was very small compared with what we would have had to pay for a pony if Mrs Allen hadn't been so generous and given us Annabella. A saddle would have cost at least five pounds. I *was* worried, but something would turn up before our financial situation got desperate again. And if I couldn't get on with the new book I could write something to keep us going until the real inspiration came.

The rolls of linoleum had been delivered to Butcher's Folly and they would be coming out with the removal van in the morning. We planned to have it all laid before any of the furniture was carried in, and what we must do now, as soon as we had some tea, was start the scrubbing of all the floors so that they would dry overnight. I put my hands on the cylinder. It was still cold, but the inlet pipe from the boiler was definitely warm, and even from upstairs we could hear the fire roaring. We were on our way downstairs again when there was a knocking at the front door. It was Mrs Briggs. She had seen smoke coming from our chimney, she said, and took that as a sign that we'd soon be moving in. If we needed any help she and Sam were ready to give us a hand. Besides, she wanted to know about the milk.

She and Dain had already met. We asked her to come in, for she was naturally curious to see what the place was like now that it was finished. She was deeply impressed, especially by the stove and the sink and the abundant daylight given by the two opposite windows of the living room.

"Eee! It's champion. It's got so much room in it, and it's so light. And I do like that cooking-stove, and fancy having gas too, and a bathroom. It makes me wish we could have our spot pulled down and built up again. We've always had it in our minds to put a new cooking range in the living-room, anyway, and have a proper sink, but there wasn't even water laid on when we bought it. It had belonged to that squire who built all them daft cow houses and pigsties, although he hadn't done owt fancy to ours, which maybe was as well. Sam had to rebuild the cow house, anyway, and lay water on to the dairy for the cooler or otherwise the Milk Board wouldn't have passed our milk, which is the only thing that pays in farming now. We've spent so much brass on the buildings and stock and fertilisers, we've just had to make do with the house. And now Sam wants to go in for a tractor. But wait till he sees all this. I'll try and coax him round into a stove like yours, anyway."

The kettle was boiling. Dain made the tea, but Mrs Briggs would not stay to join us. It was just on milking time. But she'd come up after, and give us a hand scrubbing the floors, and if we didn't mind she'd bring Sam up too. She wanted him to see that stove and the sink. Going out, however, she turned and said:

"Eh, but I haven't told you the latest about Sam and Jimmy. Sam tackled him about that saddle again a day or two ago. And last night, just about dark, there was a knock at our front door. Sam goes out, wondering who on earth it could be, and there was Jimmy, and he'd got the saddle with him. Sam asks him in, of course, but Jimmy wouldn't come. He sounds quite polite at first. He says to Sam 'I've fetched your saddle back and thanks very much for the loan of it. I've had it to the saddler's too, and had it stitched, and I hope you'll find it's in good fettle, and better fettle than when you lent it to me.' 'Thanks very much,' says Sam. 'I didn't expect you to get it mended.' 'Maybe not,' says Jimmy, and then of a sudden he gets real vexed. 'Maybe not, but I doubt you'd have had plenty to say if I'd brought it back with half its stuffin' hanging out. I've paid over ten bob to get it stitched, so you haven't done so bad out of it. And now I'll tell you this. I'll never borrow another thing from you so long as I live,' and with that hands Sam the saddle and stamps off, leaving Sam just about speechless.

"He's a coughdrop is Jimmy. I think he must have had one or two last night to make him so bold. He'll be all smiles next time he meets Sam, and I shouldn't be surprised if he's asking to borrow the saddle again before this winter's out."

We could not have had a better day for our moving in. It was calm and warm and dry, real Indian summer weather. It was not a big job. We had few material possessions; no piano for example, or bedroom suites or sideboards, the things that are usually disgorged from removal vans and pantechnicons, and when the two warehouse men in charge had carried the really heavy rolls of linoleum into the rooms where they were to be laid I got them to dump everything else just outside the front door, and let them go.

The laying and fitting of the lino presented no serious difficulties to us. We'd had so much practice cutting and fitting the old sails and tarpaulins to the crazy shapes of our hut. Here everything was square and regular. The walls had no conventional skirting boards. Instead we were going to use narrow strips of plain moulding, triangular in section which would actually cover the edges of the lino, streamlining them, so that there would be no crevices to hold dust. These could not be nailed on until the lino had been down a day or two, and had stopped spreading, a thing you had to allow for between all adjoining strips.

We did the ground floor rooms first, and the first furniture we moved in was the table, the one that had served us in our Cornish living-room. We had bought this originally at a sale. It was a conventional deal kitchen table with two drawers and a removable top. Because of the sloping floor, and because the only convenient position for it was close up to the transverse partition, we had sawed off two of its legs, reduced the width of the top by one board and made the whole thing a fixture against the partition wall, something like a quick-lunch counter. I had restored the amputated legs, and also the board, and the table fitted close up to the front window, yet being on castors it could easily be moved to a more central position in the room.

The dresser came next. We had been lucky in finding one that was the exact width of the partition wall that divided the living-room from the day nursery. It was in two detachable parts, the lower one having three drawers with cupboards below; the top part consisting of plain shelves with scrolled sides. It had been varnished and painted, but we had scraped it bare to find a nicely-figured yellow pine, and we had made wood handles for the drawers and cupboard doors. There were hooks on the edges of the shelves, and thin wood fillets so that plates could stand on them on edge.

We could not resist unpacking our new crockery to see how it would look on the dresser. We *had* let ourselves go over this crockery. It was called Cornish kitchenware, and as well as ordinary dishes, mugs, jugs and basins, there were labelled and lidded jars for various dry foods, and they bore a simple ringed pattern of blue on white. The dishes looked particularly good, but the mugs and jugs looked better for having just one or two odd and differently coloured pieces hanging among them to break the tone of blue.

Everything was turning out better even than we had expected. We had damped down the kitchen stove when we had packed up last night. We had found the cylinder too hot to touch on our arrival, and no sooner had we opened the damper than the fire was roaring again. It looked as though we could have the oven just as hot as we wanted.

I'd made a fireguard for our Cornish living-room stove out of a brass grid which originally had protected the skylight of the cuddy of one of the old sailing ships. This grid measured two feet six by one, and I'd fitted it into a wooden frame which had also formed a kerb, and it hadn't been difficult to adapt the whole apparatus to fit our new fireplace. The grid could slide up and down the frame and could easily be removed. When polished it would be most pleasing to look at and it would be still another link between our old and our new home.

But how much better, I kept on thinking, our new home was compared with our Cornish one, especially for the children. Amelia was loving it, although she had disconcerted us by complaining that the walls of her bedroom were not pretty like those of her room at Butcher's Folly, the room which had been decorated with the jays and vine leaves. Jane, too young yet for art, good or bad, took happily to the day nursery and its ample crawling space. We had fixed a low board across its doorway into the living-room.

The aunt, who liked children, and housework and cooking and gardening, was going to stay with us for a while. Our first lunch was a success, proving not only that the stove was all right, but that for cooking, eating, for *living* in, we had planned our living-room well. With the table flush up to the front window, and the window, with its entrancing view so big, it was almost like being in the open air.

It was only the aunt who found the traffic arrangements for washing up not so good. She was left-handed, and would have preferred sink and draining board and dresser the opposite way round.

It was significant that on that last day of September our dessert was blackberry tart, made from fruit we'd picked within a few yards of the house. In Cornwall the blackberries would have been over weeks ago, although the first ones would have been ripe so much earlier than they would have been here. There, too, the bracken by this time would have completely turned to its winter brown, and the oaks at least would have been patched with yellow. Here, but for a few streaks of gold among the bracken, there was little sign of autumn's approach. The oak wood was still green.

The furnishing of the lounge was very simple. We had one large divan which in daytime could go alongside either of the two windows, but could be drawn up to the fire at night. We had three easy-chairs, one of them bought, the others homemade. One of them we had contrived from a motorcar seat, the other, our most successful piece of furniture-making, from the two elm slabs of a blacksmith's bellows. Originally, we had made the seat of this with plaited motor-bike inner tubes, but the rubber had wasted and we had replaced the tubes with Sandow developer springs.

We had no real table for the lounge for it would have taken up too much room. Our books would go on shelves in the recess between the fireplace and the staircase, and for the blind wall just clear of the staircase foot we had a large cupboard with panelled doors we'd bought second-hand and stripped of its paint. The curtains were of hand-woven material, of pleasant design and colour. The divan was covered with some material the aunt, who had lived in India, had given us. It was a sort of brocade, with shades of blue and red and yellow. We had a small Chinese carpet, grey in tone, and two Kelim rugs, predominantly red, for the floor, and a thick knitted wool rug to fit up to the hearth.

We had told Amelia that she should stay up to see the lighting of the lounge fire, the climax of our house-warming. The lorry had brought down to the house some of my dried turves. After tea we had gone up our beck as far as the island and had got as many dead oak branches as we could carry, together with some dead whins for kindling.

Dusk, noticeably earlier than it would have been in the latitude of Cornwall, was falling by the time everything was ready. It would perhaps have been more appropriate to the occasion if there had been a corresponding difference in temperature; if there had been at least a suspicion of chill in the evening air, better still if there had been a storm like the one that had caused us to take shelter in the barn and make our fire long ago. It was exciting enough.

We drew the curtains, but we did not light the gas. I struck a match and held it to the dry kindling. It caught fire instantly and the flames lit up the whole room, as the flames of our fire had lit up the bare stone walls on that other occasion. The turf took hold, flaming first, then glowing red and emitting plumes of thick velvety brown smoke which curled up the fire back and then rose out of sight up the well-planned flue, so that I had to scoop some of the smoke forward into the room with my hand so that we could savour the sweet scent of it.

We were all there; the genial aunt in the blacksmith's bellows chair on one side of the fireplace, Dain sitting opposite, holding our blissfully smiling last born in her arms, Amelia bathed and in her girdled dressing-gown kneeling on the hearthrug, staring at the flames with her hands uplifted from the elbows in the unconscious gesture of a priestess performing a religious rite.

We were home!

PART TWO

1

WE WERE happy.

We had made for ourselves an almost ideal home, in an almost ideal place, and, in a little less than four years, our family had been enlarged by the arrival, at convenient intervals, of two sturdy sons, Angus and Timothy. Although this had meant having a nanny to live with us (the aunt had a passion for travel, and her visits although frequent were brief and intermittent) our accommodation had not as yet been seriously overtaxed. We had, however, built an extra and bigger playroom outside at the back of the house, along the blind wall, a single story timber lean-to. It ran continuously with the porch and a new and bigger larder.

For the children it was a perfect life. They breathed the clean moorland air, salt and ozone tanged when the wind blew from the sea. They had good and abundant food. We had our milk, cream and butter from the mill farm. Sam had a small but pedigree T.T. herd of shorthorns. His wife, Becky, as we had soon come to call her, kept their modem equipped dairy as clean and aseptic as a hospital operating theatre—a great improvement on the dairy that existed when the little squire had owned the farm.

We had our own poultry: a flock of Rhode Island Reds of staggered age groups, which gave us big brown eggs all the year round. The only snag with them was that, because of the numerous foxes in the district, their run had to be enclosed with tall wire netting, and had to be shifted from time to time as the ground got fouled, and that Annabella took a perverse delight in using the stakes as rubbing posts, although she had hundreds more substantial posts and stones and tree trunks to choose from.

I had a single barrel twelve-bore shotgun and I could get a rabbit whenever our larder was otherwise low. There were several coveys of partridges on the land. In winter there were woodcock in the copse above the island, and during the acorn season several large flocks of wood pigeons haunted the mill wood. Sam, because of the harm these birds did to his crops, encouraged me to shoot them.

There was also one famous cock pheasant. It obviously roosted in the wood, and spent most, but not all, of its daytime hours foraging among the fallen leaves under the oaks. Sam, always too busy to indulge in any sort of pastime, had let the shooting of his land to a Burnharbour sportsman. Apart from the pigeons I strictly respected this reservation, and it seemed almost as though the cock pheasant knew that the wood was sanctuary so far as I was concerned. Several times I had encountered it on my way to the mill farm, and it merely

216

scurried away, not troubling to take wing. But whenever a shoot was in progress (the sportsman and his party usually began in Sam's stubbles and swedes for partridges) it would cunningly leave the wood and come over to our side of the boundary, never, however, visibly, so that I'd have a clue to its approximate whereabouts.

There never was a more elusive and unpredictable bird. I'd never seen it on the ground here, but I would flush it, always in the most unexpected place, and always out of range of my gun if I happened to be carrying it. Once I was clearing a clump of whins with the slasher quite close to the garden fence and it got up almost at my feet and with such a sudden clatter my heart came into my mouth with fright. Another time I was repairing the boundary wall and it emerged from a hole in the wall itself, not more than a couple of strides away, but again I was unarmed, and the cackle it made as it flew away, offering a perfect shot, seemed like derisive laughter.

I was not a very good shot at moving game. As with fishing, I could never be sufficiently calm and detached. I was a snap shooter, and I had acquired this bad habit by learning to use a shotgun in the African bush, where, without a dog, with flushed birds like quail or partridge or guinea-fowl, your quarry would be in sight among the thorns or trees for seconds only. There was no time for steady aim. As with fishing, too, the more desirable the prize the more prone I was to get excited. That pheasant became a family joke, for often Dain or the children would see it while I was in my hut writing and come and tell me, but when I rushed to the place where it had been seen, it was never there.

There was a December afternoon when the shooting party had been out and ended up by drawing the mill wood. I'd heard some close shots and seen a couple of pigeons drop, but I had no doubt that the pheasant had behaved with its usual wiliness and moved out of the wood at the first sound of guns in the distant fields.

It was calm misty weather, not cold, and it was round about four o'clock when I set out, with winter dusk approaching. We needed a rabbit for our next day's dinner. I knew I could get one easily in the gloaming close by one of the several warrens. If the pheasant was on our land it would certainly fly back to the wood at the sound of my gun. I decided to walk up to the top fields first, try the whins that bordered them, then move down to the copse above the island, and return along the beck path down to the mill wood wall.

Although I saw plenty of rabbits, and was offered a long-range chance at a lone partridge which probably had been driven across by the shooters on Sam's land, there was no sign of the pheasant and when at last I got down towards the beck I knew that I must give it up, for there would not be sufficient light to get my rabbit. There was a small warren here among the whins and bracken close to where the copse began. I approached it warily but without excitement. The rabbits were out and very deliberately I waited so that I could select one that I could drop without the risk of it falling into a hole. I was crouching among the tall whins. The range was not more than thirty feet. I took my pick, and with nerves completely steady, fired. At the same instant there was a harsh clatter of wings in the whins between me and the warren, and up got the cock pheasant flying low across the warren towards the edge of the copse, again offering a perfect shot.

Had my gun been a double barrel I could have used the second one and hardly missed. Yet it hadn't, for once, flown towards the wood and its sanctuary. Its visible flight had taken it to the copse, where it had risen to clear a thick straggly holly tree, and there was still a possibility that its flight was short, that it had come down again in the copse, which had a thick undergrowth of bracken.

My rabbit was stone dead. With fingers trembling and my heart beating uncomfortably fast, I reloaded and began to move towards the copse, steering up the bank so that I could get above the level of the tallest. trees in it and have a clear field of fire if the bird did get up again. This time, in spite of my excitement, it would not catch me unprepared.

I moved stealthily, every few yards taking a deep breath in an effort to calm my nerves. I reached a good vantage point. It was above the highest tip of the holly and there were only a few bare and thin branches of alder to mask any possible line of flight. The copse was about twenty yards across its widest point. If the bird was in it it would, I judged, have selected the densest part of the undergrowth just beyond the holly.

I waited a moment, then, noticing a loose stone close to my feet, I picked it up with my left hand, took another deep steadying breath, and heaved the stone into the bracken, and had the gun at my shoulder before it dropped. The stone must have hit a dead branch before it touched the ground, for there was a definite crack. At once there was another sound and in the bracken something moved. I held my breath. I tried even to avoid blinking as I looked at the spot from which any second now I expected the pheasant to rise.

All was still for a time. Then about ten yards up from the point where I had dropped the stone, where there was a patch of bare soil from a deserted rabbit burrow, I saw for one moment part of the head and shoulders of a fox. In that moment it was dead still. I saw its eyes fixed on me, and they might have been the glass eyes of a stuffed fox in a glass case. Then it was gone. As I stared at the place where it had stood I saw another movement on the ground. Something was lying there and it was alive.

With gun still at the ready I forced my way through the undergrowth. I reached the old rabbit burrow. There lay the cock pheasant, on its back, with its feet in the air, its feet and its crumpled wings still moving, but only in the convulsions of death for its head had been bitten off.

It was clear what had happened. The fox had been lying up in the thicket, probably like the pheasant itself, having been driven from the mill wood by the shooting party. By a million to one chance the pheasant, when put up by the sound of my gun, must have alighted on the very spot where the fox was lying, and had been caught as though it had dropped on a spring trap.

I picked it up and looked at it with mixed feelings. It was an acquisition to our larder. Roast pheasant! It would have to hang for a few days, like any other sort of game, but it would be no worse for its mode of death. I was primitive enough and vain enough to wish that it had fallen to my gun. I also felt more than a little sad that this bird which had eluded me and fooled me, and even mocked me on so many occasions, had met its death by such a fantastic piece of ill luck.

We were not completely self-supporting in the way of food. Apart from rabbits, and how we got sick of them at times, we could only get game in season. We had to have butcher's meat, and this came out to us twice a week with the grocer's delivery van which also brought our bread, and, alas, most of our fish, and, in winter, fruit like oranges and bananas.

We grew all our own vegetables. Our garden soil was not quite so fertile as that of our Cornish garden, but neither was it so productive in weeds and other pests. There *were* docks and nettles and thistles, but they were normal in size and rate of generation and we could keep them in check. We had no accumulation of dried goat-droppings here although Jimmy's sheep, before the erection of the fence, had undoubtedly paid tribute for their free grazing. We had no seaweed at the garden gate like we had in Cornwall. Sam would have let us have a certain amount of farmyard manure, but there was no means of transporting it in bulk up the bridle path through the wood.

Annabella, too, might have helped, but she had an extraordinary delicacy in her natural functions. She would never leave any of the by-products of her digestive system near the house, always selecting the most remote corners of the land for this purpose, although the children, once they had learnt the principles of soil fertility, would eagerly collect these deposits in a

221

little handcart I had made for them especially as a boost for their own plots of garden.

Annabella could have helped us if, during the cold weather, she had used the stable I had built for her close by the house. She hated it, preferring to shelter in the lee of a wall or a clump of whins even in a snowstorm. There was the poultry, of course, but all the books I had read advised that this was too rich to be used neat, and as artificials were dear I had adopted the compost method of manuring, using oak leaves from the wood, and dead bracken doped in alternate layers with lime and soil and poultry dung.

Apart from our latitude we were five hundred feet above sea level. We had snow and really hard frosts, and in almost everything we were at least a month late compared with Cornwall. Yet our garden was sheltered from the strongest winds and was actually more exposed to the sun, and there were very few plants which did not ultimately thrive in it just as well, and some did even better. We had never successfully grown strawberries in Cornwall. Here, although I had to protect the flowers against frost with dead bracken, we had magnificent crops. Our early potatoes were late, but they were clean and free from disease, and had a delicious flavour. We found strains of broccoli that would withstand days of the hardest frost and give perfect heads in early spring and on into summer. They were sweeter and had much more flavour than the conventional cauliflower.

We grew broad beans, carrots, swedes, onions, leeks, lettuces both cabbage and the cos variety. We had successions of peas throughout the summer, and of runner beans which lasted until the first autumn frosts. We had gooseberries, raspberries, logans and blackcurrants. We planted apple and pear and plum trees. Except for a pair of Victoria plums, none of these had yet produced much fruit, for I had not been able to nurse the blossom through the spring frosts.

With flowers we could not possibly emulate the semi-tropical luxuriance of our Cornish garden where hollyhocks grew to a height of eight feet, and, provided we could beat the weeds, almost any seeds would germinate and get established as quickly as in a heated greenhouse. Yet many things did well in the beds we made on both sides of the little stream which came from the spring; and in a small walled garden at the south end of the house irises by the stream itself and in the beds, sweet williams, phlox, marigolds, wallflowers, snap dragons, and early-flowering chrysanthemums.

Again with its wild flowers Cornwall beat us. We had no foxgloves; the campions, which on the banks of our cove above the oaks were tall and thick stemmed and almost poppy red, were here short and thin of stem and the flowers an anæmic pink. Yet down by the beck the primroses grew in profusion in spring, and there were clumps of native daffodils far lovelier in their simplicity than the cultivated, variegated Cornish type, and we increased their number by digging up the clumps in autumn, separating the bulbs and replanting so that at the island in particular were thick patches of them which the children could pick to their hearts' content.

Except in the coldest days of winter the island was their favourite playground. It was an easy job building the low dam wall for the pool. When finished the pool was forty feet in length and eight feet from bank to bank, and about a foot deep with a shingle bottom. We left two big boulders in it at its top end to give cover for the trout, which soon adjusted their feeding times and hiding times to the play times of the children.

I built a flat-bottomed dinghy of plywood on a light batten frame. It was really nothing more than a box, six feet long and three feet wide, tapered slightly at bow and stern. With thole-pin oars, made to the pattern of those of a Yorkshire coble, it was at least pool-worthy even for an adult, and soon the only member of the family who could not row it (and also swim) was our baby son, and he would howl to be in it.

As well as the trout, the pool had another occasional inhabitant: a water-shrew. It was shy, and to see it we had to approach the pool more warily than if we were stalking trout. It was about the size of a frog with the characteristic shrew snout. Its fur was more like that of a mole in texture and colour. It was always moving, and moving quickly underwater, zigzagging from one side of the pool to another, and on the way jabbing at the small stones, turning them over and snapping the tiny grubs and sandhoppers which took shelter there from the trout. As it swam bright little air bubbles were pressed out of its fur and trailed behind it like strings of pearls.

Sometimes, too, we would see a water-ouzel bobbing up and down like a wagtail on the boulders at the head of the pool, and then suddenly fling itself into the water and actually walk along the bottom, nosing the shingle like the shrew; but if anything the ouzels were even

224

shyer, and mostly when we saw them they were in flight up or down beck. A pair of them nested under a waterfall just below the ruins of the old mill. The nest, built of moss and with a canopy like that of a wren, was on a ledge almost hidden by the main curtain of water, and the birds had to fly through the curtain to reach it.

We had built a permanent picnic fireplace at the island and usually had tea there in fine weather. We built a shelter hut, African style—of branches and reed thatch, and in the oak which supported the swing the children themselves made a tree-top shelter in the same style, but smaller, into which they could climb.

I never grudged them their delight in this place, but I could not help thinking sometimes of how perfectly suited it was for the fulfilment of my long-cherished personal ambition: the making of a big double-purpose lake.

Our bottle-gas was a success as an auxiliary to the kitchen cooking-stove, but for illumination it was not so good, for the jets of the incandescent burners were very fine and were apt to get choked. Mantles were easily broken and had to be replaced frequently. The storage cylinders, which were heavy and awkward to handle, usually ran dry at the most awkward moment, and, while normally we had a full one in reserve, sometimes we hadn't and we had to wait for the next coming of the grocer's van, and in the meantime fall back on oil lamps and candles for the bedrooms.

Undoubtedly the best illuminant was electricity. But I was almost certain that there was not, except during floods, enough volume and velocity in the beck alone to produce even a current for our lighting needs. A reservoir was essential, and the only feasible site for it was the island.

Someday, most likely it would be when the youngest of our family was adolescent and the others grown up, and we had attained financial security, I would do it. I would dive and swim in that lake. I would angle with a clear conscience for its big trout. And I would watch the waterwheel turning, driving a purring dynamo, and I would click a switch in the house, lighting a forty-watt lamp, and gloat on the fact that the current that did it was homemade and free.

2

THE CHILDREN did not spend all their time at the island, and none of its delights could rival those provided by their pony Annabella.

I was still a long way from sharing either their or Dain's enthusiasm for horses and ponies. I could take no joy or find any satisfaction, as they so obviously did, in the daily ritual of grooming, of rubbing down and curry-combing. I felt privately that an adult animal should be capable of managing its own toilet. All wild animals did this, and so did the cleanest and neatest of domestic animals: the cat.

I could never feel, either, that Annabella had any

beauty of form or character, or that she was intelligent. The fact that Dain or any of the children had only to call "Annabella" to have her come charging down from the remotest part of the land and meekly submit to being bridled merely proved to me the inherent stupidity of her species, and that she was only capable of an elementary association of ideas. Bridling was always followed by a lump or two of sugar or a handful of oats. She fell and surrendered her freedom just for that.

Yet if I wanted to catch her she would never come at my call. I would have to find her, and keeping the halter or bridle behind me, approach her warily, holding out in my free band the bait. She'd submit in the end, but only after several abortive approaches in which she would back away just when I was in arm's length. Yet if I didn't want to catch her and was doing any job like mending a fence or moving the chicken run she would canter up and, if my back was turned, try to nuzzle me, and nothing seemed to give her more delight than to find a post that I had just driven into the ground, get her backside to it and knock it down.

She would never go into her stable of her own free will, but she made repeated efforts to get into the chicken house and once, when the back door was left open, she actually got into the living-room of our house and made a grab for the sugar bowl, sweeping the whole table clear of crockery. Fortunately she didn't try to go upstairs.

In spite of all this I had to admit that Annabella inspired in me a deep and lasting affection. She was indeed one of our family and she made possible, as Dain had argued she would, the enlargement of our horizons, which with our young family would otherwise have been cramped.

We could, although Dain never felt completely happy about it, safely leave our last born at home in charge of our nanny. Bridled and with a felt saddle, and Amelia, Jane and Angus taking turns, sometimes with all three of them up together, we could wander for miles over the moors, following the meandering sheep tracks uphill and down dale, and no matter how rough the going was, or steep or boggy, Annabella never showed resentment.

Usually we had some definite objective on these excursions: an ancient moorland cross marked on the ordnance map in special characters, a ring of standing stones, a campsite, a group of tumuli usually on a hilltop. Always we were on the lookout for flints, arrow and spear heads, axes, knives, scrapers. They were commonest in the close vicinity of the tumuli or campsites, and the best hunting grounds were the patches of bared and weathered subsoil from which the turf had been stripped for fuel.

We were just as interested in the living things around us, however, varying according to the time of the year: the rare flowers and plants found on the margins of the bogs, the butterflies and other insect life, the reptiles and birds.

Many of these expeditions took us past the trout mere. I never tried to fish in it again. For one thing I was certain that the trout I had caught was the last survivor of its original population, and I still had twinges of conscience about that affair especially as Mrs Allen had assured us that the Colonel was so good-natured.

My continued interest in the mere was that we had, as slyly as we had once poached it, started to restock it, using fry from our own beck and Sam's, transporting them a few at a time in an innocent looking quart milk can. The fact that in appropriate weather we could see trout rising in the clear patches of the mere again (very, very small) proved at least that some of them were established, and was the most certain proof of all that no big cannibal fish was left. It would be years before any of them reached a really tempting size.

Whatever the season, there was always something to interest and delight us on the moors, and yet it was no use pretending that they afforded us a completely satisfying substitute for the sea and the seashore. The moors had the advantage of being at our gate. Actually, we didn't need Annabella to enjoy them. The nearest accessible shore of the bay was in horizontal distance, just under three miles from the house, and in certain conditions of light and atmosphere looked half as much, as though indeed you could run down to it in a few minutes.

But to the actual horizontal distance one had to add the dimension of altitude, more evident on the return journey, and also the numerous deviations from the straight in the nearest route, the one old Isaac had brought us by on that first occasion. Walking alone and full out, my shortest time from Adder Howe to the beach was an hour, and the return an hour and a half. To take the whole family there amounted to a major operation needing at least the better half of a day.

It had to be a fine day too, tolerably warm and the

tides had to be right. It meant taking the material and utensils for at least one meal, buckets and spades and shrimp nets, changes of clothing for the children. We could have done all this fairly simply by engaging a taxi to take us as far as the cliff top, and bring us back, but no one would hear of this while we had Annabella and the trap, which, failing all efforts to buy a suitable one second-hand, I had designed and built myself.

Perhaps trap was the wrong name for it. It was a composite affair. Basically it was the trap that old Isaac had used with Snowball. Isaac, in spite of his gloomy predictions still very much alive, had sold us the harness for ten shillings. It was too big for Annabella but it could be tailored to her size, and he had included the trap in the bargain. It had no wheels. What remained of the body was worm-eaten and rotten, but the shafts and all the iron furnishings, including the springs were sound. In any case, it would have been too big for Annabella.

To carry our turf from the moor I had, before Dain had convinced me that Annabella could be used for this purpose, designed and made a handcart with the front axle and pneumatic tyres of a dismantled Austin Seven chassis I had bought for a few shillings at a Burnharbour garage. The tyres were in excellent condition. I had made a flat top and a single shaft with a crossbar. It had proved another white elephant.

On the level, even when fully loaded, I could push it with one hand. Even unloaded it took me all my strength to push it up the hill from the house to the level of the moor, and the first time I tried to bring it, loaded, downhill it took charge and only by frantically pushing the shaft round and capsizing the whole thing had I saved myself from disaster.

To marry this contrivance to what remained of Isaac's trap, and the harness, and finally Annabella herself was not a simple matter. It was indeed more complicated than the building and rigging of a sailing boat, yet fundamentally there was the same problem of stability.

I had been alarmed by the ease with which I had capsized my handcart. The wheels of a car are small, those of a horse-drawn vehicle relatively big in order to bring the shafts to a convenient height along the animal's flanks. The body of the vehicle which carried the load was higher still, producing a tendency to top-heaviness. I felt that for carrying children the body should be low so that they could get into it, or in an emergency get out of it, without needing a step such as most traps have.

After much thought and experiment with models and toy ponies from the nursery farmyard, I evolved what was really a cross between an Assyrian war chariot, a French Revolution tumbril, and a modern milk float.

The body was essentially a box with its sides made like our dinghy of plywood on a light but strong frame. The thick butts of the shafts instead of reaching along the floor of the body to their tapering open ends were bolted to the sides halfway up, and they made bearings for the detachable plank seats. The Austin axle was too short for the body to lie between the wheels. I solved this problem by cutting it with a hacksaw and, with U-bolts securing each half to an oak beam, leaving a gap between the cut ends. This increased the width by several inches and had the same stabilising effect as increasing the beam of a boat.

The first try-out had been as momentous, and for me as anxious, as the launching of a boat, for I could not believe that Annabella would submit without vigorous protest to being strapped up in the harness, backed between the shafts and then move forward with the thing behind her. I would not have dared to have done it on my own.

Dain made no more fuss about it than if she had been strapping up our last-born in his pram; and Annabella, even more meekly, submitted.

We were near the house at the foot of the road up to the moor, the gradient that had caused me to capsize my cart. I insisted that none of the children should get in for at least the first stage and that I should hold Annabella's head until Dain was aboard with the reins in her hand; and when she said quite calmly, "All right, let her go," I did so with a muttered prayer.

She just flicked the reins, said, "*Gee up!*" and without the slightest hesitation Annabella moved forward, got the strain of the traces and broke into a gallop straight up the hill faster than I had seen any car doing it. The children shouting with delight ran in pursuit, and I followed. At the top of the hill on the level, Dain was waiting, with Annabella blowing a bit, but otherwise perfectly happy and eager to be off again, and we all got in, Dain flicked the reins and away we went on our first drive.

The trap *was* a success.

The truth was, I think, that Annabella was so devoted to Dain and the children, especially to the children, she would have cooperated in anything that pleased them. I never felt, in spite of my growing affection for her, that I was included in this benevolence. She made me feel that anything that she did for me was a condescension.

With the seats removed the trap would hold enough turf to keep our fire going for a week, and yet the weight of it would not be as much as the combined weight of the family when we were out for a drive, and on the level at least I could have pulled it myself. But if I tried to do the loading and leading on my own she would show her resentment by objecting to keep still during the operation of loading, then by objecting to move at all when the load was on board, and then, just when patience was exhausted, by suddenly bounding forward and breaking into a canter or gallop, usually in the wrong direction and choosing the roughest ground to see if she could capsize the trap and its load. She seemed to know that I would never whack her or express my exasperation with anything more violent than verbal abuse.

The children adored her. Whether they had been riding her or not, always before dark they would go to where she was grazing, give her some oats or a carrot or some lumps of sugar, make certain that she was all right. This in winter usually happened just before teatime. It was an afternoon in early December of our second year, with Angus still in arms, that Amelia rushed into the living-room in a state of panic, followed by Jane weeping bitterly.

"Annabella's *gone!*" Amelia cried. "She's gone, she's *gone*. The top gate's wide open. We've seen her footprints. There's dozens of cars on the highroad. She'll be knocked down and killed."

"Darling Annabella!" sobbed Jane, flinging herself into Dain's arms. "*Darling* Annabella."

It was our nanny's day off. I'd been helping Dain get tea ready, and had been pleasantly contemplating the approach of night, the lighting of the lamps, the drawing of the curtains, the usual noisy but happy teatime, an hour's play in the warm nursery with Amelia and Jane before bath time, the prelude to their going to bed, and for us the evening peace and quiet of our fireside.

I was alarmed, but at first not quite convinced. Amelia had a strong sense of the dramatic and was prone to exaggeration.

"Are you sure? Have you looked everywhere? When did you last see her? Who could have left the gate open?"

"Oh, Daddy!" she cried tearfully. "*Please* don't stand there asking questions. Do come and find her before it gets really dark. I don't know who left the gate open. We haven't seen her since dinnertime. If she's out on the highway she might be killed by a motor car. She might be stuck in a bog and be drowned. Someone might have stolen her. Oh, *do* hurry!"

"Two men came up past the house about an hour ago," Dain put in. "They must have been to the farm and left the car up on the moor. Perhaps they left the gate open. She won't be far away. Nothing will have happened to her, Amelia. We'll soon find her."

I knew that Dain was eager to go. But it was a man's job, I felt, and I was already putting on my gumboots.

"I must come with you!" cried Amelia. "If you find her you'll have to put the halter on her, and you know how you hate doing that and how she teases you."

I knew that, I said, without being told. There was snow on the ground, however. It would be treacherous going on the moor, and both children were alreacly wet and cold.

"Don't worry," I said. "I'll find her all right by myself, and if I can't catch her I'll drive her back."

Amelia looked slightly reassured.

"Then you must take something for her. Look, I've got some sugar and Jane had a carrot if she hasn't lost it when we ran down the hill. Oh, I *do* hope Annabella's all right."

She took from her coat pocket a handful of sugar lumps and Jane, also cheering up, produced not one but several carrots. No wonder, I thought, that Annabella was so submissive to them when they bribed her in such wholesale fashion. Amelia gave me the halter, Dain produced a torch and insisted I should put a scarf round my neck, and, nobly refusing a cup of tea first, I set off.

Night had practically fallen. The sky was nearly overcast and there was every indication of further snow, although that which lay on the ground was thin and soft. A raw moist wind was blowing from the north, more noticeable as I reached the top of our hill and came in sight of the moor. But the snow itself, so long as no more fell, favoured my quest. If the children had been right and found her tracks leading out through the gate all I would have to do would be to follow them, and no matter how dark the sky grew the ground would never be completely so. I reached the gate which the children had shut. Because of the tradesmen I had abandoned the padlock and fitted a spring latch, with a notice on both sides of the top bar:

PLEASE SHUT THE GATE

I climbed the stile. On the moor side close up to the gate there was a confusion of tracks, with those of the children overlaying those of adults, and the tyres of a car that had obviously been halted and turned, and it wasn't until I got about twenty yards along our own road that led to the highway that I picked up Annabella's tracks, with Amelia's too showing where Amelia had halted and then turned back to bring us the dramatic news.

Annabella's trail continued along the road towards the highway, and it dawned on me what might have happened. The men Dain had heard passing the house had left their car or van outside our gate. They had opened the gate instead of using the stile, letting Annabella out, and she with her customary contrariness had eluded their efforts to drive her back. She would, I knew, have watched them getting into their car, just keeping out of touching range, then, when the engine had started, sheered off along the track towards the highroad, perhaps a little frightened, but as likely as not thinking it was fun beating the car. The men, and I was assuming that they were not maliciously-minded, must have thought it wisest to leave the gate open believing she would make her own way back.

Yet, if this theory was right, it had happened at least an hour ago. Why hadn't she come back? Surely there was nothing on the desolate snowy, windswept moor that was preferable to her own grazing, not to mention the titbits the children always brought her before dark.

How awful if Amelia's first tragic conjecture had been right, that she had been knocked down by a car. It had happened to several of Jimmy's sheep at one time or another, and I had discovered that one reason for his constant vigil was to keep his flock away from the unfenced highroad. The sight of a car with its headlights already on, speeding along the road, increased my apprehension. I hurried along the track following the hoof marks, over the two railway-sleeper bridges, then up the last stretch of track to the road itself. And there they ended in the slush which had been flung on to the verge by the traffic.

Another car whizzed past me as I examined the last definite hoof marks in the beam of my torch. All they told me was that Annabella had moved on to the highway which ran at right angles to our track. But which way then, right or left? The crown of the road was bare of snow. She would have made no marks on the hard macadam, and even if she had they would have long since been obliterated.

I turned left to where the road dipped into the upper valley of our beck. She wasn't afraid of motor traffic as a rule, but she wouldn't like it, and the chances were that if she had persisted on the crown of the road some motorist would have hooted her off. If so I should pick up her tracks on one of the verges again. With my torch trained alternately on both verges I carried on almost to the bridge over the beck, then, finding nothing, I turned back, reaching our track end again and passing it. And I hadn't gone more than fifty yards up the highway than I saw definite marks on the offside verge. They were

Annabella's. They followed the verge for about another twenty yards and then, where there was an old milestone, turned on to the open moor.

I was relieved. Whatever had happened to her there was less danger on the moor than on the road with its traffic, and I was further relieved to find that it wasn't a haphazard course she had taken. There was a rough bridle path leading over the moor that we had often used for riding on for it led to one of the ancient stone crosses, and a favourite hunting ground for flints. It was called TOM CROSS and was about two miles from the highway.

On a fine dry day even in winter it would have been a lovely walk. Under present conditions I could not have imagined anything less attractive. The path was narrow and in parts almost overgrown with tall heather from which the wet snow dropped in clumps on to my legs, and, melting, oozed into the tops of my gumboots. The snow, too, stuck to the soles of my boots so that I had to walk slowly, stopping every few yards to kick the stuff off. I had no overcoat and no hat. The north wind was like a current of icy water swirling about me, penetrating to my skin.

I plodded on, glad at least that Annabella had kept to the path and hadn't apparently thought of striking an original trail through the virgin heather. But what had she been thinking, I wondered? Did ponies think? Certainly not *sensibly*. I felt angry with her. I knew that this was only an emotion rising from the deep anxiety I felt, and my affection for her. I kept on, flashing the beam of the torch ahead and to each side of the path, praying that I should see her. All I saw were the eyes of the moor sheep glowing like phosphorescent jellyfish in the beam of the torch.

Halfway to the cross there was a narrow but treacherous bog, one of the sources of our own beck. Even in dry weather the only safe way across it was by the path where a ford had been made with stone. I approached this place with special apprehension. The snow lay evenly on the sphagnum moss in the bog itself, giving a perfect illusion of solid ground, yet at the crossing there was running water, dark, evil-looking, several inches deep and about eight feet wide. Any animal or human not familiar with the place might have hesitated here and decided the snow covered bog was safer, or more likely still turn back.

It was soon clear that Annabella hadn't hesitated. Her hoof marks ended at the water's edge. I waded across, and there they were on the other side where the path now ran slightly uphill clear of the bog.

I plodded on (and I couldn't help thinking of Good King Wenceslas) following the trail. I had no doubt now that she had for some peculiar reason decided to visit the cross. I began to hope that I would find her there, that when I let her sniff at the sugar and carrots she would contritely submit to the halter and to being led back home. I imagined how joyfully the children would greet us.

The cross, it was a cross in name only for only its stump had survived the centuries since its Saxon origin, surmounted a low hill. Even without the torch I could see it as I at last drew near for it stood out dark against the snow: a massive stone pillar about seven feet in height.

Annabella's trail led unhesitatingly towards it, but with a sinking heart I saw no other sign of her.

The trail stopped at the cross itself and there was a confusion of her prints suggesting that she had walked round it several times wondering what to do. Then by the light of the torch I saw signs of her rubbing on the stone, a little tuft of hair, and. by the shape of her hoof prints here I had a picture of what had happened, and an explanation. She had remembered the stone from our many trips to it and that it was especially suitable for rubbing, and, finding herself free on the moor, she had taken it into her stupid head to make her way to it. But where had she gone from here?

The wind was rising. Odd snowflakes were smiting my cheeks. Even a moderate fall would quickly obliterate her trail. This might easily develop into a real blizzard. The path carried on in a westerly direction for miles to an even more desolate and boggy and dangerous area of the moor. There were no more crosses there and nothing else I could think of, except her own perversity, to have encouraged her to go that way. Clearly she hadn't returned home; at least not by the way that she had come and I had followed.

Often, however, we had not returned that way ourselves. There was another bridle path between the cross and the highway. It joined the highway about half a mile to the north of our own road end.

Hopefully, I moved away from the trampled ground about the cross to where the path began. And there, clearly, was her trail leading along it, and, I dared to hope, homewards, although by a considerably longer way than the other, for to avoid the bog it made a wide circuit to the north. How old was the trail, I wondered? How long had Annabella stayed rubbing her backside on the cross? It looked comparatively fresh. If I hurried I might overtake her.

I started off again at utmost speed, but the wind was now in my face and every minute it was getting stronger. Soon it started to snow heavily, and the flakes were such as I had never seen before. They were congealed into lumps almost as big as hazelnuts, which, although wet and soft, fell, or rather were driven by, the wind with considerable force and stuck on to my face and clothing like clots of mud which quickly caked me from head to foot, and, what was worse, nearly blinded me.

It was fortunate that the path was less grown over than the other, that the falling snow as yet was too wet and heavy to drift. But it was laying and before I had got half a mile from the cross Annabella's trail had become indistinguishable. I could only pray that having obviously decided to choose this route nothing had diverted her, and that at least she'd got home before the snow had started.

I was cold, wet, and my feet felt as though they were shod with lead like a diver's. To protect my eyes I took the scarf from my neck and wrapped it turban fashion round my head. Even so I had to keep scraping the snow from my face, and all I could see was the path itself in the circle of light cast by my torch. And the path was distinguishable only because of the thick heather on each side of it. Ahead and around me the driving snow made a curtain thicker than any fog.

Gradually as I plodded on the wind grew stronger and the character of the snow changed from the congealed flakes to a finer and dangerously drier type. I was really frightened. Unless I reached the highway soon the path would fill up to the height of the heather. I'd have nothing to guide me at all, and I was struck with the terrifying thought that even now I was on the wrong path.

Normally it would have taken about half an hour to make the return journey home from the cross, excluding the stretch of about half a mile along the highroad to our own road end. I seemed to have been plodding on for at least an hour before I heard ahead of me the incredibly comforting sound of a motor car. It was going slowly in bottom gear. I switched off my torch, and I detected a faint moving orange luminescence made by its headlamp in the curtain of driving snow ahead. It faded as the sound of the car receded, and then I heard a familiar human voice, the bleating of sheep, the barking of a dog.

I made a spurt. Suddenly just in front of me there loomed through the driving snow the shape of a telegraph pole. The path ended in a partially snow-filled ditch and the level verge of the highway. I crossed the ditch and at once found myself almost surrounded by moving bleating sheep. Then I saw the glow of a lantern moving nearer until it pierced the fog and I saw my neighbour Jimmy, and he saw me. He was caked from head to foot with snow. He had a long stick in one hand and was holding the lantern high with the other, and with the sheep all round him I could not help thinking how like he was to the Biblical shepherd. He stared at me with astonishment, and it wasn't until I spoke that he recognised me, and said:

"Why, it's you! I thought you must be an Indian with that thing on your head. What's up? Are you lost?"

"I'm not now," I said. "You haven't seen our pony, have you? She's strayed on to the moor."

"Nay. I haven't seen owt of her. How long has she been gone?"

"Since before dark. Someone left our gate open. I've followed her tracks as far as Tom Cross, and halfway back, but lost them soon after it started to snow."

"Why, now. You'll not find her in this muck. I've seen nowt of her. I came out when this started. I thought I'd better get my sheep driven down to lower ground where they can find a bit of shelter. But I reckon she'll find her own way back. Hosses have more sense then we have, you know. You'd best keep to the road and not get on to the moor again in this. It's coming on real bad. You'd best get home quick as you can and let your gallower look after hersen."

We parted. She might be all right, I thought. But what would the children say if I had to tell them that I had failed to find their darling? I moved across the road in the rear of the flock, and, finding the further verge, followed it. The wind was at my back and although the snow was packing the macadam it was easier going than the path had been. There was no more motor traffic. For the benefit of visitors I had fixed a board on a post at the end of our own track, and I was glad that I had put it near the verge or I might easily have missed it. Fortunately, too, I had dug deep ditches on each side of our track for the track itself was packed almost as high as the heather. I came to the first of our bridges, then twenty yards to the second one. I was only about fifty yards from our gate and I breathed a prayer that Jimmy was right and that horses had more sense than humans, that our wandering pony had found her way home. And my prayer was answered. I heard ahead of me in the swirling snow a familiar whinny. I shouted:

"Annabella. Annabella!"

I ran those last few yards to our gate. She was standing there with her stern to the blizzard, caked with snow, looking indeed as though she was made of snow, but she turned her head and whinnied ingratiatingly. I put my numbed hand in my pocket and pulled out a sticky mess of melted sugar, and offered it to her. She took it shamelessly.

"You bloody bitch!" I cried. "I could slay you!"

Then I put my arms round her neck, hugged her, and nearly wept with joy.

3

WE WERE HAPPY, and perhaps the main reason for our happiness was that we were too busy to be otherwise. There was always something to do, for ourselves and the children, inside or outside our home.

Dain had a gift for decoration. I painted the walls of our bathroom with flat neutral paint, and on this she did in oils a gay mural of tropical fish and twining weeds and corals. She decorated the walls of the nursery and playroom with circus scenes and fairs with horses and clowns and roundabouts. She carved wooden knobs and handles for all the cupboards we built. She designed and made nearly all the children's clothes. One summer we had a Norwegian girl to stay with us. From her she learnt the art of knitting in Norwegian style, on one long, double-pointed flexible needle, and she made pullovers and gloves using wools of different colours to form a unique and lovely pattern.

It was in many ways a less primitive and Robinson Crusoe life than the one we had led in Cornwall. One concession we had made to civilisation was the telephone. Apart from our immediate neighbours we had many friends. The mansion where the little squire had lived had been transformed into a private co-ed preparatory school, run on lines which more or less agreed with our own ideas of how children should be educated. The married principals, Bill and Mabs, were both intellectuals with university degrees. They were not pedants, however, and both of them had a happy, humorous outlook on life. They had a daughter Claire, the same age as Amelia. Bill's chief interest was science, Mab's literature and languages, yet they believed that handicraft, drawing and painting, music, dancing and play-acting were important things in a school curriculum, and that games, while important, should not be regarded as a fetish. It was a boarding school, but Amelia went at first as a day scholar, riding Annabella.

Bill and Mabs were regular visitors to our home, and so were two members of the staff: Sylvia, who taught dancing, and Marie, who specialised in elocution, and produced the plays and tableaux which were performed on the lawn in summer at the end of every term. Mrs Allen was also an occasional, and very welcome, caller, especially for Dain and the children. One summer afternoon, it was our third year, Dain and I were having lunch coffee in the lounge when I heard the sound of a car coming down our hill. It was a Rolls-Royce, and with alarm I recognised it as the Colonel's. He was there in the back seat with a lady.

"It's Mrs Allen!" Dain cried excitedly, adding quickly: "Oh, dear, and everything's so untidy. Do go out and meet her and keep her talking until I get things straight."

She did not at first appreciate my own alarm. I had hung the cast of the great trout above the mantelshelf.

"My god," I gasped, reaching to take it down. "Don't you see who she's with? It's the Colonel!"

Amelia, fortunately, was at school. Jane and Angus, who had been playing outside, had already rushed up gleefully to the car. I hid the fish in the fireside cupboard, and dashed out, praying that I did not look as worried as I felt.

Mrs Allen and the Colonel had got out. I had never seen the Colonel at close range before. He reminded me at once of the squire who had owned the mill dam when I was a boy. He was elderly with white hair and close-cropped moustache, very tall and straight, piercing grey eyes, a long aquiline nose, a mouth which before he spoke suggested the closed jaws of a steel trap. He was an aristocrat, a magistrate, a squire, an ex-commanding officer, and even if my conscience had been clear he would have scared me.

But when he did speak it was with a smile and a twinkle in his eyes which instantly convinced me that Mrs Allen had been right about him; that he had a genial nature, and a sense of humour. Yet his first remark after we had been introduced did nothing to put me at my ease. He had been reading one of my books about fishermen and fishing, a subject that interested him very much, although most of his own fishing had been in fresh water for salmon and trout. He had been looking forward to a chat with a fellow sportsman.

It was a good job that Mrs Allen was with us that afternoon to talk ponies, to help me to keep the conversation as far as possible away from fish. Dain must have thought that I had become a complete enthusiast on the subject. The Colonel, however, would not be completely side-tracked. It was particularly so when, after we had shown him round the house (he congratulated us on the way it had been planned), we sauntered down to the beck and the island, and he saw our little trout. I could not resist telling him about my ambition to build a dam and install a waterwheel for generating electricity, and incidentally to make a fishpond. He was enthusiastic about it, but I talked fast, dreading that he would at any moment mention his own pond on the moor, and I created a temporary diversion by telling him about my pheasant and the fox. The awful thing was that 1 liked him immensely, and although in one sense I was relieved, it really saddened me when he told me that his own fishing days were over. He was suffering from a heart disease, and for the last five years he had been forbidden by his doctor to engage in any form of sport, including the gentle one of angling.

I was bothered. I believed that I would have felt happier if I had told him frankly of how I had poached his mere. He was a sport, and he had a sense of humour, and I felt instinctively that he would have taken it in good part. But I knew that my motive in telling the story of the big fish would not be purely ethical. I wanted to boast about it, not confess, and I kept silent. The load on my conscience became even heavier when, after an early tea, our guests took their leave, for the Colonel shook my hand in the most friendly way and then, as he got into the car, said:

"Oh, by the way, I meant to tell you that there's an artificial pond of mine on the moor which used to contain a few trout. I haven't seen it for a long time, but my gamekeeper said he'd seen some fish in it this spring. Go and have a look at it if you can find the time, and try a fly if you see anything worth catching. And don't hesitate about taking a gun with you on to the moor when the grouse are in season. You may find mallard at the pond in hard weather."

Becky, Sam's wife, had an eagle eye, and the Rolls-Royce did not escape it.

"You're hobnobbing with the nobility now, aren't you?" she said when she brought the milk that evening. "Fancy His Highness coming to call. And wasn't that Mrs Allen he had with him, the one you got your pony from? She's a widow, isn't she? I wonder if she's got her eyes on him, him being a widower himself and plenty of brass. But then she's not hard up by all accounts. It's funny, though, how brass attracts brass. Them that's got it always wants more. Of course, with me and Sam it was t'other way round. Neither of us had owt when we got wed."

We had a deep affection for Becky. She was an inveterate gossip and scandalmonger. But this habit I felt had dramatic and romantic roots, and there was no real malice in it. She was kind-hearted. No one, friend or stranger; ever called at the farm without being offered food and drink. The children loved her. She got on very well with Sam. It was sad that they had no children of their own.

Sam attracted me chiefly because of his enthusiasm for his job. He was at it all the time and seemed to think of nothing else. We helped him at hay and harvest time. I was particularly interested in his reclamation activities. He had still many acres of rough ground that he was bringing under cultivation.

It made me long to start on our own derelict land. Apart from the fields I had let to Jimmy, there were at least twelve acres of ground that were fairly level and ploughable on our side of the fence. Jimmy, as Sam had predicted, had done nothing at all to the land on his side. He had paid the rent, and our relations continued to be amiable, but I felt that I would be justified in retaking possession at any time. Yet I had to accept Sam's assurance that it would be a very costly job. It would not be justified unless we intended to go in seriously for farming. I had no fierce desire to do that.

Dain's idea and ambition was to have more ponies and breed them. We could, she contended, start in a small way and specialise in children's ponies. If they were of the same breed as Annabella we should not require stables, and all we need do with the land was to improve the pasture and have hay and, say, one field for oats, although it would be nice to have a cow or perhaps two cows and produce our own milk and cream and butter.

I suspected that in this she was inspired by the example of Mrs Allen, but Mrs Allen herself did not disguise the fact that pony breeding was not a very lucrative business, and that it had its special risks. Annabella, for example, although she had been mated every year to one of Mrs Allen's own stallions, had failed to produce a foal. While heavily in foal, a pony could not be worked, and for some time after the foal might be a nuisance, and it would be two years at least before the foal was rideable.

Besides, I was a writer, and until I had published a bestseller and made a lot of money and paid off the mortgage on the house we must not risk incurring new liabilities. Having a family was in itself an expensive business, no matter how simply one lived. Our last published book had been well received by the critics and its sales had been bigger than the others. but it had not been a bestseller, and what it had earned had barely been enough to keep us solvent.

I had been right in thinking that the Cornish story, which had been inspired the evening we had gone to catch the trout, was going to be a long and difficult job. It hadn't been for want of trying. Religiously I had imprisoned myself in the hut every morning from half-past nine until the call came for lunch, and often I worked or tried to work late into the night in the lounge when the family was in bed. I had made innumerable starts and, dissatisfied with them, turned to writing articles and short stories, but chiefly as a matter of duty and because these, when sold, produced immediate cash.

It was not indeed until the second year that the book began to take shape, and I had written enough of it to feel justified in concentrating on its completion, which I knew would take me at least another year. I had read these opening chapters to Dain. I had described how we had first found the derelict hut, and how we had moved in the night of the storm, the rescue of the kitten, the starting of my first book. How we had laboured at the hut itself, mending the roof, covering the walls with sailcloth, making furniture. I had described our gardening and our first fishing trips. There had been tears in Dain's eyes when I got to the end of what I had written, but I suspect that her emotions had been roused more by the happy memories that had been evoked rather than by the story itself.

"It's lovely," she said. "It's all so real, just as though it was happening again. Do go on and finish it. It's just bound to be a success, a huge bestseller. It will make thousands of pounds. Think what we can do when we have all that money. We could farm all the land. We could have more ponies. We could have more children too. We could make the house bigger, build on an extension, if it became too small. Do go on with it."

I *had* gone on with it, and for several months had made slow, but on the whole, satisfactory progress. Then, at a chapter which I judged to be about halfway to the end, I had got completely stuck. This had happened with other books and after a time I had surmounted the difficulty and got on to the end. It had also happened with books I had never finished, and had finally abandoned, and in spite of Dain's unflagging faith and encouragement, and that I went on trying, I began to fear defeat.

Late one October night when I was fighting this fear, wrestling with the dreadful problem of how to go on, of what word to write next, drinking black coffee, and smoking cigarette after cigarette, I decided to have a walk down to the shore. Everyone was in bed and asleep, and I turned out the lights and slipped quietly out of the house.

It was a splendid night, with a full moon high in a cloudless sky. A strong north-westerly wind which had been blowing for several days had completely died. It had left a heavy ground swell, however, and as I turned the corner of the house I heard the booming of big waves breaking on the scaurs of the bay like that of distant thunder. It would be low water of a spring tide, I thought, as I hurried down into the shadows of the mill wood. I'd go to Browe Beck Cove (where we'd first planned to build our house), then down to the beach and walk out to the end along the longest scaur, watch the rollers sweeping in, breaking in the moonlight. That alone should be more stimulating to my thoughts than all the coffee I had drunk, the cigarettes I had smoked.

But when I reached the farm and the group of cottages (one of them old Isaac's), where the bridle path branched off to Browe Beck, I changed my mind. I had an impulse to see my own village, a thing I had been diffident about during the holiday season. I carried on straight down the mill cove, to the shore, walked round the Nab and saw the sea walls of the village itself less than half a mile to the north.

The stretch of beach between the Nab and the village was the equivalent of a marine parade during the summer months. There were donkeys, bathing-tents, ice-cream and tea kiosks, often swarms of trippers, and it would be littered with newspapers, paper bags and bottles. Now it was deserted, and swept clean by the great waves of the stormy spring tides, which had ebbed and would soon be flowing again. The village also seemed deserted. There was not a single light in view.

I hurried on, aware of a strong sense of elation, such as one feels just before the curtain rises for the opening of a play. My mind was clear now. But I wasn't thinking of the Cornish story. I felt that I was stepping into my further past, the past of my boyhood. I reached the slipway up which the heavy fishing cobles of Bramblewick had to be hauled every day in wintertime and down which the lifeboat would be launched, often at tremendous risk in sudden storms, to heroic feats of rescue, and it was as though I could see those men, the fishermen, the sailors, the old and the then young, my own playmates and enemies, and the women too. That I was surrounded by ghosts.

I stopped at the slipway foot. From it an expanse of level shale and sand reached seawards between two enclosing scaurs, each of which in the old days was marked with stout posts for this was the landing and the farthermost pair marked its entrance. There were no posts now, but I could see at low water the rollers coming in, rearing up and crashing into white foam on the scaur ends. On one side of the slipway was the old coastguard station, rounded and buttressed, and on the other side the main sea wall, arched and bridged to make an outlet for the little beck which ran through a big culvert under the whole village.

I walked up the slipway into the dock. The dock was an irregularly shaped space elevated above the level of the highest tides to which the fishing cobles and pleasure boats were hauled except in spells of calm weather. Here the two narrow main streets of the village, with their tributary alleys, converged. Here, in my boyhood days, had stood the lifeboat-house, Reub Bulmer's boatshed, four of the nine village pubs (including The Mariner's), a bakery, the grocer's shop, and the general store and post office.

The lifeboat-house was still there, but the lifeboat had gone and the building had been converted into a public convenience. The Mariner's had become a *Tea Shoppe* (closed for the winter), Reub Bulmer's boathouse had become a *Fun Fayre* (equipped with slot machines and a soda fountain) also happily closed for the winter, and outside the grocer's shop, which had changed hands, stood a gaudy telephone kiosk. In the dock itself there were only two small pleasure boats and a parked tradesman's motor van. There were no human beings in sight, no lights except the light of the moon, no sounds except the booming of the surf, and without closing my eyes I saw the Dock as I remembered and loved it best.

I saw the cobles, beautifully shaped, gaily painted, each on its launching wheels with its lean bows elevated and facing the sea: *Harvest Home, The Brothers, The Two Sisters, Smiling Morn, Rebecca, Susannah, Lydia, Fanny Rose, Star of Bethlehem.* I saw the fishermen gathered round them, mending nets, lobster pots; old Tindal Avery, Neddy Peacock, Matt Cooper, Willy Allen, the Storms and the Knaggs, the Screetons and the Dukes.

I could see my two especial friends and heroes Captain Bunny and the Irish foreigner Mike Regan. I could see old Janey Steel the landlady of The Mariner's (who did her hair in long ringlets and always dressed in black with a gold cross on her bosom and looked like a madonna) standing at the door of the pub, fiercely upbraiding an ejected customer for misbehaviour. I could see the village drunks Jack Peacock, Boozer

Lingdale, old Jake Bransby.

I could see the dock on a dark stormy night when a sign of distress had come from the bay and the lifeboat gun had been fired. The fishermen (and the women too, with shawls over their heads) hurrying down the cobbled alleyways. Flares lit at the slipway top; the double doors of the lifeboat-house open; the men shouting gruffly at each other, the great hawsers snaking along the ground, the boat on its steel carriage slowly emerging from the house, moving to the slipway top, then down to the sea itself, stopping when the front wheels of the carriages were awash; the crew (already in oilskins and lifebelts) climbing in, manning the oars, the bearded coxswain at the helm shouting, "Let her go." Then one of the launchers knocking out the steel pin that held the keel of the boat to the greased runway of the carriage, and the boat sliding down out of the light of the flares into the darkness and danger of the sea.

I crossed the dock to where an alley led upwards behind the one-time boathouse. There were steps, for the gradient was steep, and the alley twisted between the tightly-packed cottages. There were alleys to right and left of me as I ascended, some level, but none straight, and there were no spaces between the cottages other than these. There were no gardens, very few yards. There were no lighted street lamps, or any other sign of life in the cottages.

Most of them, I knew, were now owned by people from industrial inland Yorkshire, who used them only in the holidays. The fishermen and sailors who had lived in them when I was a boy were either dead, or they had emigrated to the bigger fishing ports of the coast, or (and this was especially so with the sailors) had gone to live in 'Up-Bank' Bramblewick.

In the old days, although the alleys had names like Tyson's Steps, and Fisherhead, and Slam Gutter, and The Opening, and The Bolts, and Grainger's Yard, no one had ever thought of labelling them with nameplates. Nor had any of the cottages been numbered. Everyone, including, of course, the postman, knew where everyone else lived. This apparently wasn't so with the new and transient population, or they had brought with them an urban or suburban custom. The cottages I passed had names on the doors or above their lintels, some just painted, some with chromium letters on varnished panels; such names as The Nest, Chez Nous, The Harbour, Osokosi, Captain's Cabin (this one incidentally had been the cottage of Will Tonbull the chimney sweep) and—it was the cottage in which old Captain Binns had cut his throat with a razor the night of his wife's funeral—Just a Cot.

They were deserted and dead, as the whole village was deserted and dead. Yet the alleys were unchanged. The walls of the cottages, the red pantiled roofs were as they had always been, and because there was no space there had been no new and incongruous building.

And to me, in my imagination, the place *was* alive, and in my mind, too, was the quickening of another book.

The Cornish story, I suddenly felt, was dead. The fact that I couldn't get on with it, after all my months of trying, was proof that it was no good. It was too personal, too much about ourselves. There were not enough characters in it. The few people we had got to know in

Cornwall, apart from Joe Hoskins, were, from a writer's point of view, flat and uninteresting compared with those of my own village. I had used some of these village characters in my other books, but these books had been mere sketches compared with what I might do now: a *big* novel about the people and the place I really knew and loved. That was more likely to be successful, to make us a fortune than the story of our personal adventure. All I needed was a plot or theme. I had a thousand characters to choose from and in every way this was a better setting than the Cornish one. It was unique. There was not another village like this in the world.

I walked on, up one alley, along another, up steps and down steps, admiring as I had never done before the beauty of the place which in the past had inspired so many painters (including my own father) yet not, so far as I knew, any novelist. This was my own.

I passed along Fisherhead, where the Fosdycks and the Emersons had lived. I paused outside the cottage of my beloved Captain Bunny. It had been named (in Woolworth metal letters) The Nook, and it looked as though its new but absent owner had installed a bathroom and a W.C. for there was one window with frosted glass that hadn't been there in the captain's day. The moon glittered on the letters, but I was not troubled. For in my imagination the front door was open, and there was the captain himself, in cheese-cutter cap and black reefer jacket and leather sea-boots, his box of whiting and mackerel lines in his hand, smiling at me, his eyes twinkling, just as he'd be when we were off for a Saturday afternoon's fishing in the bay.

I walked down Slam Gutter, past the Congregation Chapel and I crossed the stone bridge at the foot of Bramblewick Bank, and I saw what had been the smiddy, now a shop (closed) selling summer fancy goods. Here the brawny dark-visage blacksmith Will Knaggs shod horses for the farmers, forged anchors for the fishermen. He was a splendid craftsman, self-taught intellectual and atheist, argumentative, self-opinionated, and I had a vivid picture of him bending over his anvil, beating a piece of white-hot iron, the light of it on his grimy sweating cheeks, the sparks flying, pelting him so that he looked like Satan himself.

I passed the Laurel Inn and went up another steep alley behind it, and saw the cottage where the infamous Boozer Lingdale had lived. I reached The Openings and another one-time pub, in front of which I had seen a bloody fight between Boozer and my friend Mike Regan. I was out of sight of the sea, for the whole village was packed into a gorge behind cliffs, but I could hear it all the time booming and roaring. I moved on, seeing, hearing, talking to my ghosts, thinking of my book. It had no shape, no pattern but the stuff of it was in my mind, working like leavened dough.

I was on the north side of the village now. I took an alley that led down into the wider and level alley called Chapel Row, and came to the Wesleyan Chapel and the door of my old school, to the cobbled yard where the scholars foregathered to wait the arrival of our dreaded master, Slogger; the scene of some of my own bloodiest fights. Both chapel and school had been closed for some years. A new chapel had been built 'Up-Bank'. The building was now a furniture store, but its walls and pantiled roof and chapel windows were unaltered, and all its ghosts—the ministers, the local preachers, choristers and organists, the chapel-goers, the scholars of the school and Slogger—were vividly with me. I carried on to an alley called Coblehead, which lead steeply back to the dock. I moved down it and came once more to the slipway top. The whole of the bay and the open sea were in sight again in the clear light of the full moon.

It was an enchanting spectacle. There had never been anything in Cornwall to compare with this. The flood tide was pressing in to the shore and the outermost scaurs were already submerged. The great rollers were moving in in slow procession in long dark lines which threw a deeper moon shadow as they reached the shallows and heaved upwards, curved over and split into white boiling foam. Yes, here was the book! The sea and the village and the people I knew, and the things I remembered woven together in a different pattern from anything I had written before. The stuff was here. All I needed was a plan.

Suddenly, to my astonishment, the figure of a man, a real man and not one of my ghosts, appeared round the sea wall at the bottom of the slipway. He was of medium height, of slender build, wearing a cap and a dark shabby raincoat and decrepit rubber deck-boots. He was moving slowly, with a stagger, as though very tired or at least slightly drunk, and as he set foot on the paving of the slipway he stopped, and with a weary gesture put down a basket and a coil of fishing line he had been carrying, and started rubbing his hands together as though the fingers were numbed.

He had not seen me. He was looking out to sea, with his back towards me, and I watched him, wondering who he was. The fishing gear and basket told me at least that he had been down the scaurs taking up a set line which probably had been inaccessible on the morning ebb. There would be bait in the basket, but certainly no sizeable fish. Shortly he picked up line and basket, turned and started to move with slow unsteady strides up towards me, and I saw his face in the moonlight. It had a deathly pallor, and it was thin, almost emaciated, with deep lines like scars made by a knife reaching from his nostrils to the corners of his mouth. The cheeks were hollow, the eyes deep sunk, the lids half closed, and their stare was vacant as though he were in a trance. Or was he drunk?

I stood where I was. He drew nearer. I could hear the squelching of water in his boots, then the sound of his heavy breathing. Suddenly I recognised him. It was Captain Tom Bransby. I coughed and for the first time he seemed to be aware of my presence. He stopped, at scarcely more than arm's length. He did not speak. He just stared vacantly and I spoke.

"Hallo, Captain! Any luck?"

He continued to stare at me in silence, but without any sign that he recognised me. Then he muttered something that was quite inaudible, and moved on past me up the slipway towards the dock, and at last out of sight. As he passed me l had caught the unmistakable whiff of stale alcohol. He wasn't drunk, but he had been drinking, and drinking heavily. And yet it wasn't only

261

the marks of dissipation or illness I had seen on his face. There had been something inexpressibly tragic in it. It was the look of a man haunted and hopelessly unhappy.

I stood where I was, watching the great waves rolling in to the shore, thinking of what had just happened, and what I knew of Tom Bransby. I had never known him very well. Although he had gone to the village school he was my senior by several years, and like all the other male members of his family he had gone to sea straight from school and was only home occasionally. His family had been Bramblewick for many generations. As ships' officers (and also as owners) the Bransbys had a high reputation. They were known, however, for their hard drinking, and old Jake, Tom's grandfather, had been one of the most notorious of the village drunkards. At sea the Bransbys were known for their strict sobriety and discipline.

My own war service had been with the Air Force in German East Africa. I'd had malaria and dysentery and a final crash which had produced that condition known then as war neurosis. Our war had been a mild affair compared with what had been going on in Europe and at sea in the U-boat campaign. It had its horrors, however, and I had become inured to the many aspects of human suffering and death. There had been no airmail for the troops in those days. There had been a strict censorship, home news scanty and infrequent.

It was not until my return to England, just before the end of the war, that I learnt what had been happening in my own village. So many of my closest friends had been lost, chiefly at sea, by U-boats and mine, that I had not been especially concerned by hearing of what had happened to the Bransby family.

I recalled now that Tom Bransby was sailing as a junior officer on the same locally owned ship as his own father, John Henry (the son of the infamous Jake), and that his youngest brother had been making his first voyage as an apprentice. That the ship had been attacked by a U-boat, set on fire, and that Tom, blown overboard in the explosion, had seen both his father and his brother trapped and engulfed by the flames. Grimmer things than that had happened in the war. Now, in my mind, it became significant.

I remembered how before the war I had once seen Tom Bransby spick and span in apprentice's uniform, walking down from Matty Brewster's Wood on a sunny spring day with his young brother Harry (it must have been a Sunday, for Harry was in his best clothes), each carrying a bunch of daffodils. He was holding Harry's hand.

Tom was very good looking, deeply sunburnt (his last voyage probably had been to the tropics), and he seemed proud and arrogant. He must have been fond of Harry, however, I thought. I must have seen him several times at a later period, for I had another picture of him grown up and not in uniform, but in the neat serge suit and dark overcoat and trilby hat usually worn by ship's officers on shore leave, waiting for the train at Bramblewick station, a sextant case in his hand, a telltale gleaming white sailor's kitbag among the luggage on the rulley ready to go into the guard's van, and with him, to see him off, a well-dressed, good-looking girl and a small child, his wife and daughter. That must have been before (or in the early days of) the war, and I could not remember having seen him since, but that was not surprising seeing that I had spent so many of the post-war years away from Bramblewick.

Yet I had heard about his tragic downfall. He had suffered a nervous breakdown after the sinking of his ship, and spent many months in hospital. He had recovered and it was after the war, and he was in command of a ship, when disaster befell him. His ship collided and sank another one. At the official inquiry it was found that at the time Tom was under the influence of drink, and his master's ticket had been suspended.

The Bransbys had always been hard drinkers ashore. Old Jake, having amassed quite a fortune when he had retired, had died a pauper. Tom had started boozing. He had apparently made no effort to rehabilitate himself in his profession. He'd gone down the slippery slope with a vengeance, and I had an idea that his house and furniture in Up-Bank Bramblewick had been sold over his head, that he was now living in one of the old cottages I had just seen, obviously one that had not been bought and renamed by one of the holiday residents. Which cottage? Were his pretty wife and daughter still living with him? Was he going back to them now, half drunk, waking them up, quarrelling—perhaps beating them up as old Jake Bransby had often done with his wife and family?

What a situation! What a character! And, I thought suddenly, what a theme for a book! Did it matter where he was living, whether his wife and child were with him or not? Already I was beginning to invent, to place Tom

Bransby dominantly among my ghosts; his wife, too, and daughter, and old Jake Bransby, of course, and the Bransby double inheritance of splendid seamanship and liking for drink, through three generations, and possibly, if I made Tom's daughter grow up, a fourth. Will Knaggs, the blacksmith, could come into it. I could set him against one of the local preachers, or perhaps a revivalist. He could have a son who could fall in love with Tom's daughter. But it was Tom himself who must be the main character; it must be the story of his life.

I was getting more and more excited. I knew something about drink, although I had never been much of a drinker myself. I knew something about war neurosis. One of our best pilots in the East African war, a peace-time white hunter, was an ex-planter and a bottle-a-day man. So long as he had his whisky his skill and control were faultless. But if, as occasionally happened, our mess ran out of liquor, he was nervy and incapable of flying. Towards the end of the campaign I'd had the experience of sharing a field hospital tent with this pilot, who on top of malaria was suffering from D.T.s. Suppose that I gave Tom something of the character of this man? He'd had a frightful experience in the war. He'd come back after the shock of it, but it was feasible that he had not made a complete recovery, that he was drinking to give himself that confidence essential for the duties and responsibilities of a ship master. It was feasible that in the collision, instead of being drunk, *he hadn't been drunk enough.*

I pictured him as I had just seen him. He was a man at the end of his tether. It was easy to imagine him going home, having a scene with his wife, beating her up. I recalled how, when this had happened with Jake and his wife, the then vicar of Bramblewick (a stern old autocrat) had given Jake a dressing down, and actually made him sign the pledge, and that he had remained sober for several months. Suppose that something like this could happen in Tom's case? Suppose that he became really ill, had D:T.s (he'd looked not far off it), that the vicar, or better still, a chapel preacher, got hold of him, converted him like the man in Masefield's *Everlasting Mercy*; that Tom made a comeback, a thing that might well provoke the atheistic blacksmith, especially if Tom swung completely over and became a religious fanatic.

I'd got it! Tom does get religion, and he gets it bad. His daughter is beautiful, and talented, has a flair for elocution (there was a village girl who had made quite a name for herself as a concert pianist), wants, to Tom's horror, to become an actress. The blacksmith has an only son, and his ambition is for this son to go to university, to take a science degree and become a second Charles Darwin. There is something satanic in the blacksmith's character, and something Christ-like in that of the preacher. One of the resident ministers at the Wesleyan chapel, one of my ghosts, had been a Welshman, the Rev. Cuthbert Jones. He'd had long hair, and was a most eloquent preacher. His wife taught at Sunday School, organised the children's concerts. Dancing and acting were taboo among the old type Wesleyans, but she could be the one to recognise and even encourage the talent of Tom's daughter.

What a book! It could be terrific. Yet the main

character must be Tom himself, and I must be sympathetic to him as indeed I was deeply sympathetic to the Bransby I had just seen. He was a victim of the war. His state was pathological and vicious. He was a fine man, like all the Bransbys had been. He might, for the purpose of my book, become a religious prig, but this must be a phase of his disease, and somehow or other the pendulum must swing back, and he must find his true self again, as the master of a ship.

That I could work out later. The book was alive, as the Cornish book was dead. I looked around me at the deserted dock then towards the sea again. The flood tide would soon be reaching the cliff foot. I must hurry home, and in the morning start writing again. It would be the biggest and the best book I had ever done.

4

I HAD WORKED hard all that winter and into the spring and summer of the following year at the Bransby book.

At first, Dain had not been convinced that it was going to be a better book than the abandoned Cornish one, and more likely to prove a financial success.

"I do think it's a fine idea," she said. "You've got some wonderful characters to bring into it, all those old sea captains and fishermen, and the preachers and the blacksmith—he *must* have been a character, and you've got a wonderful setting. But it does sound a bit gloomy and tragic to me, almost like a Russian novel. The Cornish book is so cheerful, and I should have thought that most people these days would prefer to read about cheerful and lovely things."

"Yes. But it won't all be gloomy and tragic. There'll be the love interest in Tom Bransby's daughter and the blacksmith's son although that wouldn't be the main theme of the book. And somehow or other I will contrive a happy ending. You wait till I get it all worked out."

"Of course. I'm certain that it will be a grand book. Yet I just can't believe that you'll never finish the other one. I hope you will, anyway. But this one sounds wonderful, and after all, you know best."

I was never quite certain that I did know best. Dain's intuition had so often confounded me. Yet, as the book progressed and she read the finished chapters, she seemed to become completely convinced that I was right.

I had almost forgotten the Cornish book. I was too full of Tom Bransby and the other characters I was weaving into his tale. I was as sure as I could be of anything that this was the book that would put an end to all our worries about money, enable us to do all the things we wished to do, even, although I kept this to myself, give me my lake and waterwheel.

The character of Tom had developed well. I had invented a suitable wife for him. She was the daughter of a local farmer who, as often happened in reality as well as in fiction, had a strain of the aristocrat in his blood. Not all of the squires of the district, or even the lords of the manor, need have been as virtuous as the ones I had known. This could account not only for the unusual beauty of Tom's wife, but also for the beauty and potential talents of his daughter.

It was a fascinating job building up the characters of a novel. You could take a person and use him more or less as he was in real life, or you could mix him with one or several other characters to make a composite portrait, and make him behave exactly as you liked. You could make him fall in love, make him rich or poor, famous or notorious, a crook or a saint.

Actually, there had been a local girl with good looks and voice and a natural gift for acting. She had won prizes at the Burnharbour musical festival, and some wealthy person had offered to pay for her to go to London and be trained. Nothing had come of it. The girl had grown up and married, and produced a family. I was not certain that I wanted this to happen to Tom's daughter. My idea in making her a would-be actress was to create a dramatic tension between herself and her converted prudish parent, to emphasise *his* character.

My Wesleyan minister, although basically the Welshman I had known, was a composite of several parsons I had met at one time or another, including a Roman Catholic African missionary, and a Unitarian minister. I had given him a Celtic ardour, but also a strong sense of humour, and I felt that I liked him, and that the reader would like him too.

In Cornwall we had been friendly with the chief of one of the laid-up ships. His wife was living with him on the ship and both of them were Welsh. She came from Cardigan. She had raven black hair, beautiful grey eyes with long lashes. She was vivacious and had a Rabelasian wit, yet at home she was a chapel-goer, leader of the choir and a Sunday school teacher. She had a lovely singing voice. She had organised concerts (including plays) with her Sunday school children. She was just right for my minister's wife. I had made her teach at the Bramblewick Wesleyan School, at which for a number of years I had been an unwilling scholar myself and made Tom's daughter her brightest pupil.

I had not yet worked out the climax to my novel. I didn't know how the story was to end. Tom himself had died, a few weeks after I had seen him, unromantically, but not surprisingly, of pneumonia. I had made him turn farmer after his conversion, his wife's father having conveniently died and left his farm to her. I had located the farm near High Batts with its fields coming down the cliff edge so that always the sea, and its shipping, would be in sight and hearing of him, reminding him of his other life, calling to the real Bransby in his blood. Somehow or other I had to get him back, sailing as , and master again, as I liked books to end happily there must be a final dramatic episode in which his life would come to full circle, yet not with his death.

I was still a long way from the end however. Indeed, I was about as far as I had got with the Cornish book when I got completely stuck again. As before, my mind simply refused to work.

It was July then, and we were experiencing a heatwave. Day after day there were blue skies, brilliant sunshine. The children loved it. Naked and sun-tanned they played at the island all day long, and were quite satisfied if we made only an occasional full-scale excursion to the shore with Annabella and the trap. Certainly weather such as this was not conducive to writing, yet dutifully I shut myself in my hut every morning, doing my best to forget what it was like outside in the sunshine, coaxing my mind to work. In vain! I was faced with the growing conviction that once again I had tackled something beyond my powers, that I was beat.

Dain had done her best to renew my faith and optimism. She kept on praising the chapters I had done. She said that I was taking a gloomy view of it because I'd got stale and that it would be a good thing to leave it for a time, take a rest, or at least do something different.

There came an evening during that heat-wave (and this was six weeks before the expected arrival of the fourth member of our family) when she made a more concrete suggestion: that we should have an early supper, that I should put the book completely out of my mind and go down to the sea and fish and enjoy myself all on my own.

I could not pretend that her proposal was completely unattractive. We had been in two minds as to whether we should have a seashore picnic that day. We had decided that it was too hot, especially for Annabella, to make the long double journey. All day, however, I had been aware that for a certain type of fishing the weather conditions were tantalisingly ideal. The sea had been dead calm, the tides neap. The herring sile was in the bay. Even from our windows and without glasses I had watched the telltale flocks of gulls circling over large dark patches of water which showed where the immense shoals of sile were moving. They were far out, but always towards evenings, in this weather, the bigger, predatory fish like cod, mackerel, and billet, would drive the shoals shoreward, and at dusk they'd come into the shallow creeks between the scaurs, especially at the south end of the bay at the foot of High Batts. In their frenzied pursuit of the sile the big fish would snap at anything that resembled them: a white feather, even a bare shiny hook.

It *was* an attractive proposition. The only thing I did not like about it was that it meant going by myself. It was too far, and it would be too late, for me to take Amelia. Dain had shared so many of my exciting fishing expeditions. She'd never seen this sort of thing, however, and I knew that she'd find it even more exciting than the big trout if the shoals behaved as I anticipated.

It was nearly four miles to High Batts, eight there and back, with much of the going very rough. Obviously she should not risk it. I suggested that instead we should have a walk across the moor to the trout mere and see how our transplanted fish were getting on, and that later I'd have still another shot at getting on with the book.

She laughed.

"Darling, we can go there any time. There wouldn't be much attraction in looking at the fish and not fishing, and there'd be no point in fishing until they've grown much bigger. Besides, it isn't so much fun fishing there now that the Colonel has given permission. You've said that the weather and the tide are just right for High Batts and the weather might not last. It would be a pity not to take the chance. It would be a complete change for you. You first got the idea for the book by going down the shore and the village by yourself. Very likely you'll find the inspiration for getting on with it by going again. Besides, it would be nice to have some fresh caught fish for breakfast."

I gave in.

5

I HAD RARELY known conditions so propitious as they were that evening. The place where I proposed to fish was called the Billet Scaur. It was a long high reef reaching out from the foot of High Batts cliff on the north side and there were parallel scaurs on both sides of it, forming narrow tidal creeks. Scaurs and creeks would be submerged when the tide was in. During spring tides this happened quickly, and you were given only about two hours' fishing, and if there happened to be a swell less than this. It was no good trying to fish on the ebb tide. It was no good fishing in daylight except in winter when the water was cloudy. The ideal combination of circumstances for summer billet and cod was calm warm weather, a dead neap tide, just starting to flow at dusk.

Dusk *was* falling when I reached the scar. The tide, dead neap, was just on the turn. There was no wind, not a suspicion of swell. The air was as warm as I had ever known it during our warmest days in Cornwall. Everything was exactly right. I ought to have been feeling very happy and excited as I walked down the scaur, and saw, not more than fifty yards seawards from its end, a dark patch on the water. The sile was in. Before I had fitted my rod together there was a hissing sound (like the falling of hailstones) and the patch was furrowed and broken by the dorsal fins of several big fish, one at least as big as my record trout, charging through the shoal, causing some of the sile to shoot up and fall in a glittering cascade.

Normally that sight would have made me tremble. I was aware instead of a peculiar sense of foreboding, of impending misfortune. I wished that I hadn't come, that I had stayed home and made another determined effort to get on with the Bransby book.

All the way down I had been thinking of it, trying to recapture the belief and enthusiasm I'd had for it up to the point where I had stuck. I had come by a route which should have evoked the atmosphere of the book. I had deliberately taken a lane that led past Matty Brewster's Wood, where I had once seen Tom with his young brother in daffodil time. In building up Tom's pre-war character I had brought in this incident.

I had, too, described his courting of the farmer's daughter, their first meeting on the cliff shore near Mill Nab, his proposal to her, and a romantic love scene on a warm July evening similar to this one, by a cliff-top stile near to her father's farm. The fields of the farm, in which so much of the action would be developed, came down to the cliff edge just above the Billet Scaur, and I had planned, although I hadn't written it yet, a scene where Tom then turned farmer gazes down from the cliff at the scaur when fishing looks good, and in his exalted self-righteous state of mind considers how even fishing, as being a waste of time, can be a sin and a temptation of the devil.

The more I thought of the book the more discouraged

275

I had become. My walk, instead of soothing and inspiring me, had only exacerbated my feelings of revulsion towards it and all its characters, particularly towards its chief character Tom. It was as though I had taken a drink or a drug, and that it hadn't worked. Or was the dose not strong enough?

I didn't think that my idea in making Tom regard fishing as a sin, in his peculiar circumstances, was very far-fetched. Certainly it *was* a form of intoxication which if indulged in immoderately might be regarded as a vice. I thought, rather gloomily, that if I had spent one-half of the time I had devoted to this fascinating pastime to my job of writing I might have done much better for myself and those who were dependent on me. Really, I ought to pack it up now, and go home and work, and, if I couldn't do the Bransby book, get on with something else.

The shoal, however, was coming nearer in. I'd got my rod fixed, and almost mechanically I locked on the reel and threaded the line. It was my old stout sea-rod this, designed for casting out from the beach with a sinker and it was anything but ideal for fly fishing. It would do, with a very light lead, provided the fish did come near enough in, and I quickly fixed lead and cast and cuddy fly (simply a white feather tied to the hook with tinsel) to the line. I was ready now. I moved to the edge of the scaur, and at once all my feelings of remorse vanished.

Although the stars were out there was an afterglow in the western sky over the distant moors and there was still a fair amount of light. The water was crystal clear. It should have been possible for me to have seen the butt of the scaur, a miniature cliff falling underwater to the bottom two fathoms down. There was a patch of shingle here surrounded by the brown stems and fronds of oar weed, which dried out at spring low tide. Now the bottom was obscured by an almost solid mass of fish.

There were thousands of them identical in shape, colour and size. They were sile, immature herring. They were, seen from above, greenish grey in colour, about three inches in length. They were packed close together in depth as well as horizontally, their heads all pointing the same way, and momentarily they were not moving. The foremost of them had found the solid face of the scaur, one wall of the trap towards which all day the bigger fish had been driving them.

Suddenly, like an explosion, a light ripped through the shoal. The fish had turned about, each obeying the warning signal of its neighbour, the flashing of its silvered and phosphorescent belly; and then as the shoal moved away from the rock, there came another flash and another in quick succession.

The shoal had been split. Part of it was coming back towards the rock. Before it reached it a big fish, I could not tell whether it was a cod or a billet, sped round so that it almost grazed the rock, turned and charged with open mouth straight into the shoal. Out from the rock a loud splashing, a furrowing of the water, the gleam of silvered bellies of the terrified sile, told me that this was not the only big fish. The massacre had begun.

I started to fish. From a strictly sporting point of view there was no comparison between this and the stalking and hooking and landing of a seven-pound trout with a fly rod and fine tackle. My sea rod would have lifted a fifty-pound fish. The cast I was using would at least have stood up to half that strain. There was no advantage in trying to cast my fly far out. In their greedy pursuit of the sile the big fish had their fear of shallow water. If I'd had a large enough landing-net I could have caught some of them as they dashed by the rock at my feet.

It was exciting enough. I simply cast out, let the fly drop in the water, and drew it in with a slight jerking motion. I hooked a fish at my first cast and swung it on to the scaur behind me. It was a one-pound billet, the Yorkshire name for half-grown saith or coal-fish. I was fishing for the pot, but I was confident that I was going to get something better than this, and as it was only mouth-hooked I threw it back, and soon I hooked another about the same size.

Then I did get something better. It snapped at the fly before it reached the water, like a salmon. I struck, the rod bent, and I gave the fish a few yards of line before catching it and getting its full weight. I knew then that I could manage it all right, and I reeled in quickly until it was within range of my gaff. It was a codling about four pounds in weight, in prime condition, and as I unhooked it it spat a number of still-kicking sile from its mouth. I killed it and cast again. My next fish was not so heavy yet it fought more gamely. It was a grey gurnard, a fish which my friend Captain Bunny had prized above all others for the sweetness of its flesh.

I went on fishing. I'd forgotten my book and all the worries of it. I was intoxicated, oblivious to the passing of time. Yet even a neap tide flows, and steadily the water was rising round the scaur, and the lagoon dividing it from the other scaurs was widening. At three-quarters flood it would cease to be a lagoon, and a trap, and the shoals of sile would be able to disperse along the shore line. Before then I must start for home.

The lagoon, however, was still packed with the sile. As the sky had grown darker the fish grew even bolder. They ploughed through the shoal in all directions, making trails of phosphorescent light like meteors. Most of the fish I caught I threw back alive and uninjured. I had a long way to walk back and I didn't want to overburden myself. I'd got two codling as well as the first one I'd caught. There was the gurnard, half a dozen mackerel (I must have caught at least a score of these), and several large whiting.

I was seeing fish, they looked like cod, that must have weighed at least as much as all these put together, and I was still hopeful of getting one. Suddenly, quite close to the scaur end, the surface of the water was split by a large black triangular fin, dripping with phosphorescence. There was a splash. I thought for a moment that it was a gigantic cod, but as the fin vanished another appeared close by, and another. I heard a peculiar grunting sound. They were not fish but porpoises, a school of them. The hunters of the sile were being hunted. The night's drama had come full circle.

It was the end of my own fishing. I watched the porpoises for a while. There were about six of them. They did not come close in. They were not interested in the sile. They were after the billet and codling and mackerel, and these, aware of their peril, would be trying to escape back to deep water. I dismantled my gear. I gutted my catch and started to string the fish together still watching the porpoises out of the tail of my eye. I had just about finished the job when I heard a low ominous rumble.

It came from the west. I looked apprehensively towards the moors and Adder Howe, which, if there had been a light in any of the front windows, should have been visible. There was no light. As it was now past midnight that was not surprising. Dain must have gone to bed long ago. As I looked there was another, and louder rumble, definitely from the same direction, and this time definitely thunder. Yet in the whole sky there was not a sign of cloud. The stars shone brilliantly and although the air was warm it was not close as it would have been before the gathering of a storm.

I tied the knot in my string, slung my catch on to my disjointed rod over my shoulder, took a last glance at the cavorting porpoises, and started along the now very narrow scaur towards the cliff and beach. There was another rumble, which hadn't died before there was another. I saw a reflected flash in the sky over Adder Howe, and before I reached the short end of the scaur I saw that the stars that had been visible over the moor were being hidden, that a regular bank of dark cloud was swiftly rising, moving east.

I was not at first alarmed. The storm, and it certainly was one, was still a long way off. It might be mild and quickly dissipate. Overhead the sky was still completely clear. Yet unless I climbed up the steep path to High Batts top there was no shelter nearer than the farm and the cottages above Browe Beck Cove a good two and a half miles along the shore. I was wearing flannel trousers and a bush shirt, with rubber ankle-boots on my feet. If it rained hard I'd have an extremely unpleasant journey. I hurried. When I reached the beach my view to the west was temporarily blocked by the cliff, and I had walked about a quarter of a mile before the view cleared. I had no doubt then that the storm was coming my way and that it was one of unusual type and severity.

There was none of the characteristic cauliflower type of cloud. It was more like a bank of dense black smoke which had now risen almost halfway up the western sky above the moors. It was arched from north to south. Its still rising and advancing front was even. It was lit spasmodically with lightning flashes. They were not forked. The thunder was not loud, and obviously they were reflected from the centre of the storm still far off.

Then, just as I thought that I'd got the bearings of Adder Howe (still with no light in it), there came a single gigantic spark. It extended from the edge of the cloud to the earth at least close to where I reckoned our house stood. It lit up the whole countryside and the shore as clear as day. In seconds, which I dared not count, there was a violent peal of thunder, and then another wicked flash which seemed to come to earth in the same place as the first one. I had the thought that either or both of those flashes had struck the house itself.

I started to run; looking towards my home. I knew that at this distance even in daylight it would have been difficult to see. A light, and it was almost certain that the storm would have awakened Dain, would have been visible, and coming now it would at least have been evidence that nothing had happened. The next flash, nearer to me, and even more vivid than the first, revealed that a curtain of rain, falling from the base of the cloud bank, had obliterated the contour of the moors and was evidently moving rapidly down the vale of our beck. If there had been a light I could not have seen it now.

I was scared. I knew that the chance of any house being struck by lightning in a British thunderstorm was millions to one against, that the odds against a fatal accident were even greater. Yet, whenever there were severe storms, houses were struck, people were hurt, sometimes killed. I remembered that a young farmer riding a horse along the beach between Bramblewick village and Browe Beck had been struck by lightning. His horse had been killed, and he had been crippled for life. I remembered that several farm buildings in the district had been struck at one time or another. At one not far from Adder Howe the chimney of a farmhouse had been struck by a flash which had travelled through the living-room, set fire to a rug and fused all the cutlery on the kitchen table. Sheep, cattle, horses, were struck and killed, and usually this happened when they sheltered under trees or grazed on hilltops. Lightning usually went for prominent points or objects.

Our house was in a prominent situation and the mansard roof was sharply pointed. Many times, during storms less violent than this one promised to be, I had wondered whether it wouldn't be a good thing to have a conductor fitted. When I'd discussed this with Will Stainforth he'd told me that the only house he knew of that had been badly damaged by lightning was one near Burnharbour which had a conductor. It would cost about twenty-five pounds, it would spoil the look of the roof, and certainly he wouldn't go to the expense if it had been his house. The barn had been there for more than a hundred years without anything happening to it.

I wished now that I'd had more sense, and not been swayed by this scientific heresy. Of course conductors gave protection to a building. Their function was not to attract and divert the electric spark to the ground, but to dissipate the potential charge that invited it. Although I could not see the house or the land near it, it was clear that the centre of the storm was moving directly over it. Yet there was nothing I could do but get home as fast as I could, and pray that everything was all right.

It was hard going, for with the tide nearly up I was forced to keep to the shingle near to the cliff foot. Between the flashes which were becoming more frequent the darkness was intense. I could not run without stumbling. The weight of the fish on my shoulder didn't help things. I thought of making a cache of it above high-water mark, covering it with stones so that I could come for it in the morning, but decided it wouldn't make that much difference to my speed, and that I'd feel a fool if I got home with nothing to show for my evening's fishing. Besides, the storm travelling at its present rate should soon pass over.

Its rate was astounding. The arched but still even front of it was soon overhead and closing to the north and south. Only to seaward was there clear sky and stars. Before I had gone another quarter of a mile there was no visible sky, and north, south, east and west the lightning was ripping the pall of cloud in all directions.

I had seen many thunderstorms in East Africa, where during the monsoon season they were of daily occurrence, but never one as violent as this. Some of the flashes appeared to reach from horizon to horizon. Some came down vertically to the earth, and also to the sea. There was scarcely any pause between them, no moment of darkness longer than the blinking of an eye. I had never heard such thunder. My ears ached with it. My eyes ached with the glare of the light as though it was actually burning them.

And then came the rain. There was no wind. It fell absolutely vertically and in an almost solid torrent. Before it came I had seen that I was still about half a mile distant from Browe Beck Cove and I had recognised the very strip of land at the top of the bridle-path, where we had planned to build our house, and how I had wished that it was there, and not on the distant moor. There were no warning drops and, because of the crashing and echoing of the thunder, no noise. It smote me on the head in a sudden deluge. Instantly I was drenched. But worse still I was blinded, for I had no hat. The water streamed down my face. I could not see a yard in any direction.

I dropped my fish, knelt down on the shingle, and to protect my face bowed my head like a priest before a shrine. I shut my eyes. I could still see the lightning flashes through my eyelids, only tinted red. One flash must have struck either the beach or the cliff not more than fifty feet away. The flash and the noise and the blast came simultaneously, and I thought it had actually hit me. I smelt the ozone made by the discharge as one smells the fumes from a burst shell. That was the nearest flash, yet there were brighter ones, and noisier ones, and there was no sign that the storm was passing over. The rain went on pelting down on to my arched back and whenever I opened my eyes it was to see nothing but rain and the lurid lightning.

I must have remained in that undignified and uncomfortable and yet inevitable position for at least half an hour. I was cold, wet and frightened. There were so many lightning flashes, such a crashing and tumult of thunder, such a deluge of rain, that it seemed unlikely that any house, or any animal or tree within the area of the storm, could have escaped injury of some sort. What *had* happened at home? I was completely impotent. I could do nothing until the rain stopped, and I could see to walk.

Then, as suddenly as it had started, it did stop. I stood up, pressed the water out of my hair, rubbed my eyes. At once I was reassured. Although the lightning was as frequent and violent as before, the storm was definitely moving out to sea. I was too close to the cliff to see the moors, but in the west there was a narrow belt of clear starry sky, and to the north above the village of Bramblewick, still partly obscured by rain, I could see houses, several with lights in their windows.

I slung the fish over my shoulders, and started off. The beach ahead of me as far as Browe Beck was clear, but here and there the rainwater pouring down the cliff face from the fields above had cut deep gullies in the shingle and the going was rough. As I neared the cove, I heard, between the thunder claps, a steady roaring sound and I was glad there was a footbridge over the

Beck for it was in full spate and the shingle which dammed the big pool had already been washed away. I climbed up the bridle-path where we had first seen old Isaac. The path itself was a miniature beck. I reached the top and the piece of land where our home was to have been built, and I paused here for breath.

The storm *was* over. Half the sky was completely clear, and the clouds were moving away rapidly eastwards over the sea. It was still an active storm, with almost continuous lightning, which now illuminated the upper areas of cloud. They rose to an immense height like a mass of rounded snow-clad mountains, and these were reflected on the unruffled mirror of the sea, making a magnificent spectacle.

I hurried on, along the lane which was to have been our connecting link with the main road. It was more than ankle-deep with liquid mud. I came to the road and I saw the farm and old Isaac's cottage. There was no sign of any damage. Against the starry western sky I could see the moors and the Mill Wood, and the top fields of Adder Howe and there was nothing except a few puddles and the rush of water in the gutters of the road to tell that there had been a storm.

I followed the route that old Isaac had taken us. I passed many trees and several farm buildings. Not one apparently had been struck. I heard and I saw moving cattle, horses and sheep, lying down or grazing just as though nothing had happened. I climbed the hill above Browe railway station, and reached the level of the moors, and then moved down through the plantation into the upper valley of our own beck, and as I neared the wood I heard the roar of the beck.

The wood was dark, the trees still dripping. The track was familiar, however, and I came to the ford, ankle-deep when I had crossed it last, now a raging torrent. I waded through it, carried on up through the wood, came to our gate in the boundary wall, and then saw above me the ridge and gable-ends of the house silhouetted against the stars. Tired though I was, I ran the remaining distance. There were no lights in any of the windows, but everything was all right. Nothing had happened. As I neared the door I saw Annabella, standing near to her despised stable, and she whinnied. I opened the door, stepped inside, put my fish down on the draining-board, found a match and lit the gas.

The range, damped down, was on, and the kettle was simmering. On the table a meal was laid for me. What a nice warm, comfortable room this was, I thought. I took off my boots and wet socks and with a flashlight walked through the lounge and tiptoed upstairs. I peeped into the children's rooms, saw they were all sleeping peacefully. I quietly opened the door of our own bedroom. Dain, too, was asleep.

I closed the door and opened the airing cupboard. The tank was hot, and my pyjamas were lying on top of it. I took them and went downstairs again, turned on the bath and removed my wet garments. I made some tea, and while it was brewing, took my bath.

It was not until I was drying myself that it occurred to me that in the course of my night's adventure, from the start of fishing to this happy return to my home, I hadn't once thought about my unfinished book, let alone solved the problem of how I was to get on with it. The bath refreshed me. My mind was clear. I sat down and started the meal which Dain had so thoughtfully prepared for me.

I tried to concentrate. It was no good. I was sick of Tom Bransby and his story. I got up to refill the teapot from the kettle on the stove. I noticed for the first time that a chair had been drawn up towards the stove, and that on it, open but face down, was a familiar brown-paper jacketed typewritten manuscript. It was the Cornish book. It was clear that Dain had been reading it last thing before going to bed. I picked it up, put it on the table, and went on with my meal.

I had not looked at the manuscript since I had started the Bransby book. The last time I had read through it I'd had a stronger sense of revulsion than I now had against the other. I hesitated for a while, then bracing myself for another wave of dislike, I started to read, not from the beginning but at the page where evidently Dain had left off. It was the chapter in which I had described how, when our financial troubles had been at their worst and the manuscript of our first book had been rejected by one publisher after another, we had received a telegram of acceptance. That episode certainly had been one of the most dramatic in our Cornish life. I'd liked it when I'd written it. Dain had liked it more than any other part of the book. Then after re-reading several times I had come to dislike and finally detest it.

I did not dislike it now. Indeed, I found it most exciting. I turned back and read part of another chapter. Then I began at the beginning of chapter one. And I hadn't got very far before I put it down, not with disgust, but with elation. Dain had been right. *This* was the book! It was the Bransby book that was dead. I could and I *must* carry on with it at once, finish it, let the other go hang. I could have danced with relief and joy.

6

IT WAS the last week in August. The year was 1939. The Cornish book had been published on Bank Holiday. It had been chosen by the Book Society as the monthly choice.

With one or two exceptions the critics had given it high praise. One distinguished critic, writing in a distinguished provincial newspaper, said that it bored him. Another complained that the only character in it that really came to life was our cat. Another, writing in a highbrow weekly journal, said it was just the sort of book the dear old aunties of the Book Society would make their August choice, and that it had no more reality than a paper rose.

Other critics, equally distinguished and one with an international reputation, used such gratifying words and phrases as "charming", "idyllic", "enchanting", "written with endearing simplicity", "a book in the tradition of *Crusoe* and *Bevis* and *Swiss Family Robinson*", "desperately exciting", "perfect characterisation", and several of them prophesied that it would be likely to prove the most popular novel of the year.

I had scores of adulatory letters from complete strangers. True that some of the writers seemed to have been inspired by motives not wholly altruistic. Some were struggling authors themselves or had children or other relatives who wished to become authors, or had novels or plays or short stories they hadn't been able to place and the account I had given in the book of my own struggles suggested that I should be able to help them, by reading and criticising, and perhaps revising their manuscripts, and even introducing them to a publisher. Some, evidently convinced by what the critics had said that I had struck oil, simply wanted financial help for various reasons.

All were, in one way or another, gratifying. Of more practical interest were the letters I got from the editors of newspapers and magazines, asking me to write articles or short stories, and those from my agent telling me that several American and Continental publishers had asked for copies of the book to be sent to them, and that a famous British film producer was deeply interested in it as a possible for two of his most famous stars, now making a film in Egypt, and that I might expect an offer when these stars returned to this country.

It looked as though we were going to be rich. My publisher hadn't told me yet what the actual sales had been, and his letters had been guarded. He had said that they were good and that if they continued so he would have to order another printing. No matter how well a book was received on publication it usually took some weeks to get really going. We should know more definitely by the end of September if the favourable reviews it had got, and his advertising campaign, were going to establish it as a really outstanding best-seller. The sale of the film rights would naturally help in this matter.

Neither of us wanted to be very rich. The thought that we might be sometimes worried me. Poverty was hateful, yet we had found our greatest happiness in making or contriving things for ourselves. There were plenty of things we still wanted. We wanted to travel and see, and perhaps live, in other countries. With great wealth this would be possible, yet it would mean leaving our present life and home, and there would be the problem of deciding which country we should go to. There were so many. You could only live in one place at a time. You had only one life. There were only twenty-four hours in a day, and one-third of these you had to spend asleep, unconscious.

It was true that great wealth gave you the power to help others, to do what the *Codex Sinaiticus* lady had done for us with her cheque for twenty-five pounds. Even philanthropy could not be simple for there were so many good causes, it would be an awful job deciding which should get help, and in what degree. The possession of wealth carried heavy responsibilities.

The brother of the *Codex* lady had shelved them by refusing to accept his inheritance. That seemed a cowardly way out, and yet the greatest danger of all was that, confronted by the difficulties of deciding how, and in what measure to give or distribute, one might be tempted not to give at all, to become mean and a miser.

On the whole, it was better to have too little money than to have too much. The ideal would be to have an income which would act like the governor of an engine, a device that automatically controls its speed, not too fast, not too slow.

Every day of that month the mail or the telephone had brought us good news of some sort. The news that came to us over the radio, that made the headlines in the newspapers, obligingly brought to us by our postman, if it still contained elements of optimism was anything but good. The threat of a second great war was in the air.

I did not believe that it would, or that it could, happen. It was against all reason that any civilised nation, aware of the cost in human lives and suffering and hard cash of one great war, and the complete futility of it, could start another one. Hitler, judged by his personal appearance in some of the news reels I had seen, by his voice, and some of his writings, was a conceited and unpleasant man. He was clearly not a fool. He had been a soldier himself and he must have known that as a method of settling international disputes physical fighting was out of date.

Remembering some of the propaganda we had used to decry the Germans in the Kaiser's war, the "corpse factory", for example, I thought that many of the things we were saying against them now, and against Hitler, were at least exaggerated.

There were indeed plenty of superficial grounds for optimism in that summer of 1939. If Munich had been a victory for Hitler the events that led up to it and followed it had been a stimulant to British industry. The rearmament drive was under way. The slump was over and giving way to a boom. There were no laid-up ships now such as we had seen in Cornwall. All of them were in commission and British shipyards, which had been idle for years, were working overtime, building new merchant ships as well as ships of war.

We had evidence of this in the constant stream of traffic passing up and down the coast in sight of our windows. When we had first come to Adder Howe the passing of a single cargo vessel would have made us rush for our binoculars. Now often there would be scores of them, and almost every week we would see a brand new ship, on trial, from one of the Tyne or Tees yards, or away on her maiden voyage.

It was an end to unemployment, and the dole. Coal mines, furnaces, steel mills, textile factories were all busy again, and in that summer there came for the British workman the first holiday with pay. The seaside resorts, Burnharbour and Bramblewick included, were crowded with holiday makers. Our moorland highroad, so lonely in winter, bore on it especially at weekends a ceaseless traffic of buses, motor coaches, private cars, caravans, motor and push bikes, cyclists and hikers. The roar of it was like the roar of the sea. It was perfect holiday weather.

New life, too, had come to British farming. Sam, who did not completely share my optimism about the international situation, made some pointed comments upon this subject.

"It's taken a lot of red lights," he said, "to frighten the government about farming. It doesn't matter which party has been in power, Tory, Liberal or Labour, they've gone on letting things slide, except, of course, during the war, when the U-boats nearly starved us out and then they were on their knees to persuade farmers to plough up more land and grow more food.

"And yet as soon as the war was over they forgot all about us. It only paid, they said, to produce milk, which we couldn't import, although, I bet, if they'd invented a way of shipping milk in tankers so that it could have been kept fresh, they'd have done that.

"It's the factories and the rich owners of them that they've always put first in peace time. They had to sell what they made to foreign countries or the colonies, and these countries had to sell us *their* farming produce to pay for them. We've produced milk, all right, but chiefly on imported fodder. If farmers had been given a square deal and more encouragement they could have done without most of this imported stuff and produced meat as well as milk. And that's what they'll have to do if the Germans start war again, and we are to beat 'em."

Sam was himself starting to reap the reward from his years of hard work and intelligent planning. All the fields that he had cleared and ploughed up were doing well. This had enabled him to increase his stock considerably. He never gave me details of his financial position. He told me, however, that he wouldn't have been able to buy his own farm and stock it without a bank loan. To get a bank to help you, apart from material security like the farm buildings and the land itself, the main thing was to show the manager, by what you were earning, that you were a good and safe investment, and it was easier now that the government was backing the banks. Clearly *he* had done this. In addition to buying new stock he had bought a brand new tractor complete with plough and disc harrow.

He had done something more important. Our common neighbour, old Matt Pashby of Bog Hall, had decided to give up farming. Bog Hall had been sold, and Sam, with a mortgage, had bought it lock, stock and barrel. Its fields, one boundary was our beck, extended to the mill farm above the wood, and there was the cart track joining them. They were all neglected for Matt, like Jimmy, had been mostly a moorland sheep farmer. The house and all the farm buildings had been in disrepair, and the price had been moderate. Sam had taken possession on Lady Day. He had let the house to a young newly-married couple, Len and Ida Bradley. Len was a farmer's son, Ida, a very pretty vivacious girl, a farmer's daughter, and they were both as keen to get on as Sam and Becky. And Len, who could drive a tractor, was helping Sam in running both farms as one unit. Jimmy had bought Matt's flock of moorland ewes.

I was not envious of Sam's growing prosperity, yet when I saw his tractor at work, ploughing up the neglected fields of Bog Hall, I longed more than ever to make a start on our own land, and if this proved a success to reoccupy the fields I had let to Jimmy and do the same.

I wasn't worried about doing this, for Jimmy, although he had paid his rent, still hadn't done a thing to improve the land. He, too, was deriving benefit from the rearmament drive. The price of wool (and lambs too) was going up. As well as taking over Matt's flock he had taken over the extra moorland grazing. It gave him farther to ride every day, a thing he loved doing. He was always affable when we met. I noticed, too, that he had got an almost brand new saddle and bridle for his mare. His combined flock now numbered nearly three hundred. He knew and it seemed that he loved each one.

Dain and I had often talked of what we should do as soon as it was absolutely certain that we were going to have a lot of money. Certainly we should start the ploughing up of the fields, and if Sam could not manage it because of Bog Hall we should get some other tractor owner to do it, or we might even get a tractor ourselves. I'd have to take lessons first, perhaps with Sam or Len. We had agreed that although we must travel, and live in other countries, it would be difficult to do this while the children were small (there might be more children, too), and that whatever we did we should never want to give up Adder Howe.

Yet, already it was getting a bit cramped. We could do with some extra bedrooms, another bathroom, and we had worked out how we could do this by building, either in stone or timber, along the blind wall of the house where the wood playroom was, using a flat roof to join the middle ridge of the mansard giving us two stories, with a bridge over the existing porch and paving.

We had discussed this with Will Stainforth. He thought it feasible and that it was unlikely to meet any opposition from the authorities. He was ready to give us an estimate at any time, although he warned us that we mustn't expect to get things done so cheaply as the original building. Cost of material, now that the trade depression was over, was going up. So were wages. In the big housing estate contract he was just completing it was going to be a near thing for him to come out on the right side.

Neither of us had any ambition to own a motor car. If ever we wished to get anywhere quickly it would be much simpler and cheaper to telephone for a taxi. It would be pleasant to own a cruising yacht. This, however, would definitely commit us to leaving Adder Howe and again it would be so complicated with a large family like ours.

There was the subject of ponies. Amelia soon would be wanting something bigger than Annabella. We ought, Dain suggested, to buy just one other pony like Annabella at first and two bigger ones we could ride ourselves, and to which the children should gradually get used. Mrs Allen would advise us as to which was the best type to get. They would all be mares so that we could breed them eventually. Whatever we did with the land we must make allowance for grazing for the ponies. And seeing that Annabella would not use her stable we could pull it down and build a more substantial one, with a harness room.

We were painting an agreeable future for ourselves. It did not as yet include the likely realisation of my ambition to make a lake and install a waterwheel. Yet, I had seen how one half of my dream might be fulfilled. I had carefully surveyed every foot of our beck from boundary to boundary. I had taken measurement of the flow of water, and I was convinced that except in prolonged periods of drought there *was* sufficient volume to drive a wheel that would at least give us electric light.

And there was one place close to my hut and to the boundary of the mill wood where there was a drop of at least nine feet in a distance of twenty feet. The bank was suitable for the building of a double wall to support the bearings of the wheel. All that would be required was a sluice twenty feet in length into which the beck could be diverted; all, that is to say, apart from the wheel itself. Unless I could get one second-hand it would be an expensive thing to have made. It would need special castings. What would it matter when we were rich? Anyway, if it worked all right, it would pay for itself in course of time in free electric current.

Were we being too optimistic? On the last Sunday of that memorable August the two leading literary Sunday newspapers contained large display advertisements quoting some of the reviews, and describing the book as *the* success of the season. One of these papers, which every week had a column entitled BESTSELLERS IN LONDON and had not hitherto mentioned our book at all, put it first, and called it "the topical favourite".

The postman brought us dozens of fan letters next morning. I was in the middle of reading them when the phone rang. It was my agent speaking from London. He'd just had a long talk with the film producer. The two stars were home, they had read the book, and were enthusiastic about it. He would be making an offer during the course of the week. The sum they discussed was five thousand pounds. We might get a bigger figure than this if we waited for American publication, but as we hadn't got an American publisher yet, and as it might not prove so popular there as in this country, he would advise strongly to accept when the offer became definite, and he was confident it was going to be that.

I was trembling when I put the receiver down and for a time I stood staring dazedly at the telephone, wondering whether I was not in a dream. Then Dain came into the room, and she said in a scared voice:

"What's the matter? Is it bad news?"

I tried to tell her calmly what the agent had said. She looked incredulous. Suddenly I flung my arms round her, hugged her, and shouted exultantly:

" Five thousand pounds—five thousand pounds! And that on top of everything else. We're going to be really rich."

We danced, and the children came in. Amelia, Jane, Angus and Tim (now a toddler).

"Let's celebrate!" Dain shouted. "Let's ring up everybody we know, and let's go down to the beach and have a super picnic. Let's ask Becky and Sam, Bill and Mabs and Claire and Sylvia and Marie and Will Stainforth."

"We *must* take Annabella," cried Amelia. "And the trap. I wish we had more ponies and another trap. There won't be room for everyone."

"We'll soon have plenty of ponies and traps," I cried recklessly. "But we'll have cars for today. Let's make a list of everything we need for the picnic. I'll ring up the garage to send out at least two cars and they can collect from the grocers and confectioners. Tons of cakes and ham sandwiches, and ice-cream and—yes—why not for tonight when we get back?—champagne! Let's celebrate. We're rich at last!"

It was a perfect day, calm, sunny and warm. The heather was in full bloom. The cornfields, sweeping down to the sea were ripening, the woods and pastures were bright green, the sea a pale opalescent blue, and I thought, as we drove along the highway for the road that led down to Browe and the shore, that I had never seen our countryside look more beautiful, and that we could not have found a better place to live in than this.

How lucky and how happy we were! The highroad was still crowded with holiday traffic, but not so heavily as it had been at the beginning of the month. Britain's first holiday with pay was nearly over, and many of the cars we saw were obviously homeward bound. Their occupants were sunburnt. All looked happy.

We were a smaller party than we had hoped for. Sam and Becky were too busy cutting their first field of oats. Bill and Mabs had prospective parents to interview and only Claire could come. They would look in in the evening and share our celebration. So would Will Stainforth, only it would be late, he said. He had never been so full of work.

I hadn't told him how much I was going to get from the film, but I had told him that I could give him the green light for the extension to Adder Howe, and that I hoped he'd give me an estimate as soon as possible. He had sounded delighted.

Sylvia, the dancing teacher at the school, had been coming to lunch, and she was with us with her little niece Jane. Our friend Marie, who taught drama, was away on holiday; the aunt was in Switzerland.

Our permanent nanny had left us to get married. Taking her place for the summer at least we had a charming Norwegian girl Marith (her home was Trondheim) and she was with us, and we had all managed to pack into the large car the garage had sent out. The fact that it was a Rolls-Royce had helped to console the children for not taking Annabella and the trap. And I took it as a propitious symbol of our new and certain prosperity.

I hadn't as much as glanced at the newspapers the postman had brought with our letters. We hadn't listened to the radio.

The car took us to the start of the little lane that led to the Browe Beck Cove, and the place where we had planned to build our house, and it would pick us up there again at half-past six.

The tides were neap and at about half-ebb, exposing a strip of clean hard sand between the scars. The beach was too far away from the village to be crowded. The sea was warm. We paddled and bathed, and shrimped and built castles and made sand pies, and we played games and we danced, and made a driftwood fire near the cliff foot and had our picnic with all the things that had come out with the car.

It was indeed a perfect day, and that night we drank champagne with our friends, and we didn't listen in, even to the midnight news. During the rest of the week, the last week in August, the fan letters continued to arrive, and there was one from my agent notifying me that he had received offers for the Dutch and Italian translation rights of the book. In each case the advance on royalties would be twenty pounds.

He made no mention of the film in his letter, but on Friday came one from him which if it didn't tell us the worst at least prepared us for it. The producer had told him that because of the international situation he could make no definite commitments at present with regard to the film rights of the book. If war came the deal was off.

On Saturday came the news from my publisher that because of the possibility of war he had not been able to put in hand the new printing of the book which otherwise its sales would have justified.

On Sunday came the news that Great Britain was at war with Germany. I needn't have worried about being rich after all.

7

AND SO we were at war again.

After my final crash and illness, I had been discharged from the Royal Air Force as "permanently unfit, pilot or observer", and what notions I might have had of taking part in another war were dispelled by a letter I got from the Air Ministry in reply to my inquiry. There was no suitable vacancy for an ex-officer of medical category P.U.P.O., whose only flying experience was with aircraft long since obsolescent.

I could not pretend that this letter, and a similar one I got from the War Office, distressed me deeply. I was susceptible to patriotic appeals, I thought it would perhaps be more pleasant to be wearing a uniform than civilian clothes, but I hated war, and the discipline of any sort of soldiering, and, besides, I had the responsibility of a wife and family.

The film was off. It looked as though the book itself was dead. In its short run, however, it had earned several hundred pounds. Some of this unfortunately had been paid to me as royalties in advance when the manuscript was delivered. Yet we should still be able to pay off some more of the mortgage, and have enough to live on for at least a year, and, although the Germans had already inflicted severe losses on British merchant ships, it looked after the first few weeks of war as though the threats of heavy air attacks and actual invasion had simply been bluff.

Many of the children who had been evacuated to the country from London and the large seaports and towns had gone back to their homes. Theatres and cinemas which had been closed were opening again. And with us, apart from rationing and the discomforts of the blackout and the daily passing of huge convoys of merchant ships, escorted by warships and aircraft, there were few signs of war.

We had been obliged to give up the idea of building an extension to the house. We had to give up, temporarily at least, the idea of buying more ponies, and my project of installing a waterwheel seemed farther off than ever, which was a pity, seeing that it would be a saving in a product likely to prove of vital importance in what already was being called Britain's war effort. Bottle-gas was a derivative of petroleum. All petroleum had to be imported from overseas, and the Germans would do, and already were doing, their best to cut off supplies by sinking tankers. Although there was no difficulty yet in obtaining our gas cylinders, there might well be soon. Then we should have to fall back on paraffin oil or even candles for lighting. Both of these were petroleum products. My wheel and a dynamo would have made us independent.

The convoys of merchant ships which each day steamed past our bay in both directions were doing so without any apparent interference from the enemy. It seemed that the methods of detecting the presence of and attacking U-boats developed towards the end of the Kaiser's war had made it impractical for them to operate in shallow coastal waters. The traffic lane along our coast to which the convoys rigidly kept was also regularly swept by minesweepers which we could watch operating in pairs. Each week the radio and our newspapers recorded the ever-mounting toll of British, Allied and neutral merchant vessels sunk by torpedo and mine. It was clear that the Germans were going all out to cut our lifelines of food, fuel and raw material with the rest of the world. We were told, and soon exhorted, by the government that we must grow more food in our own country. If not the war would be prolonged; at worst, we might be defeated. We must, as far as it was possible, become self-supporting.

To what extent could we do this on our own neglected land? Dain was enthusiastic in her belief that we could go a long way towards it. We'd got plenty of land. We'd got a *bit* of money. We ought to go in for farming. What was farming after all, but gardening on a bigger scale, and having animals? The garden we had made proved that our soil was all right once it was cleared.

"It will be like our Cornwall life all over again," she said. "We *had* to be self-supporting then, in almost everything. Wouldn't it be exciting if we could grow our own wheat, and thresh it, and grind it and make our own flour and bread. It *is* a pity we can't have that waterwheel."

We hadn't been completely self-supporting in our Cornish home. We had grown all vegetables and fruit, but we were not vegetarians. In our leanest days we had been obliged to subsist largely on the products of our garden, and fish of our own catching. Poultry was a capital investment we hadn't been able to afford, and we'd had to buy our eggs or do without them, although in the nesting season we'd had plenty of herring-gull eggs from the sea cliffs. We would have been miserable without bacon, and at least an occasional steak or mutton chop. We had made our own jam. Jam needed sugar we could not produce ourselves. We had to buy, or do without, bread, milk, butter or margarine, tea, coffee, cocoa.

What *could* a British farm produce to replace or augment the food stuffs which had been and were being imported? Obviously not tea, coffee, cocoa, rice, bananas, oranges, or grapefruit, prunes, raisins and currants. Obviously, and I wouldn't have been so certain of this had I not listened to Sam holding forth on the subject, what a British farm *could* produce was butter, cheese, eggs, and above everything, meat: beef, mutton, pork and bacon.

It could produce wheat itself, but never more than a fraction of what the population required, and in this part of Yorkshire it was a risky crop to grow. The same applied to sugar-beet, which was right enough for the big farms in South Yorkshire and Lincolnshire and the Midlands. Meat was the main thing apart from milk. And to produce both you had to have good grass, oats, beans, kale turnips or mangolds, and for winter feeding hay or silage. Winter feeding, too, at our altitude would mean housing for animals.

The first thing was the land itself. We had helped Sam with his double harvest, which from his own farm had been a bumper one. We had done this voluntarily, because we liked him and we liked the job, and because it gave us a certain patriotic satisfaction. I couldn't settle down to writing anyway. He had promised that as soon as he had completed his own ploughing, he would start on mine, and one afternoon in early October he came up to Adder Howe to have what he called a scout round.

I had never known him so matter of fact and business like.

We walked round the whole of the tolerably level land on our side of the fence that divided it from the fields I had let to Jimmy. There were three fields, marked by the remains of dry-stone walls and here and there a stunted, wind-bent hawthorn. Together they amounted to about twelve acres. One of them was almost entirely grown over with tall whins, and all had patches of bracken in them encroaching on the coarse grass which Annabella had only lightly cropped.

"It would almost have been better," was Sam's first rather discouraging remark, "if you'd let Jimmy's sheep roam over these fields. They'd have trampled the bracken down if nowt else. The worst thing about bracken is that you can't tell what's under it when you're ploughing, whether there are stones or not."

He had a short, pointed iron rod which he kept on poking into the ground as we walked backwards and forwards over the whin-free areas of the land. In places it went down easily for several inches, in others he had to jab at it hard, and in one place it obviously struck rock not more than four inches from the surface. He made no immediate comment, and I was starting to feel worried, for not more than ten yards away sticking out of the bracken was one large slab of the hard grey stone which he had called flint.

"I suppose," I said diffidently, "you could plough round a block like that, or would it have to be broken up and cleared?"

He smiled dryly.

"You could plough round it, only it would spoil the shape of your furrow. It would be best broken up of course, and got out of the way. It's the stones you can't see that will give the trouble in a job like this. Tractor ploughing has got to be done quick, and there's more force on the points of your shares than you'd have with a team of horses. Points break and they're expensive things. Besides, there's a shortage of them with so much ploughing under way. Break two points and your job may be held up perhaps for the whole day."

I was getting worried. There was worse to come. I had told Sam of our ambition to make a farm of Adder Howe, and he had expressed a general approval. This had been some weeks ago. Now standing on the very rock I had spoken about, he said:

"I don't want to put you off about all this. I know how you feel about it, owning all this land and wanting to turn it back to summat useful. If I owned it, I'd have to do it somehow or other. But it's no use me pretending it's going to be easy and cheap. I could bring the tractor and plough round by the highroad from Bog Hall, and have a go at this straight away, but I reckon it would be a waste of time and brass. This land will grow crops all right. There'll be plenty of fertility in it, as much as in any of the land I've broken up. But so far as rocks go, it seems to me there'll be as many here as in the fields you've let to Jimmy. In fact, I'd rather tackle them than these. Did you say you could get them back from him?"

"I think so. He hasn't kept to his bargain about liming them and putting on fertiliser."

"I told you he wouldn't, long ago," Sam reminded me.

I was still very fond of Jimmy.

"But he might," I said, "want to plough them up himself, now that all farmers are being persuaded to grow more food, and that farming is beginning to pay."

Sam laughed aloud.

"You still don't know Jimmy! I doubt if he's quite realised yet that there *is* a war on. He hasn't got a wireless. He never reads a newspaper. He rarely goes to a pub. He never thinks of anything but his sheep. All he knows is that the price of wool and mutton is going up. So long as there's plenty of fodder on the moor, he'll not bother. If he wanted to plough up he's got nearly fifty acres of his own that's been good arable. He's not going to spend any brass on your fields. And you'll need those fields if you're going to make any sort of farm of Adder Howe.

"What I would do if it was my land would be aim at getting it all to good grass with oats as a first cover crop, then buy some young store cattle and fatten them for the market. Never mind cows and milk. And you'd only have to build a shelter for them for really hard weather. You could have some barley of course. You could keep pigs. It *is* good land this, once it's cleared of stones and muck.

"You should start by burning off all the whins and bracken. You'll have to get the whin roots out, of course. You'll have to find out where all the stones are, dig round them, and then get someone from a quarry to blow 'em up. I'll plough it for you then, and harrow and sow it. It will all need lime and fertiliser, but it would be worth it in the end."

Once again there was enthusiasm in Sam's manner.

"Do you still feel," I said, "that you couldn't take it on yourself, that we couldn't go into a sort of partnership with it?"

"No. If it wasn't for the beck, and there being no proper road up from my spot, I might have thought of it. But I've got as much as I can manage with Bog Hall. It will take me five years at least to get that into shape. By then," he added dryly, "the war should be over, and maybe farmers will be forgotten again until the next war starts."

I met Jimmy later that same afternoon. We had gone on to the moor to load turf, with Annabella and the trap. We were all there for it was a Saturday and Amelia and Jane were not at school. The aunt was with us too. She had hurried back from Norway at the outbreak of war. She thought it was going to be safer in England.

Ironically enough, in view of what was to happen later in the war the father of Marith, our Norwegian friend, had sent an urgent telegram to her from

Trondheim, insisting she should return at once. He thought it was Norway that was going to be safe. Her going had saddened us all. The return of the aunt had been a compensation, for the children adored her.

The weather was still fine, dry and very mild. It looked as though coal might soon be scarce. There had been many government radio appeals for economy in its use and I had cut what I hoped would be an adequate supply of turves for the winter. They were dry. We were making one big stack of them just inside our gate. The children at least were happy, for as well as the fun of carrying the turves and piling them into the trap they were all keeping an eager lookout on the patches from which the turf had been removed for flints, and there was immense excitement when Angus picked up an arrowhead.

In spite of the news we had heard of the Nazis' march into Poland, of Russia's impending invasion of Finland, of the sinking of more merchant ships by torpedo and mine, and of air attacks on the Orkneys (including the sinking by U-boat of the *Royal Oak* in Scapa Flow with a terrible loss of life), it was hard even for us to realise that we were at war, for here everything seemed so peaceful, and so very beautiful.

The heather bells were fading but there were still streaks of purple in the warm browns of the moor. The bracken, I had not yet come to regard it as among the major pests of farming, had turned yellow and brick red. The rowans on our hilltop were hung with clusters of scarlet berries. The summer green of our own wood and the mill wood had changed to the glowing reds and yellows of autumn. A thin mistiness made the calm sea a pearly-grey. A large convoy had moved south during the morning. Now the only ships in sight were the herring drifters, scores of them steaming north to the still-unrestricted fishing grounds.

We saw Jimmy a long way off in the direction of Tom Cross, to which Annabella had led me on that stormy winter night, and it seemed that he was riding home. But when he reached the deserted highroad he turned on to it, and trotted down to our road-end, and along our road towards us. I'd had no chance of a talk with him since he had paid his midsummer instalment of rent and the Michaelmas instalment was overdue. He was going to pay it now, I thought. It would be a good chance to have it out with him about the tenancy. He rode up, stopped and touched his hat to the aunt and Dain. The children who liked him crowded round him, and Amelia and Jane stroked his mare.

"Now, then," he said, beaming, "I see you're all busy. It's a good idea too, getting turf. I only wish I could find time to cut a load or two. Perhaps I can later on if you can give us the loan of your spade for a day or two. You've got some bonny bairns. They look well. It must suit them living up here. What's that you've got?"

This was to Angus, who was holding up his treasure for Jimmy to see.

"An arrowhead," said Angus proudly. "*I* found it."

Jimmy dismounted. He looked at the arrowhead a little doubtfully.

"Aye? " he said. "Aye? It does look sharp, doesn't it? Did you say it was an arrowhead? It must have been shot with a bow. It's a long time since anyone used things like that."

"It belonged to an early Briton," Amelia explained with the superiority of her years." Angus doesn't quite understand that yet. They lived up here on the moors. They hunted for all sorts of wild animals, and used their skins for clothing. We've found the flint scrapers they used for cleaning the skins. Here's one."

She took from her dungaree pocket a handful of flints, and Jane immediately produced her collection, and the two of them began to give to Jimmy a rapid-fire archaeological dissertation. Fortunately, Annabella suddenly decided she'd had enough turf-leading for the afternoon and started off for home, and the lecture was broken off while we captured her.

I then had a chance of a talk with Jimmy, more or less privately. I had no resentment against him for his failure to keep to the terms of our agreement. I was not, however, going to lose the advantage this gave me, and I reminded him about the lime and the fertiliser. He made no protest. He didn't seem in any way put out. He just smiled benignly.

I went on to tell him that it was important, because of the war and what the government was asking us to do, that the fields should be properly farmed, and made to grow crops. Did he intend to plough them up himself? If he didn't I would have to get someone else to do so, in which case I'd have to call our agreement off and take repossession. I had no doubt then as to how the wind was blowing with Jimmy. He positively beamed.

"Why," he said. "It's queer you should have said all

this, for that's why I rode up to see you. I wanted to get things straight about them fields of yours. Now that I've taken over Matt Pashby's ewes and his moor stray, I'm not wanting any extra grazing. If it suits you to have them fields back it suits me. There is a bit of rent owing. I'll let you have that next time I see you. I haven't got it on me now, but you'll get it all right."

It had been so easy I felt that I could afford to be magnanimous.

"It doesn't matter about that," I said. "We'll call it quits, and I'll take the land back at once."

"That's very kind of you. Very kind of you."

He mounted his mare.

"Is it true you're going to start farming? You might do well if you've got plenty of brass to lay out on it. I wish I had. But I'd still think twice about ploughing up them fields of yours. There's too many rocks in 'em, and I doubt whether if when you get it ploughed it'll grow owt but thistles. Well, I'll have to be getting on. Good luck to you anyway."

He rode away, and once again I was left with the impression that Jimmy had got the better of me. Dain could see nothing but good in what had happened.

"It's wonderful," she cried. "And how nice he was about it. I thought he'd be furious. We've got the whole land back again. The whole forty-two acres. We *can* make a farm of it. Let's start clearing it at once. Let's get all the whins and the bracken burnt off, and then start on the rocks. I'm sure we can do it and I'm sure it will be a success."

"Right," I said. "Let's make a start tomorrow. It's too

late to start burning now because of the blackout. Let's finish the stack and take one load down to the house."

We were on our way down to the house (it was teatime and the light by then was failing) when we heard the drone of an aeroplane out at sea, where three herring drifters were just visible through the haze. We could not see the plane, but I guessed it to be a Coastal Command Lockheed or Anson on routine patrol. Then, near to the stern of one of the drifters, and on the sea, there was a vivid flash, then another, and another. I saw smoke and I saw that all three drifters which had been in line ahead were turning, first one way and then the other, zigzagging, and it seemed at increased speed. There came the sound of explosions, and there were several more flashes on the sea, and then a series of bright flashes in the air above the ships which I recognised as machine-gun fire, before I heard among the rumbling of heavy explosions, the familiar rattle.

We had stopped, Dain holding Annabella's head, the children all looking. I was thankful that they were too young to understand what was happening, that the drifters were being attacked with bomb and machine-gun by a Nazi plane. We still could not see the plane. Soon we could not see the drifters because of the smoke from the bombs and furnaces. Then both the sounds of firing and bombing ceased, and the drone of the planes died away to silence. The smoke cleared and from it shortly and to my huge relief there emerged all three drifters, with smoke coming from their funnels only, steaming ahead again, apparently unharmed.

That night we were told on the radio that in the

course of the day a Nazi raider had made a bomb and machine-gun attack on fishing craft off the North-East Coast. There had been no casualties and no damage.

We were lucky with the weather. It continued dry, and although, because of the blackout regulations, we had to be careful not to leave any smouldering vegetation after dusk, we successfully burnt off not only the whins and bracken but much of the long tussocky grass on the fields which we had once regarded as being on our side of the fence. Jimmy's sheep had at least helped to keep the grass on his side fairly short, and until I fixed a new outer boundary fence they would continue to do so, and they would be getting their grazing free. We had decided to clear the smaller fields first.

I was not underrating our task. All the burning did to the whins was to expose their main stems and branches so that they could be cut, either with saw or slasher. After that, each one had to be uprooted and my experience with the clearing of the garden patch had shown me what a tough job this could be.

Dain and the children helped. I had to do the uprooting with the spade and some of the roots went down well over a foot and were enormously thick. That encouraged my belief that there was a good depth of soil, that all our labour would be repaid in the end. And wherever we cleared or dug there was the chance of finding things, for all this land had obviously been in the occupation of the early Britons. When the whole of it was ploughed up and the soil exposed to the weather, before our crops were sown we should have a wonderful

316

hunting ground for flints.

We piled the charred whin branches into heaps. When dried and brittle they would make good kindling, and if coal really became scarce we could use them with turf and logs in our kitchen range.

Gradually that part of the land that had been hidden by the whins was cleared and regained shape as a field and our clearing had revealed only an occasional rock close to the surface. Some of these were soft sandstone. Some, and these were the biggest, were the white flint, whose exact nature I still did not guess. The burning of the bracken had revealed a larger number of them. There might, as Sam had suggested, be even more hidden under the soil. He had told me that the deepest furrow his plough could cut was seven inches. Anything below that could do no harm, and I made the discovery that if there were stones at less than this depth the vegetation above was scanty giving a clue which could be proved or disproved with a probing rod.

I had a crowbar, a ten-pound sledge hammer, and my Cornish visgy. One afternoon I started work on one of these rocks and the day was memorable because after the one o'clock news there had been a talk on fuel economy to which we had all listened. The speaker had said how important it was for domestic users to save coal which was so vitally needed for our furnaces, power stations, and munition factories.

He talked about grates, and cinder sifters, and coal substitutes like wood and peat and turf. He mentioned how in desert countries the natives had to burn dry camel and cattle dung, which they made into bricks and dried in the sun. And he said that one good way to save coal was to use the slack or dust that was found in every coalhouse, either for damping down the fire when its full heat was not required, or by making it into eggs or briquettes. To do this you mixed the dust with lime or cement mortar, or wet clay, moulded it, and left the eggs to dry arid harden when they would make a first-rate fuel.

I said, when the talk was over, that we must have a try at doing this, for there was plenty of slack in our own coalhouse which I had built near to Annabella's despised stable. I had been too eager to start work on my rock to start the experiment then, and it did not strike me as significant that for once Jane and Angus didn't want to come up with me to the fields.

The rock itself was roughly oblong in shape, about five feet in length, three across. An average of about a foot was exposed above the ground. I selected one corner and whacked it with the sledge. The steel head bounced back from it as though it had been a spring, and without making the slightest impression on the rock itself. I tried again and again, and at last succeeded in breaking off a small chip, no bigger than one of the flint implements which the early Britons had left behind on the moor and interested us so much.

Those implements, however, were all made of the dark-brown and semi-translucent flint (actually fossilised sponges) found in the chalk of the East Yorkshire wolds and cliffs. This, although as hard, was a pinkish white, and although crystalline, quite opaque. It had no cleavage planes. Obviously it was going to be the very devil to smash up. Sam had been right again. The only way of removing the rocks was to blast them. But to do even this I should have to get under them. Drilling, I imagined, would require a diamond drill. How deep was this rock buried. Was it just a single rock, or, awful thought, was it an outcrop of solid continuous formation?

I set to with the visgy, making a trench from its exposed face. To my relief I found that at a depth of little more than a foot the face ended, but I had to dig nearly another foot and widen the trench, before I could start undercutting, and even then I had no definite proof that the whole rock was bedded on the under soil, and independent. I would have to trench completely round it, undercut it, and then for positive proof, lever it up with the crowbar.

It was a big job and I tried not to think that this was only one of perhaps a hundred rocks I'd have to clear before the whole of our land could be ploughed, that there were many bigger than this.

I worked like a navvy. I lost count of time. And it must have been nearly four o'clock when I heard a shout and saw Dain with Timothy in her arms walking towards me. By then I had at least proved that three-quarters of the rock *was* resting on subsoil, for I had undercut it several inches for this distance, and I was able to give Dain an encouraging report. She was worried, however.

"Where are Jane and Angus? Haven't they been with you?" she asked.

I hadn't seen or heard them all afternoon.

"They said they were coming up to get some sticks. They left soon after you'd gone."

319

"Perhaps they're down at the island."

The island was not more than two hundred yards down from where I was working. I gave a shout. There was no answer.

"Perhaps they've gone down to the farm. Or they may have gone to meet Amelia."

We made no strict bounds for the children, but it was a rule that before they went off on their own they had to tell us where they were going, and for how long; a rule they usually kept. There was nothing very alarming in their absence. It was nearly teatime, however, and leaving my tools I took Timothy in my arms and we walked down towards the house. As we reached it we saw Amelia riding up the path from the wood on Annabella. She was alone. We gave her a hail. Had she seen Jane and Angus?

"No, I haven't seen them anywhere."

"Did you call at the farm?" I asked.

"Yes. I saw Mrs Briggs. She asked me if we wanted any cream. Jane and Angus weren't there."

The aunt had come to the door. Jane and Angus were not in the house, she said. And tea was ready. I did feel slightly alarmed now for being late for meals had never been a failing of any of our children. We were all in front of the house now. Amelia had dismounted. I set Timothy down.

"I'll go and look for them," I said. "They must be somewhere down in the wood."

And then there was a noise from inside the coal shed, the door of which was shut had now suddenly opened. And there was Jane and, behind her, Angus, both looking rather sheepish, but also, Jane in particular, rather pleased with themselves. Dain gave a cry of horror.

"Whatever have you been doing? What a mess you're in."

Both of them, indeed, were in a mess. Their hands, their faces, their clothes, even their hair, were smeared with what looked like black mud, and Angus had his hands full of it.

"It's all right," said Jane. "We've been making coal eggs like the man told us to. We've made such a lot. Come and look. But they're not dry yet. And they do smell a bit. We had to use Annabella's manure to mix with the coal."

Smell! We moved to the doorway of the coal shed, and although I should have been the last person to discourage originality in any of our children, I was at first appalled by what I saw. I had myself sifted our stock of coal with the solid lumps on one side, the fine dust on the other. It was the dust that Jane had been working on. She, with Angus as mate, had mixed this with a quantity of Annabella's manure which they must have gathered on the top fields, but keeping out of my sight. They had made a heap of it, just as they had seen me mixing concrete or mortar, and they had added water to make it all into a sticky mess. And they *had* made eggs, scores of them, which were laid out in rows along the concrete floor like buns from a baker's oven.

We had to laugh in the end. We had to admire and give praise for what indeed was a war effort. And using a shovel I moved the eggs to a shelf in Annabella's stable, and I promised Jane that when they were dry we would see if they would burn, at least in a picnic fire. They did dry, eventually, but in the process they disintegrated and the final residue was carried to the garden. We used lime with the rest of the dust, and, suitably clad and with washing facilities handy, the children made coal eggs on frequent occasions. They helped considerably in keeping our home fires burning.

8

THE FIRST winter of what was already being called the phoney war drew on. We had rain, frost, a little snow, but, on the whole, the early part of the winter was dry and mild, giving no indication of what was in store for us later on, and on most days I was able to work at the job of clearing round the rocks and, what was almost as important, the repairing of the old, and the erection of new, fences. They would have to be sheep-proof to protect our crops and wire-netting and barbed-wire seemed the only effective method.

It was clear that the reclamation of the whole land was going to be more difficult and expensive even than Sam had prophesied. It was also clear that sooner or later I must get down to making some money and on the wet days I did try to write. I found it extremely hard to concentrate. I had no new book in my mind. One morning, and this was during our first light snowfall, I picked up the manuscript of the unfinished Bransby book. It seemed to me, particularly in the Kaiser's war atmosphere I had tried to create, unreal, uninteresting and even boring. Who would want to read what had happened to a sailor in the Kaiser's war now?

Christmas came. It was not as the children had hoped a white Christmas. There was neither frost nor snow. We all went down to the school for the breaking up concert and party. Marie and Sylvia had collaborated in the production of a pantomime, *Cinderella,* with Claire as the principal boy. Amelia had a part as an attendant page.

Bill gave us a Christmas tree from what had once been one of the little squire's plantations, and we brought it home in the trap. We had our own Christmas party. There were Christmas stockings, and we had roast turkey and Christmas pudding and mince pies. There was as yet no serious shortage of food in Britain.

We had a big ash log on the lounge fire. We roasted chestnuts in the embers. We had crackers and balloons, singing and games, and perhaps it was as well that that day our radio was out of order, and that there were no newspapers. There were only the convoys, and the minesweepers and the aircraft patrols of Coastal Command to remind us of the war. We heard no guns or bombs.

It was a night towards the end of January when the first of that winter's many storms began. The day was frosty with the sun, red as a harvest moon, shining without heat through a grey haze which lay upon moors and sea. There was no wind.

Sam was threshing at Bog Hall, and after lunch Dain

and I had gone over to help. Not that our help was really needed, for, as Sam said dryly, it had been a poor harvest from this land which had been neglected for so long. There were just two small stacks of oats and the sheaves were full of thistles. They were from fields which Matt had himself sown, and he had given them no fertiliser or lime for years. Len would work on them in spring, dress them with lime and get some manure on to them, and it would be a different do next harvest. Arable land that had been neglected was much worse than land that had never grown crops at all, as we'd find out to our advantage when we came to crop our own land.

We liked Len and his young wife very much. They had no capital, and it had been a wonderful opportunity going in with a man like Sam who was always so willing to share his own knowledge and experience as well as giving practical help. As we had not succeeded in getting a new permanent nanny, Ida was coming over to us for a couple of hours most days to give a hand with the cleaning. She was good with the children and obviously was looking forward to having a family of her own. Jimmy, too, was helping with the threshing. Because of the ice on the road he had been obliged to walk and he left soon after we had arrived, explaining that he'd have to do his shepherding on foot.

"It's the first time," Sam remarked sarcastically, as soon as he was out of hearing, "that I've known Jimmy pack up from a job just before a meal was due. Still, it was nice having him, and all he's borrowed is a couple of sheaves of oats for his mare."

We felt a little diffident in joining in the meal that had

been laid out in the farmhouse kitchen by Ida for the end of threshing, for we hadn't done more than a couple of hours' work. She would have been offended, however, if we had refused. It was a smaller house than that of the mill farm. It still had an open fireplace, but Sam, as the new landlord, had begun improvements, and had already got water laid on to the kitchen sink, and how proud Ida seemed of it all. As we walked home, arm-in-arm across the field which led down to our beck, Dain said:

"Won't it be exciting when we have our own threshing to do? Let's have a walk round all our fields now, and just imagine what they are going to look like. I'm glad Sam said that about land like ours being better than fields that have been badly farmed." And she added inconsequently: "I do hope that Ida and Len will have a baby. They do seem so happy with their farm, and that would make it perfect for them."

We crossed the beck, and walked up through the copse where I had robbed the fox of its dinner, and up to the first of the fields we had cleared of whins. Will Stainforth, who had come out rabbiting one day, had promised to find a man who would do the blasting for me, but it wouldn't be for several weeks. He approved of what I was doing with the rocks, digging well under them so that a charge of gelignite would lift and split them.

We had decided, and Sam had approved of this, to do just the fields on our side of the fence first, and by this time I had cleared all the visible rocks in two of them. The soil had been frozen too hard for me to do any digging today. Now a change had come in the weather. The frost had suddenly gone. A wind, and it was a curiously warm one, was blowing gently from the east. But the haze which had hung over the hills and sea showed no signs of clearing, and it was getting dark. There was just enough light for us to see, towards the highway, the figure of Jimmy, stick in hand and dog behind him striding towards a scattered group of his precious sheep. A solitary bus with its headlamps shaded was passing our road-end. There was still nothing to suggest that a storm was impending.

For security reasons the BBC no longer gave weather forecasts. It started to rain. We abandoned the idea of going the rounds. Before we were halfway down our hill the temperature had dropped again, the rain had turned to sleet, the wind was freshening and backing.

An hour later when I went out to get some turf from our stack, a blizzard was raging and there was a deep drift against the walls of the coal shed. The snow, fine and dry, was driving horizontally, and I could scarcely stand against the power of the wind. And this was only the prelude to a storm that was to continue for three days and nights.

The wind raged, and never varied in its main direction of north-east, and while there were gusts which shook the house, the lulls that followed were lulls only in a comparative sense. If there were periods when the actual snowfall ceased, or moderated, one could not definitely distinguish them as such, for all the time the fallen snow, dry as desert sand, about the house was moving, swirling, sometimes even rising vertically like sea water sucked up by a water-spout.

It was not safe for the children to venture out. But I had to go out next morning to get coal and turf and logs and, in this Dain insisted on coming with me, to find Annabella and bring her, willy nilly, to her hated stable, in which we had hopefully put a bedding of dry bracken and a rack of hay and oat straw.

Before starting on our quest we had to dig through a drift that rose almost level with the stable roof. Oddly enough, the road up the hill as far as the first level field was bare except for the snow that was actually falling on it and as swiftly being swept away. The ground was frozen hard as iron.

We found Annabella in a clump of whins, her backside to the weather, caked thickly in snow, unconcernedly cropping at the whin twigs about her. She took the sugar Dain gave her and made no fuss about being haltered. As soon as she realised that she was going to be stabled she tried every trick to defeat our plan, and we had to tow her with the halter down the hill. When we reached the stable the trench we had made through the drift was almost blocked again and Dain had to hang on while I cleared it. We won in the end, after an exhausting struggle.

Then I had to go for the milk for we guessed that Sam and Becky, it was usually she who brought it, would be finding things difficult. The bridle-path to the wood ran down a narrow gulley. This was completely filled with snow, but a detour to the left brought me to the boundary wall of the wood, and the wood itself being completely protected from the gale had only a normal snowfall on the ground, and it was not more than a few inches deep. From the other side of the wood down to the farm, where I encountered once more the full fury of the blizzard, there was a colossal drift filling the road, and piled up against the farm buildings. To the right of it, as on our own hill, the ground was almost bare.

I found Sam and Becky in the cowshed, busy, but quite cheerful. They had finished the milking and were stuffing the racks with hay brought in from the stackyard, to which they'd had to dig their way. Sam apologised:

"I'm sorry you've had to come down in this weather for your milk. It's a devil, isn't it? I'd have brought it up later but it's been a job getting the hay in. Next thing I'll go in for is a dutch barn. I thought my stack was going to blow away just now. It seems to be getting worse."

"How are things at your spot?" said Becky. "It is a wild 'un, isn't it? Have you got plenty of food? There'll be no buses running. The milk lorry hasn't got here yet and I don't think it will. Everything will be blocked up. I shouldn't be surprised if the railway line is blocked too, but you can't hear whether the trains are running or not with the wind howling like it is. Let's know if you're short of anything. I wonder how poor Jimmy is getting on with his sheep. He'll be worried."

"Yes," said Sam, "he'll have been awake all night worrying, and I bet he'll be down here before long asking for some turnips for them. It must be a devil on the moor top. He won't be able to ride round in this. You're wise to have your pony inside. You'd better have some more hay for her."

For two more days, and well into the night of a third, the storm continued with unabated fury. Not once during that period did it noticeably stop snowing, and at no time could we see, either from the house or outside, more than a few yards in any direction. Our telephone had gone dead. There was no postman, and, of course, no newspapers. Our only direct human contact was with the farm to which I made a daily journey for our milk. Sam told me that he had tried to walk down to the school to find out if there was any chance of the milk lorry getting through, but that there were drifts eight feet high blocking the road and he had given it up. Len had struggled across the fields to get some tea as his wife had run out of it, and Jimmy had been down to borrow some hay for his mare, and ask for some turnips, and both of them had spoken of drifts in which they'd sunk to their armpits.

Yet except that the children hated having to stay indoors, we suffered little inconvenience. The house shook during the fierce gusts. The slates rattled, and so did the front windows. No damage was done. We had no leaks and we had no draughts, except when the front door was open. We were well stocked with coal and wood and turf and food. All our rooms were warm. Fortunately, I had put our henhouse in a sheltered position near the wood boundary, and although I had to dig my way to it, our Rhode Islands were quite happy and some of them had produced eggs.

We could have enjoyed the storm, the adventure and drama of it, but for the certain knowledge that it was causing great hardship and loss, even loss of life, to many people, and especially to those who were facing it at sea along our own shallow and at most times treacherous coast, their perils increased by the special ones of war.

The sea was not visible, but we could hear the deep ceaseless thunder of it through the other noises of the storm. The driving snow would protect shipping from air attacks as effectively as thick fog, but fog, under normal conditions, was a greater maritime hazard than gales and rough seas. What was happening out at sea while we were warm and comfortable and safe ashore? What must it have been like for the officers of a merchant ship steaming blindly ahead, with other ships close ahead and astern, in weather like this, and throughout the long winter night knowing, too, that on the surface of the sea, or below it, were drifting or cunningly-laid mines?

We heard during the storm, at intervals that ruled out the possibility that they were bombs, three heavy explosions. They might have been drifting mines that had come ashore and exploded on the rocks, or they might have been mines that ships had struck. The radio gave us no news whatever about the storm itself, but there were further grim statements of tonnage sunk. We had already been told about the laying of magnetic mines by German aircraft in British estuaries. We had been told, too, that the enemy had made several attacks on lightships, sinking them with bombs, machine-gunning their escaping crews.

At last the storm was over. On the morning of the fourth day the sun rose from the sea through a red mist into a pale-blue cloudless sky. The shallow areas of the bay were white with broken water and the thunder of the surf came louder than ever on the still air. Farther out, the swell, although heavy, was unbroken. There were no merchant ships in sight. About a mile north of High Batts, however, and about two miles out, six minesweeping trawlers, in pairs, were steaming slowly south, pitching and rolling to the swell. Through glasses I could see that their decks and rigging were thick with snow and frozen spray.

The children were wildly excited at the prospect of going out again after their long imprisonment in the house. They wanted to toboggan, build snowmen, igloos. Their fear was that the snow would melt before they made a start.

They need not have worried. The storm had been succeeded by a frost of exceptional severity. The milk in our larder, the butter and bacon, were all frozen hard as stone. Outside the cold make one gasp. Yet it was dry, like a Canadian cold, and once I had dug a way through the deep drift that lay between the house and the outhouses, and the foot of the road, the children, clad in the woollen skiing suits Dain and our Norwegian friend had made for them, were out, and there was just enough snow on the road itself to make it perfect for their sledges. We dug Annabella out of her stable and let her free. She rolled in the snow and then galloped madly up the hill to the whins.

The sun as it mounted in the morning sky had little warmth, but its light was intense, and every detail of the landscape stood out with extraordinary clarity, as though one saw it through a crystal lens. Everything was transformed by the snow. It lay everywhere except on the grey heaving sea and the vertical cliffs, and the lee side of the tree trunks in the wood and the hedgerows. The sun tinted it with streaks of pale gold, and there were pink and turquoise and amethyst purple in the shadows of the valleys.

We had heard the comforting whistle of a railway engine. It might have meant only that a snow plough was at work on the deep cuttings of the railway. There was no sign of our postman. It was possible that a mail had come through at least on the first morning of the storm and that the postman had left our letters at the school. I had skis and, as the children were quite happy playing near the house, I set out in an attempt to reach the school. I thought it would be easier to go over the moors rather than try the lane which Sam had found so thickly drifted. I wanted to know, too, to what extent the highroad had been affected.

An astonishing sight confronted me when I reached the top of our hill. It was as though the whole expanse of the moor had been inundated by a heaving sea, whose great waves had been changed into white marble. There were rollers, running in more or less parallel lines from east to west, at right-angles to what had been the main direction of the gale. One of them extended from our own land towards the highway completely enveloping our gate and the boundary wall, and where it reached the highway it was within feet of the top of one of the trunk telephone poles. The wires of our own telephone line which joined the main at our road-end were sagging to the ground. There was no sign of traffic on the road. Here and there in the trough of the waves its surface had been swept clean and the macadam showed up in startling contrast to the snow.

I was a self-taught and not very experienced skier. I would not have known whether the condition of the snow was technically good or not. It was certainly dry and powdery, and I had proved on the drifts near the house that without skis one sank into it almost waist-deep and that it would have been almost impossible to walk far without digging. I found that the snow packed under the skis at less than eight inches, that at the slightest incline and the gentlest push with the sticks they glided. Helped by the sticks I climbed the wave that completely hid our six-bar gate, and I glided down the other side of the wave at a speed that took me halfway up the slope of the next one.

The route I intended to take was the bridle-path which skirted the boundary between farmland and moor. Except in very dry weather it was boggy, especially on the far side where the track down to Jimmy's farm joined it. The path itself was now unrecognisable as such under the undulating billows of snow up which and down which I progressed faster, and with greater pleasure than if I had been walking along the path in ordinary conditions.

I got to Jimmy's gate, which by a trick of the storm was almost clear of snow. It was standing open. The pasture that reached down to his farm was also tolerably clear and in it were a large number of his sheep, their backs thickly caked with snow, munching the hay and mangolds that had been strewn on the ground, or bleating vociferously. The way through the gate was trampled with their traffic. In the nearest drift outside it were signs of digging, and there were the tracks of a man and dog. Some distance away I saw Jimmy almost shoulder-high in a drift digging with a shovel. His back was towards me. He turned with a startled look as I glided down the slope of the drift, more startled than on the last occasion we had met in a snowstorm.

"By," he cried. "You made me jump. Them's queer things you've got on your feet. Why, I've seen pictures of them in the papers. They're what the Eskimos use, aren't they? I didn't know they were used in England. Can you wear them easy? You seem to be getting about as though there was no snow at all. They'd be a blessing for me for getting over the moor to find my poor sheep that's missing. I've never seen snow like this before. There's still more than a score of 'em to find."

There was no mockery in Jimmy's face now. He was a worried and unhappy man, and I felt very sorry for him. I said I would willingly lend him my skis when I had got back from the school, although I was afraid it would take him some time to learn how to use them. Anyway, when I got back, I would help him in his search. He looked grateful but doubtful.

"Thank you very much, but I think they'd be too slippery for me. I'd only fall off. It wouldn't be much use you looking for 'em either. You'd want Nell with you. It takes a dog to smell 'em when they're buried. There's one of 'em in this drift. I'm nearly at it."

I stood by while he dug the snow away and at last

334

reached the sheep, and I observed with what care and gentleness he released it from its prison. It was alive. It's own heat had melted the snow around it into slush and there must have been enough air in the unpacked snow to keep it from suffocation. Its legs were cramped, however, and Jimmy rubbed them, and he patted its flanks and fondled its head as though it had been a distressed child.

It was clear that I could be of no use to him, and I pushed on. I was still in sight of the sea. There was no traffic on it. The minesweepers by this time must have been well south of High Batts headland which shut off my view in that direction. Again, in the whole panorama of land and sea, there was no sign of war. It was easy to forget and be happy, to abandon myself to the extraordinary beauty of the scene, to the pleasure of moving quickly and almost effortlessly over the rolling waves of sparkling sunlit snow, in air, which, if cold, was like wine.

Then as I reached the high land above the Hall, which was surrounded by trees, I heard the distant sound of explosions. They came from the sea beyond High Batts at quick but regular intervals, heavy and rumbling, but soon they were mixed with sharper staccato explosions. I felt a horrible sensation in my stomach. The deep rumbling sounds were undoubtedly bombs, the staccato ones anti-aircraft guns. I could see nothing. Judging by the direction and distance, it was likely that it was the minesweepers which were being attacked and, unlike the unarmed trawlers, were defending themselves with their artillery.

This was war after all, and not a phoney war. Away over there beyond the headland which had looked so beautiful and peaceful after the storm, men were trying to kill, or save themselves from being killed. The ships we had seen, although undoubtedly armed, were only fishing trawlers, and were, as I knew, manned chiefly by fishermen whose peacetime vocation was dangerous enough. They would not be well-practised, like the men of the regular navy in gunnery. In any case, the odds would be against them if they were being subjected to a determined and concentrated attack by several aircraft, and by the number of the bombs it seemed likely that this was so.

All my feelings of happiness and elation were gone. I felt ashamed of them. Yet what could I do but pray that the bombs that were falling, like those aimed at the drifters, were missing their mark, that the raiders were being driven off.

Then I heard from behind me another sound. I turned to see three aeroplanes in V-formation, flying low over the moor from the north-west. They were so low that I instinctively ducked as they flew immediately over my head, at what was, compared with that of the craft I had flown in once, an enormous speed. The roar of their engines seemed to shake the ground. Their bellies and wings were gleaming silver, like those of a flying fish. On the wings was the familiar red, white and blue target of the RAF.

They were Hurricanes, the first I had seen. They were beautiful. Against the blue sky, in the sunlight they were as well-shaped and immaculately groomed as a herring-

336

gull hovering in the wind. But it was a devilish beauty, I thought. They were instruments of destruction and death, although how efficient so few of us then guessed.

I watched them flying on a dead-straight course over our peaceful, beautiful snow-clad vale towards High Batts, straight for the hidden battleground. I thought of the boys who were in them, eager and perhaps a little fearful for their first sight of the enemy. I thought of the men on the sweepers, or whatever ships that were being attacked. And I thought of the enemy too, the young Germans, essentially no different from our own, trained and conditioned to hate and kill, and destroy. I listened to the bombs and the guns and the swiftly-receding drone of the planes, and my prayers were for the victory and safety of our own boys and men, but how I hated war, and how I wished that all nations could settle their disputes and grievances with intelligence and kindness.

The planes disappeared from sight and sound. The bombing ceased and there were only a few more bursts of artillery fire before all was quiet again and peaceful. I moved over the drifted boundary wall into the field above the Hall wood. It was tolerably steep, with a good and even thickness of snow, and I prepared to let myself go in what should have been the most exhilarating run of my journey. I held back.

There was the sound of planes again, this time from the sea, and the horrible rattle of multiple machine-gun fire. The sun was in my eyes. It was some time before I saw a black object with smoke streaming from it like the trail of a rocket moving low across the bay in a north-westerly direction. There were further bursts of gunfire.

The black smoking object was zig-zagging, but drawing nearer to the land in the direction of the north end of the bay which, for me, was obscured by a clump of nearby trees. It was clear enough now, although I couldn't see its Nazi identification marks, that it was a twin-engine German plane similar to the one that had attacked the drifters. It was clear that, while still under control, it had been badly hit and was making an attempt to reach land. There was no more gunfire. I saw what looked like one of the three Hurricanes swooping over it like a hawk swooping over a terrified pigeon.

I had never had the experience of air combat. In East Africa, apart from occasional machine-gunning from the ground when we were flying low, and some inaccurate improvised anti-aircraft guns, there had been no enemy opposition to our air operations. But I had been involved in several crash landings, and could imagine the feelings of the occupants of the already defeated bomber desperately looking for a place to land, the inevitable crash, the sudden and horrid disintegration of fuselage and wings and fuel tanks, the probability of explosion and fire. I thought that if I'd had my choice, I would have preferred a crash into the sea.

Both planes disappeared behind the clump of trees, and I thought, although I was not certain of it, that I saw the other two Hurricanes, farther out to sea, circling shorewards. They were not firing, and I heard no sound of crash or exploding tanks. Later we were to hear the bomber had crashed near to a farm some miles inland from Burnharbour. One of its crew had been killed by machine-gun fire. Three others were wounded, one so seriously that he died in hospital. The wounded survivors were assisted out of the wreck by farmers and cottagers, who gave them refreshments and cigarettes, pending the arrival of the police. The bomber had been engaged in an attack on the trawlers when intercepted by the Hurricanes. One trawler had been hit, her skipper killed, and one of her crew wounded. The commander of the Hurricane flight (it was a certain man called Townsend) had deliberately held his fire after he had seen that the bomber was disabled, and had directed its pilot to the land.

I made my run down the last field to the school, taking no joy in it. Fortunately, the children there had neither seen nor heard anything of what had been going on in the air. Like our own they were all out playing in the snow, laughing and shouting and making too much noise.

I found Bill and Mabs in the staff room and joined them in coffee. They had heard the planes but not the bombs or sounds of firing. They had their worries. The main water supply pipe to the Hall (another legacy of the little squire) had frozen, and the school was without water, with burst pipes which would flood when the thaw came. The snow was not so thick down to the village, but the railway line was still blocked in several places, and there had been no mail or newspapers.

There was, as I had hoped, a mail for Adder Howe left at the school the first morning of the storm. In it was a letter from my agent saying that he was in touch with an American publisher with strong British sympathies, who was at present in London. He was anxious to let his own countrymen know that what they called a phoney war was anything but a phoney war to the navy, merchant and fishing fleets operating in the North Sea. He felt that there might well be a book in it. It should be by a British author, familiar with the men concerned, and my name had been mentioned. Would I like to take on the job? The British Admiralty had been approached, and if they were satisfied as to the author's credentials, opportunities would be given for visits to bases and ships, and a trip on a minesweeper might be arranged. If I were interested would I wire or telephone at once and come up to London for an interview with the publisher.

The school phone was in order. It was impossible, I was told by the exchange, to make a call to London owing to storm damage, but telegrams were being accepted, and I sent a telegram to my agent saying that I was deeply interested, and that I would come up to London as soon as I could.

9

I WAS AWAY three weeks.

I stayed at Harwich, the main east coast minesweeping base, at Lowestoft, Yarmouth, Grimsby and Hull. I made one short voyage in a minesweeping trawler. I met and talked with officers and men of the Royal Navy, the "regulars" and experts of the minesweeping service. I met some of the so-called boffins, then principally engaged in finding an antidote to the wicked magnetic mine. All these men excited my admiration, yet not in the same way as did the "regulars" of the service, the reservists and wartime volunteers, the skippers and hands of the peacetime fishing trawlers and herring drifters, and smaller inshore craft.

I'd always had a deep affection for these fishermen. I felt at home with them in the fuggy overheated cabins and forecastles of their docked and briefly resting ships, in their canteens and pubs. Many of those I met had experienced attacks by Nazi aircraft similar to the one that we had witnessed from our home. One of the skippers had helped to rescue some of the survivors of the Dutch liner *Simon Bolivar,* sunk with heavy loss of life in the Thames estuary by a magnetic mine. The thing that had impressed him most was the finding of a child's doll among the floating debris of the wreck.

It hadn't been easy to get them to talk about their war experiences. The chief characteristic of all these men was their imperturbability. Yet under this I had detected a cold detestation of the enemy. He wasn't playing fair. The Nazis were not only torpedoing merchant ships without warning—they were sowing their mines in waters where any sorts of ships, including passenger ships like the *Simon Bolivar* with women and children on board, could be blown up. Their aircraft were attacking fishing vessels and then deliberately machine-gunning their escaping crews. They had attacked lightships. They were breaking all the rules. They were no better than murderers.

Certainly on the east coast of England during those weeks the war was not phoney. There were lulls in the weather, but mostly the wind blew with gale force for days and nights on end with blizzards and tremendous seas. Yet the traffic lanes were being swept, and, although fishing grounds had been restricted because of the laying of protective British minefields, and so many of the fishermen and their craft were otherwise engaged, fishing was being carried on in defiance of the murderous enemy.

It *was* a theme for a book.

I was glad to get home, to find everyone safe and well, for our telephone was still dead, and the letters Dain had written had been a long time reaching me. Apart from two mines exploding on the scaurs near Low Batts, and some very distant bombing, there had been no incidents during my absence.

The moors and the whole countryside were still snowbound. The fantastic drifts on the moor, however, had flattened, and a single way traffic lane had been cut by snow ploughs along the highway, and buses were getting through. The lane from the village to the Hall and the mill farm had also been opened, allowing the milk lorry to operate and, incidentally, Amelia to go to school. Jimmy had lost only three of his sheep, and Sam had been able to take a load of mangolds with the tractor to help keep his flocks from starvation.

The frost persisted. Our beck was frozen from bank to bank, and our little waterfalls petrified. Wherever the occasional bursts of sunshine had caught the trees, melting temporarily the encrusting snow, there hung long glittering icicles and the wood was like an Aladdin's cave. It was all so beautiful and peaceful after what I had seen and heard on my journey. But I had only to look towards the sea to be reminded that what I had heard and seen was real enough, and the morning after my return I dug a way into my hut, lit my stove, and as soon as the place was warm enough, started on the first chapter of the book.

I had no ideas about this book becoming a bestseller. The American publisher had commissioned it. I was to get a fair sum as advance on royalties when it was completed. He had not disguised the fact that he was pro-British, that he would regard the book as pro-British propaganda to help win sympathy for the British in their fight against Nazism. He only wanted the truth, the ungarnished facts, as opposed to what Goebels' propaganda machine was broadcasting every day, especially to the American people. This was the aspect of the job that pleased and encouraged me. I hated war, but I was convinced from what I had seen that Nazism was an even greater evil.

Yet, while I worked on the book, I itched to be getting on with the clearing of the land, still frozen and covered with snow. The production of home-grown food was going to be of great importance in the fight against Nazism. If allotment gardeners were being beseeched to dig and grow more, how imperative it was that our own waste acres should be ploughed up and sown.

Even the children were glad when the snow went at last, with a sudden mild south-west wind and a night of real rain followed by several days of mild sunny weather. There were floods which soon subsided. The fields became green again, the moors, although streaked with the remains of the deepest drifts, turned to their more familiar brown. And in the air were the first exciting smells of spring.

Will sent his quarryman out, and he started work blasting up the rocks I had undercut. Unfortunately, the blasting only split them and lifted them clear of the subsoil. The pieces that were too heavy to lift had to be broken again with a sledge hammer. I thought that, seeing that I was writing again, I was justified in employing some labour for this job. Will helped me by sending out one of his brawniest men. We used Annabella and the trap for carrying the pieces to the boundary walls. They were practically all white flint. I still had no suspicion as to their real nature and its

344

significance.

In only one case had I failed to get under a rock, and found as I dug deeper that its base grew bigger, suggesting that it was an outcrop of an underlying bed, that the free ones were only free because of ancient glacial action and weathering. Luckily this rock was near the boundary, and when I showed it to Sam he said that it would be simple to plough round it.

It was a morning in the first week of April when Sam arrived with his tractor to make a start. As yet there had been nothing on the radio or in the papers to suggest that the so-called phoney war was nearing its end, that the real war was about to begin. Indeed, there were grounds for optimism.

The Russians and the Finns, after many bloody battles, had made peace, and Russia had announced her intention to remain strictly neutral so far as Germany and the Allies were concerned. Hitler and Mussolini had met, and it looked as though Mussolini at least was not against an international peace conference. There had been peace demonstrations in Italy. The Vatican had appealed to all nations to avoid a major conflict. The sinking of Allied and neutral ships had continued, but many U-boats had been destroyed, and in the North Sea the Hurricanes and Spitfires of Coastal Command seemed to be mastering the raiding Heinkels. Every day when the weather was clear we were seeing large convoys of merchant ships passing without hindrance. The only aircraft we heard were British.

We were all (except the aunt, who was visiting friends) there to see the start of the ploughing, for it was an occasion almost as important as the laying of the foundation stone of our house. It was a warm sunny day. The primroses and daffodils were already out. A lark was singing. From the copses and the wood came a chorus of bird song: blackbirds, thrushes, finches, linnets, the cooing of woodpigeons, the harsher notes of jays and woodpeckers, the croaking of crows and magpies. Sam started on the field nearest to the moorland boundary, and first made a single furrow round it to mark the headlands. Then using all three shares of the plough he came up the middle of the field and began ploughing up and down one half. The children ran after him, shouting excitedly. Soon they abandoned this game to look for flint implements. Our own immediate interest (Dain and I with Timothy were at the top of the field nearest to the moor) was the soil itself, dark chocolate brown in colour, turning like the bow waves of a ship from the plough.

"It *does* look good," Dain said. "It *does* look good. It's all as exciting as when we first started clearing the garden in Cornwall. But this beats gardening. It will be a real farm. Only I do wish we could be doing it ourselves. I wish it could be done with horses instead of a tractor. I suppose that would take much longer, though."

"Yes," I said. "I suppose it would."

The tractor moved considerably faster than a team of horses, and it was ploughing three furrows at once. After ploughing the field had to be harrowed, to break up the sods into a tilth; it had to be sown and then rolled (I had learnt all this from Sam) and in addition it had to be spread with lime and fertiliser. We were not going to undersow it with grass. Sam had advised that we should wait for next year to do this. I had arranged with a Burnharbour firm to supply and spread the lime. Sam had agreed, at a fair price, to carry out all the other operations, and the ploughing alone of our twelve acres would take at least four days. I was half in sympathy with Dain's preference for the more primitive methods of agriculture, but were they practical in wartime? I itched to be driving the tractor myself, and was hoping that later on Sam would initiate me into the art of ploughing.

Yet the thought came to me, as I looked at Dain and Timothy and the other children happily searching for treasures on the upturned soil, while the skylark was singing overhead in the sunshine of this lovely spring morning, that the world might have been a happier place if the internal combustion engine, which gave power to the Heinkel bomber as well as to Sam's tractor, and gunpowder and dynamite and cordite and trinitrotoluene, which destroyed ships and killed and maimed men as efficiently as they helped men to mine gold and coal, and clear obstructive rocks from fields like mine, and shoot cock pheasants, had never been invented. Horses *were* better than tractors.

Very late that night I was at work on my book in the lounge with everyone else in bed and asleep, when I heard the sound of a twin-engine aeroplane flying over the house.

There was nothing at first unusual about that. It would be a British plane, an Anson or Lockheed or Blenheim, engaged on night flying practice. But instead of its sound diminishing it went on and on, as though it were circling, and it began to irritate me like the buzzing of a bluebottle or wasp. I got up and walked through the living-room and carefully opened the back door from which one looked north and west uphill towards the moor.

It was very dark and I had no light. I realised soon that the extra darkness was produced by a mist. There were no stars. I could only vaguely distinguish the shape of the outbuildings. The sound of the plane continued. It seemed to be flying at a considerable height and over the moor, and still circling. And then there came a livid flash, and within seconds a loud explosion. There was another flash, which silhouetted the outbuildings and hilltop through the mist. Another explosion, then another and another in rapid but regular succession, all from beyond our hilltop, but each one perceptibly farther to the west.

I dare not move. I knew they were bombs, and that they must be enemy bombs. That they were a "stick", a number of them released consecutively from a rack so that they would straddle a target, and I had the immediate comforting thought that in the direction of where they were so obviously falling there was no target. They must be at least a quarter of a mile away from our house. They must be falling on the open moor.

I counted twenty and then stopped. I heard the sound of the plane again, growing louder, coming directly over the house. I held my breath, knowing there was nothing I could do but wait, and if more came and we were hit, deal as best I could with whatever happened. No more came. The sound of the plane diminished. It was flying out towards the sea. It died completely. I moved into the

348

house, found Dain in her dressing-gown downstairs looking rather scared.

"Were they bombs?" she said.

"Yes. But they were a long way off, over the moor. They can't have done any harm. It must have been a raider out for shipping deciding to loose-off his load before making for home. It's all over anyway. Are the children awake?"

"No. I've been into them. They're all fast asleep. Is Annabella all right?"

"Let's have some tea," I said. "I'll go and have a look while the kettle is boiling."

I put on the kettle. I opened the door again and looked out. At once I heard the clump of Annabella's hoofs as she trotted down the hill through the mist. Before I closed the door I heard voices. Sam and Becky were coming up the path, and I gave them a hail. Becky answered:

"Eh, are you all right? You haven't been struck, have you? They must have come near."

Sam was laughing.

"They were a long way off," he said. "I told her that, but we wanted to make sure you were all right. We were up to a calving cow. I thought it was a Jerry plane when I first heard it. It sounded different from any of ours. And when it started cruising about, thinks I, it means mischief, and I stood outside the cowshed, by that time we'd got the calf all right and I saw the first flash, but not proper because of the fog. It was more like the reflection of a lightning flash."

"Eh, but I was frightened," put in Becky. "When the

first bang came, my knees were fair knocking together. I thought it might have got your house. I'm still shaking a bit."

They came in. We made the tea. I agreed with Sam's belief that the bombs had fallen well away on the moor where there were no farms. In the dark and with the mist there would be no point in going up there. It wouldn't be advisable to use torches. We were all a little shaken, I think, but we were also elated, for we'd had our baptism of bombing, near enough to be frightening, yet apparently with no harm done.

As soon as it was daylight I walked up on to the moor. The sun had just risen. The mist had gone. There was every sign of another warm spring day, and already the birds were singing. As I got to our gate I saw well beyond the deserted highroad the familiar figure of Jimmy. His mare was with him, but he was dismounted, and he was standing looking at something on the ground.

I hurried along our road, crossing the highway, and within a hundred yards of it saw the first bomb crater. It was about twenty feet across and about eight feet deep in its centre. I judged it to have been about a hundred-pounder, big enough to sink a ship or, with a direct hit, to have destroyed our house. The second one was about fifty yards away, and I could see the mound made by another the same distance and in a straight line. And it was between this one and the next that Jimmy was standing looking at the mangled body of a sheep. Close by were several others, one decapitated, one with the whole of its side torn off, and its entrails were twined among the heather. There was a nauseating smell of blood.

There was a dead ewe at Jimmy's feet. His own face was pale and I saw tears in his eyes as he turned to me and said:

"What do you think of this? What do you think of this? Seven of my ewes killed and all of 'em with lamb. Can you see that one with its head blown off? There's one just blown to bits. And look at this one. It was alive when I found it, with three of its legs off and a hole in its side. I had to cut its throat with my knife to put it out of its misery. I've had that ewe for six years and it's never missed a lambing, and almost always it's had a couple, and never owt wrong with 'em. I tell you what, if I could get hold of that bloody German who did it I'd cut his throat for him. What harm had these poor ewes done to him?"

10

IT WAS a wonderful spring, and it was followed by a wonderful summer. Sam said that he had never known such a run of good weather for farming. Everything went right. Spring ploughing had been followed by a spell of dry easterly winds, but for sowing there had been showers that had softened the soil for the drill. There had been no late damaging frosts, and there had been plenty of sunshine to bring up both corn and grass. Everything on his own farm was doing well. He and Len had transformed the neglected acres of Bog Hall. And our own fields gave promise of exceeding our wildest hopes.

No field ever received more lavish attention than did those fields of ours. We looked at them every day and at first while the soil was dry it did no harm to wander over them. The nearest tumulus to them marked on the ordnance map was about two hundred yards on the moorland side of the boundary fence. We found dozens of flint scrapers and knives and spearheads and also several beads that were undoubtedly prehistoric. But the most exciting find had been made by Amelia and Jane. They had rushed down to my hut one morning, about a fortnight after the sowing, during the Easter holidays.

"Daddy—Daddy!" they cried. "Come and look. The

corn is out."

I was at work on my book, but it was nearly lunchtime and I broke off to walk up with them to the fields. We'd all kept an eager look out for the first shoots of corn, and there had been many false alarms. Tiny green blades which had emerged from the bare soil in places had proved to be shoots from the old buried sods. This time there was no mistake. The children led me to the first field that had been sown, the one nearest to the moor. I had to kneel down and look closely. There beyond any doubt were scores and scores of pale-green blades less than an inch in height all in line following the pattern of the drill.

Day by day we had watched those blades grow. There were rival contestants for the stored-up and artificially augmented fertility of the soil. There were thistles and the old coarse grass and later, where the bracken had been, the shoots of these emerged. We could not hoe the fields as one could a garden. We could not eradicate more than a small proportion of the weeds, but we cleared many of them by hand, and we found, as Sam said we would, that the oat plants as their roots were established began to choke their rivals. Soon all our fields were green and the green was uniform, and that of healthy vigorous corn.

But the phenomenal good weather of the spring and summer of that year, if ideal for the British and Continental farmer, was also ideal for the fulfilment of Adolf Hitler's diabolic plans for European conquest. In dry sunny May, with clear skies that were perfect for air reconnaissance and attack, his armoured columns swept

353

over the Netherlands, Belgium and Luxemburg. Norway was already in the bag. The Battle of France had begun. Before the end of May Belgium had capitulated. The Nazis were across the Maginot Line. A wedge had been driven between the French and British. The evacuation of the British forces had begun and before the end of the first week in June, with the weather as lovely as it had been in May, the miracle of Dunkirk had happened. The bells of Berlin were ringing. But in Dunkirk Hitler might well have recognised a portent that the gods were not wholly on his side.

Of all this we knew nothing beyond what we heard on the radio and read in the papers. The convoys of merchant ships were still passing up and down the coast. The minesweepers were carrying out their daily sweeps without interference from the enemy. Although the fishing fleet of Burnharbour (reduced in size because so many of the young men had joined the Navy or Naval Reserve) had been alerted for the Dunkirk operation, the authorities had decided that the distance was too great, and no boats had been called on. There had been no more bombs. Jimmy, who had been promised full compensation for his dead sheep, had benefited from the dry warm weather for his lambing season. In spite of rationing there was still no real shortage of food, no difficulties in getting coal and paraffin oil and gas. The children were happy. I was too busy with the book and the garden and the land for us to make any whole day excursions to the beach, but at weekends we had picnic rides on the moor, and always there was the island with the pool and the dinghy, and the swing. There were flowers for them to pick, birds' nests to find.

Physically, the war with all its horrors was still remote from us. But the news was terrifying. On Midsummer's Day Hitler had met the emissaries of defeated France and stated his terms for surrender. He had met them in the railway coach in the Forest of Compiègne in which, in the Kaiser's war, Foch had granted an armistice to the defeated Germans. Mussolini had declared war against France. Churchill had made the most famous of his radio speeches. Britain and the distant Commonwealth were now alone against the combined strength and evil intent of Nazis and Fascists, with the United States still only benevolently neutral.

I had finished my propaganda book. It was sent off to the American publisher with a faint hope that it might in some way help in Britain's cause. There was nothing more that I could do personally but get on with the making of the farm, the preparation of the remaining fields for ploughing.

I had already made a start on the rocks. The quarryman who had done the blasting was not available, however, nor could Will Stainforth let me have one of his labourers. His firm was busy building air-raid shelters at Burnharbour. Later on he might be able to help me, but he couldn't promise. Then, one day in July, when I rang him up he told me there wasn't a hope. The firm had taken on the priority job of building pill boxes and gun emplacements along the coast. Did I know that all the beaches were going to be closed and all roads to them blocked? He thought it was daft himself. The Germans would never land on a rocky coast like ours.

He was right about the beaches. The children had been clamouring for a seaside picnic, and one evening Dain and I, leaving the aunt in charge, had a quick walk down to see how things were. The road leading down to the mill cove was blocked with a stone wall and a number of soldiers in battle-dress were offloading coils of barbed-wire from a truck. A sentry with fixed bayonet challenged us on our approach. We were told that unless we had written permission from the commanding officer of his unit we must not go any farther. The lane leading to Browe Beck Cove, to the place where we had first planned to build our house, was also blocked and guarded. In a field close by there were a number of military trucks and bivouac tents.

As we turned rather gloomily for home, Dain said:

"Well, darling, we're lucky, anyway. How awful if we had built our house at Browe Beck. We've still got the moors and our own stream. We're lucky that we've got such a nice house, away from it all and that we've got a farm. We're not going to miss the shore so much where we are as if our house had been close to it. It's good to think that we'll be able to do something to help by growing food."

We *were* lucky. It was a very small thing we had lost. There would be no more happy bathing parties on the beach with the children; no more fishing trips to High Batts. But in Europe men, women and children had been slaughtered, towns and villages ravaged. At sea, although things had been so quiet on our own coast, the enemy was intensifying his attacks on our shipping.

Next day I was at work clearing one of the rocks in

the biggest of our remaining fields when I saw a man moving slowly along the moor boundary close up to the wall, which I had repaired with blocks of the white flint. He was dressed in tweeds with plus-fours, and he had a leather haversack over his shoulder. At first I took him to be one of the sportsmen who shot over Sam's land. As he came nearer I saw that he was not carrying a gun, but a small hammer. He was looking at the wall with great interest. I saw him put his hands on one of the pieces of flint, and I thought he was going to pull it out. It was a dry wall and it had been a difficult job making the pieces fit. If he pulled one out it might bring a whole section down. I dropped my visgy and walked towards him. He was now near the gate, but on the moorland side, and therefore not trespassing.

I was soon satisfied that his intentions were not foolish or harmful. I introduced myself as the owner of the land inside the wall. He told me that he was a Government geologist. He was engaged in a check-up of certain beds of silica rock that were known to exist in the district. This rock, when ground up and converted into a cement, had high heat-resisting properties, and was used for lining furnaces. Normally much of it was imported. Now, at a time when every furnace in the country was engaged full-out on the making of munitions of war, it was a key product. He had been looking at stones that had been used to build the wall. He'd noticed that some of them were newly broken. He'd noticed that there were further piles of this broken rock on the headlands of the growing corn. Had I taken them from the land? Would I mind if he had a walk round, not over the crops of course, and if he took samples of the rock away with him for analysis? He was certain that it *was* silica rock but its actual value could only be ascertained in the laboratory.

I told him all I knew, and that I suspected myself that at least one of the rocks, the one we had ploughed round, belonged to an underlying formation. Actually, I had suspected this of the one I had been working on in the big field when I had seen him. I had dug down to more than three feet without coming to an end of the "face". We moved over to this rock. He examined it and he took my crowbar and forced it as far as it would go into the hole.

"I think you are right about this being an outcrop," he said. "There *is* an underlying bed. It probably varies in depth. But according to the Geological Survey map it should stretch for at least half a mile in a north-south direction and down to the edge of the valley. It was surveyed long ago of course, before the war. I've only got to confirm it, and get sample specimens. I'd like to spend an hour or two looking round, if you don't mind. There'll be no need for me to walk over the crops. Were you planning to have this field ploughed up and sown?"

"Yes," I said. "I'm trying to bring the whole of this land into cultivation. Are you suggesting I shouldn't?"

He smiled.

"If I were you I wouldn't at present. It might pay you to wait, but that is just private advice, not official. You've got silica rock here. It may not be the required grade. If it is, I should say the chances are it will be wanted."

"Would that mean a quarry?"

"That's beyond my sphere. I'd say it would be an open-cast proposition, like coal. The overlay would be bulldozed off."

"And the field would be ruined?"

"As an arable field I suppose it would, for some years anyway, although the usual practice with open-cast mining is to take off the topsoil and put it back. That is with first-class agricultural land, and you would hardly call this first class, would you? I am not a farmer. I don't think you'd make much money out of the rock, perhaps a royalty of sixpence a ton, but all the work and capital outlay would be done for you. I think it would pay better than farming it."

I had once seen an open-cast ironstone mine in the Midlands; acres of beautiful wooded country completely devastated. There was nothing intrinsically beautiful about these top fields of ours, but they were a part of Adder Howe, a part of the beauty of our unspoilt and beautiful countryside. I had a sudden vision of all the land being torn up by huge and noisy excavators. All the money in the world would not compensate us for that.

"What would happen," I said, "if the rock was wanted and I refused to let it go?"

He smiled again rather grimly.

"I don't know, but I imagine that in wartime the Government can do pretty well what it likes."

I thought that, as he had more or less suggested it, I should leave him to wander round as he liked, and I invited him to come down to the house and have tea with us when he had done. He thanked me but declined as he had left his car on the highroad, and he had further sites to examine. I was feeling very worried. I wondered what I should tell Dain, and as I walked down to the house my depression grew, for I remembered that in the conveyance deed of Adder Howe with old Isaac there had been a clause stating that the mineral rights in the property were reserved by the original vendor, presumably the executors of the little squire's estate, or perhaps the lord of the manor.

It was bad news I had to take to Dain. She had bad news for us both. She was in tears. Mabs had just been speaking to her on the telephone. A large number of troops were moving in to the district. It was to be a battle training ground for a division of the new army. The moors were to be taken over for a tank and artillery range. The school itself and all its buildings were to be requisitioned for staff headquarters. And Bill was now desperately trying to find another big house. He'd gone off by car to the Lake District, to examine some properties that were to let. Definitely the school would be closing at the end of the term, but if we liked she would gladly take Amelia and Jane, when they found some accommodation.

It *was* bad news. Mabs and Bill and Claire, and Marie and Sylvia were our closest friends. There was small comfort in Mabs's offer to take Amelia and Jane, thus breaking up our family. I had another dreadful thought. If the military authorities could requisition the Hall, they could do the same with Adder Howe. We might ourselves have to quit. And where should we find another home? How dreadful if we had to go back to Butcher's Folly. I kept my thoughts to myself, and I decided that for the time being I would say nothing to Dain about the geologist. But Dain was recovering.

"We *shall* miss Bill and Mabs," she said. "But we'll just have to make the best of it. Perhaps we can get a governess for Amelia and Jane. If only we had a bigger house we might start a school ourselves. I don't want Amelia and Jane to go away, but we've got to do what is best for them. Let's have some tea anyway. Perhaps the war will be over soon. And wouldn't that be lovely!"

We were in the living-room. The aunt had taken Jane and Angus down to the island. Timothy was still having his afternoon nap. There was a knock at the door. It was Becky, looking very excited and bursting with news. She came in, but she wouldn't sit down.

"Eee! Have you heard the latest? I don't expect you have, because we've only just heard and its official. We've had an officer come to the house. He was a colonel, Sam said. He'd got red tabs on his coat, and he must have been very important. There's thousands of soldiers coming to camp on the moor. They're going to build lots of army huts close up to the highroad. There's going to be tanks and big guns, and they're going to practice on the moor. They're going to take over the Hall, and the school has got to flit. It'll be hard on them, won't it? But it's going to be a good thing for us in a way. They're going to send some soldiers to live with us. And some with Len and Ida at Bog Hall. It'll be a bit of company, and a bit of extra brass coming in, although they won't pay like summer visitors.

"The officer wanted to know about your place, and if you had any spare bedrooms. I told him that you had bairns and that you were full up, and that you were starting to farm, anyway, and he said that he wouldn't bother, but I expect he'll have gone to see Jimmy. I don't know how Jimmy is going to come on with them using the moor. It won't be safe, anyway, with guns going off. But it *is* going to liven things up, isn't it? Especially if they're going to be here all winter."

11

WE HAD to hide our feelings from the children, to pretend that there was nothing amiss. It was not the closing and likely spoilation of the moor, on top of the closing of the beach, that distressed us so, although these things were bad enough. Bill had found a large country house in Cumberland. The school term had ended, without the usual party and dancing and play on the lawn, and the staff and those of the boarding scholars whose parents lived in London and other air-raid threatened areas were starting to move in relays.

Weighing up all the pros and cons we had decided that it would be best for Amelia and Jane to go. The school had ponies which were to be taken to Cumberland by rail. We had decided (and Bill and Mabs concurred) to let Annabella go too, for Amelia and Jane were so devoted to her. All these were insignificant troubles compared with those that were being faced by many other families during the closing days of July. They were small enough for us compared with the problem of our land, and the possibility that we might be evicted from our home.

A company of Royal Engineers had arrived. A large permanent camp was being built on the moor between Bog Hall and the trout mere, now forbidden to us for the "duration". Notices warning the public against trespassing had been erected on the highroad verge. The highroad, which in last July had been crowded with happy holiday makers, was just as crowded now with military traffic. Jimmy had been told that his sheep would be allowed to roam at present, and that he would be allowed to shepherd them. It must be at his own risk.

The billeting officer had visited us. He had looked at all the rooms. We had told him that two of our children would be leaving soon and that there would be two spare bedrooms then. He had noted the telephone and other amenities. He also admired the view and he gave me the impression that he would not have been averse to living in the house himself. Officially he warned us that he might have to billet some soldiers on us later on, and that there was a possibility that the whole house might be requisitioned as it was so conveniently situated to the main camp. If we wished to let it voluntarily to the War Office we would, of course, get a reasonable rent and there would be compensation for any damage done. So long as we were engaged in farming it was not likely that we should be compelled to leave.

We had heard nothing about the silica, and I had gone on digging round the rocks. The oats now were fully grown, and in patches were beginning to ripen. Sam said that it was a finer crop than any he had produced on first broken land. I hadn't told him about the visit of the geologist. He had promised that as soon as his own harvest was completed in the autumn he would start the ploughing of the other fields.

We had told Amelia and Jane that they were going to Cumberland to live with Bill and Mabs and Claire and Marie, and their school friends. There had been tears, consoled when we told them about Annabella, and that we should be coming to see them soon. Dain had been busy getting their clothes ready. Those of the staff and scholars who had gone had travelled by coach, and our children would go with Marie and Mabs in the next batch. We were both dreading the parting, for it would be the first time that any of our children had not slept under our own roof. We knew, of course, that they would be happy at the school, well cared for, and that their education would not be interrupted.

I was in my hut engaged on some correspondence the day before it had been planned for them to leave, when Dain shouted down to me that the postman had been. The children were out. There were two letters for me, one in an official envelope. I opened it first. It was from the head of a Government department and it stated that an analysis of samples of rock found on my land had shown a very favourable percentage of silica. There were indications that the depth and extent of the deposits would justify mining operations at an early date. Representatives of a firm engaged on the mining and processing of silica would put their proposals before me. In the meantime I was advised not to proceed with any agricultural operations, which it was understood I had been planning.

I handed it to Dain.

"I don't want to read it," she said. "I know it's bad news. It's goodbye to the farm, I know. I can tell by your face. Never mind. Something will turn up. It always has done in the past. What does it say?"

I had already told her about the geologist's visit. I'd also discussed his visit with my Burnharbour lawyer, and he had confirmed that the mineral rights were reserved, actually by the lord of the manor's estate, and that they could do precisely what they liked about them, although possibly I could get compensation for damage to the land.

"It's bad," I said. "They want the rock. We can't have our farm, and that may mean the house may be requisitioned. We'll just have to wait and see. We'll be able to harvest our oats anyway, but they'll want those fields too, I suppose."

"Well, we'll have to get another farm. We've got to do something. What's in that other letter. Perhaps that is good news like the *Codex* letter and the cheque for twenty-five pounds."

"Darling," I said. "Things like that don't happen twice in anyone's lifetime, even in ours. Besides, it isn't money we need now, is it, like we did then?"

I looked at the envelope. The postmark and handwriting were familiar.

"It's from that man in Wales who wrote a fan letter a few weeks ago. It's not likely to contain anything exciting."

It had been a very pleasant letter. The writer was a consultant mining engineer, and it was on business notepaper, but not typed. The name on the heading was Jones, and there was a string of letters after it including a BSc. It said that the book had fascinated him. He took it that the story was at least based on fact, that my wife and I have found a derelict army hut and made a home of it. Were we, he wondered, still living in it?

But it was of special interest to him and his wife because for years they had dreamed of making a house something like ours, away from the noise and botheration of town life. Just before the outbreak of war they had found such a place and bought it. It was not like our place very near the sea, and it was not a hut, but a twenty-room mansion among the Welsh hills, remote from the coalfields. He'd got it cheap because it was in a terrible state of dilapidation, but he had been looking forward to the job of reclaiming it, doing, in fact, what we had done with our place. Unfortunately the war had put a stop to that, and he and his wife would have to wait until it was over before their dream could be fulfilled.

He had given no details about his mansion. But the letter had sounded sincere without any catch in it, and I had written thanking him for it. I had told him about Adder Howe, how we had started to cultivate the land, and, as he was a mining engineer, I thought that he would be interested to hear about the gannister. I had also told him about our stream and my dream of one day making a lake and installing a waterwheel.

I opened the letter. It was quite a long one. It began with a conventional expression of thanks for my own. He

366

and his wife were both sorry that we were not living in our Cornish paradise, and yet our Yorkshire home sounded just as lovely, but, of course, for the war and how that was going to affect our plans for farming. As a mining engineer he could only confirm my fear that the gannister would have priority, and open-cast mining would be the only economic way of winning the stone. It would make an unholy mess of the place, and it would be years before the land could be cultivated.

Ironically enough, things were the other way round with his own plans. He hadn't told me in his first letter that the mansion he had bought was, in fact, a farm, with fifty-six acres of land which hadn't been cultivated for many years, and had been allowed to go back to nature. There were farm buildings adjoining the mansion, a barn, stables, cowhouse, pigsties, and two cottages. They were all, like the mansion, dilapidated but repairable. But he was not a farmer, and had no ambitions that way. Now the authorities were pressing him to do something about the land, and very reluctantly he had come to the decision to get rid of the whole place—sell it. He had paid a ridiculously low price for it, seven hundred and fifty pounds, freehold. He was willing to let it go for the same figure, and with a two thirds mortgage. Would it interest me?

My hand holding the letter began to shake a little. I had to take a deep breath.

"Dain," I said. "It sounds exciting. It sounds like the *Codex* all over again. His place is a farm, fifty-six acres, and he wants to sell it, for only seven hundred and fifty pounds. There's farm buildings, a barn, stables, pigsties."

"Stables? Why, that sounds marvellous. Oh, do go on. You haven't finished it yet. There may be some snag."

I read on, but while I read I had the growing feeling that I was dreaming, that it just couldn't be true. The place was in hilly, but not mountainous, country some miles inland from Milford Haven. There was a village about three miles away with an inn and shops, but otherwise it was completely isolated. The mansion (its name was Castle Druid) was not forbiddingly large, and some of its rooms were quite habitable. It was Georgian and it was reputed to have been designed and built by John Nash. There was a story that Lord Nelson had stayed in it with Lady Hamilton. It was surrounded by a seven-acre meadow through which ran a stream, and there were signs that there had once been an ornamental lake. I had mentioned a waterwheel in my letter. The farm next, lower down the stream, had a waterwheel, now disused but there were many in the district, all disused, and it should be easy to acquire one. There was plenty of water in the stream anyway, and it also contained trout.

I had to stop.

"Dain," I said, "tell me if I am dreaming. I just can't believe it. There's a trout stream and a waterwheel, or at least we could have one. You read it and finish it. Tell me if there *is* a snag."

She took the letter and I saw a joyous excitement growing in her face as she read. Then she passed it back to me, gripped my arms, and said:

"It's true. And it's just wonderful. It's just what we want. A big house. Twenty rooms. We can soon put it right. We could have a governess. Better still, we could have a school and Amelia and Jane wouldn't have to leave us. We might get Sylvia to join us. And all that land, and the farm buildings. Stables. We could have more ponies and breed them. And the trout stream and a waterwheel. A real farm. But the main thing would be having our children with us, not having to part with them. Do let's take it. Send him a telegram at once. He sounds such a nice man. I feel sorry for him that he's got to give it up. We needn't give up Adder Howe forever. We can let it to the soldiers. But we don't want to stay on here with most of our friends gone, and watch our fields being torn up and not being allowed on the beach and moors. And not being able to farm because of that wretched gannister."

We were in the living-room. It was another perfect sunny day. I looked out through the window, at the view over the oak wood and the sloping mosaic of fields to the bay, the view that had attracted us so when we had first come up with old Isaac to find a site for our house.

It wasn't going to be easy, leaving all this. There could not be in the world anything quite like it. There was the sea, and the moors and our little beck, the island. There was Sam and Becky and Len and Ida. There was Jimmy. And Dain must have known what I was thinking, for she put her hand in mine and said, with tears in her eyes:

"It is a lovely view. We have been happy here. But we'll be just as happy anywhere so long as we're all together. We can always come back, can't we? But it's wonderful to think that we can go somewhere where we can take all the children with us, yes, and Annabella too.

And where there's a waterwheel too. Think of that."

I took Dain in my arms and hugged and kissed her, and then I said:

"Come on. Let's phone the telegram at once."

THE END

About the author

LEO WALMSLEY was born in Shipley, West Yorkshire, in 1892, and was brought up in Robin Hood's Bay on the North Yorkshire coast — the 'Bramblewick' of several of his novels. After serving with distinction in the Royal Flying Corps in the Great War, where he was awarded the Military Cross, he determined to become a writer, beginning with boys' adventure stories.

He lived for a while in London before returning to Robin Hood's Bay in the late 1920s, then settled in Fowey, Cornwall and wrote *Three Fevers* (1932), the first of his 'Bramblewick' novels, followed by *Phantom Lobster, Foreigners, and Sally Lunn.*

In addition to over twenty books, he wrote 200 or so short stories and articles prior to his death in 1966.

Other books available in this series

Three Fevers
Angler's Moon
Foreigners
Phantom Lobster
Sound of the Sea
Master Mariner
Love in the Sun
Paradise Creek
The Happy Ending (due 2013)

For further information about Leo Walmsley,
membership of the Walmsley Society,
or where you can buy these books,
please visit:

www.walmsleysoc.org

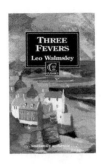  

 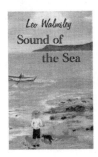

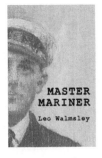 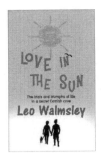 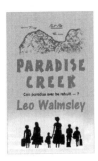

Published by

www.walmsleysoc.org